TRANSITION METAL CHEMISTRY

TRANSITION METAL CHEMISTRY

A SERIES OF ADVANCES

Edited by

GORDON A. MELSON
Virginia Commonwealth University
Richmond, Virginia

BRIAN N. FIGGIS
The University of Western Australia
Nedlands, Western Australia

VOLUME 9

MARCEL DEKKER, INC. New York and Basel

The Library of Congress Cataloged This Serial as Follows:

Transition metal chemistry. v. 1-
   New York, M. Dekker, 1965-
       v. illus. 24 cm.
   Editor: 1965-   R. L. Carlin.
   1. Transition metals.   I. Carlin, Richard Lewis,   ed.
QD172.T6T7   546   65-27431
Library of Congress   [4-1]
ISBN   0-8247-7188-5

MARCEL DEKKER, INC.
270 Madison Avenue, New York, New York 10016

Current printing (last digit):
10 9 8 7 6 5 4 3 2 1

PRINTED IN THE UNITED STATES OF AMERICA

Preface

This volume of *Transition Metal Chemistry* continues the series restarted in 1982 with the publication of Volume 8. As in previous volumes, Volume 9 contains in-depth reviews of important current areas of research in transition metal chemistry.

This volume deals with two aspects of the application of spectroscopic techniques for the characterization of transition metal complexes. Theoretical aspects and discussions of acquired data are presented; this approach results in a thorough treatment of the principles and applications of polarized crystal spectra and UV photoelectron spectroscopy. Both chapters are authored by scientists who are active in their respective areas of research. The information presented and discussed should be of interest to all researchers who have an interest in the area of transition metal chemistry.

GORDON A. MELSON
BRIAN N. FIGGIS

Contributors

MICHAEL A. HITCHMAN   Chemistry Department, University of Tasmania, Hobart, Tasmania, Australia

A. OSKAM   Department of Inorganic Chemistry, University of Amsterdam, Amsterdam, The Netherlands

H. van DAM*   Department of Inorganic Chemistry, University of Amsterdam, Amsterdam, The Netherlands

---

*Present affiliation: Research and Development, Océ Nederland BV, Venlo, The Netherlands

Contents

1

Chemical Information from the Polarized Crystal Spectra of Transition Metal Complexes

MICHAEL A. HITCHMAN

University of Tasmania
Hobart, Tasmania, Australia

I. INTRODUCTION

A. Preamble

The light-absorbing properties of transition metal ions in crystals
were studied by physicists as much as 50 years ago, and indeed it
was largely the need to explain the absorption spectra of such systems that provided the impetus for the development of the crystal
field theory of bonding in transition metal complexes by Van Vleck
and Bethe [1]. As with so many other physical techniques, however,
it is only recently that the widespread availability of cryostats
and sensitive spectrophotometers has allowed the study of the electronic spectra of single crystals of transition metal complexes using polarized light to become established as a useful tool for the
practicing inorganic chemist. A detailed list of compounds studied
in this way prior to about 1967 is to be found in the review by
Hobbs and Hush [2], and more recent results are summarized in the
periodic Royal Society of Chemistry Specialist Reports on the electronic structure and magnetic properties of transition metal complexes [3]. The more general aspects of the electronic spectra of
metal complexes have been amply treated in several books [4,5] and
review articles [6]. Several brief accounts of the fundamentals of
crystal spectroscopy have also appeared [7,8].

     It is the purpose of this chapter to put forward a "user's
view" of polarized electronic spectroscopy as applied to transition
metal complexes, with the emphasis being placed on the nature and
limitations of the information that may be derived using this technique, and how this is best obtained. Rather than giving a detailed
list of the various studies that have been made, attention will be
focused on just a few examples, with these often being drawn from
areas of direct interest to the author. The discussion will also
be limited largely to systems in which the metal complexes are
effectively isolated from one another in the crystal lattice, following what has sometimes been called the "oriented gas" model of crystal spectra [9]. In this approach cooperative interactions between
the metal ions in the lattice are ignored. The effects that such

interactions can have on crystal spectra and the way in which these can be recognized have been discussed in detail elsewhere [6,10,11] and will be touched on only briefly in the present chapter (Sec. IV.F.1). Discussion will also be limited to the light-absorbing properties of complexes; fluorescence and phosphorescence spectra, which for certain systems provide useful data, often complementary to that from absorption spectra, will not be considered.

B. Advantages of Spectral Measurements Made Using Single
   Crystals and Low Temperatures

Perhaps the most important advantage of measuring the spectrum of a single crystal rather than that of a solution or powder is that the molecule of interest is held in one or two fixed positions in space. This means that if the crystal structure is favorable (see Sec. II.C), the anisotropy of the absorption spectrum may be investigated by making measurements with the electric vector of linearly polarized light in different positions with respect to a chosen molecular coordinate system. This can often greatly assist the assignment of the peaks in a spectrum (Sec. II.B.2) as well as usually considerably improving the accuracy with which the band maxima may be resolved. Also, if the density and thickness of the crystal are known, the absorption intensities of the spectral bands may be determined quantitatively, a significant advantage over measurements made with powders. This may be of value in deciding the origin of the intensity: for example, whether the transition is allowed by a vibronic or static mechanism (Sec. IV.A), or in the studies of complexes existing in two isomeric forms in a crystal lattice, when the Beer-Lambert law may be used to determine the relative concentrations of the two species at different temperatures.

The principal reason it is advantageous to cool crystals when measuring electronic spectra is to ensure that as many molecules as possible are in their ground vibrational state. This usually simplifies the spectra, improving resolution and sometimes making it possible to observe vibrational fine structure. Cooling to the

temperature of liquid nitrogen, 77 K, generally produces a
significant improvement in spectral resolution, while if low-energy
vibrations are coupled to the electronic transitions, a further
improvement may be expected on cooling to the temperature of liquid
helium, 4.2 K (Sec. IV.B.1). Furthermore, a study of the changes
in the spectrum as a function of temperature can sometimes give detailed information about the vibrations that induce the intensity
in d-d transitions.

II. PRACTICAL ASPECTS

A. Sample Preparation

1. *Choice of a Suitable Crystal*

Often the most time-consuming part of a study of the polarized
electronic spectra of a complex is the growing of suitable crystals!
Some advice on the art of crystal growing is given in recent articles published by the Bell Telephone Laboratories [12]. The requirements of the technique are that the crystal be of good optical
quality and have one or more well-developed faces available with an
area adequate for the measurement of the spectrum. The thickness of
the crystal must also be such that the maximum absorbance falls in
the working range of the spectrophotometer (ideally, ~ 0.3 to ~ 3.0
optical density units for accurate measurements using a spectrometer
such as a Cary model 17, although good spectra with an absorbance up
to ~ 6.0 have been reported [13]). The quality of the crystal is
best checked by observation under crossed polarizers using a microscope, when it should "extinguish" sharply and uniformly [14]. A
good guide to the anisotropy of a crystal absorption spectrum in the
visible region is provided by the degree of "pleochroism" exhibited
upon rotation of the crystal with the polarizer and analyzer of the
microscope set parallel to one another [14].

To a good approximation, the light absorption of a crystal
should obey the Beer-Lambert law:

$$D = \epsilon ct \tag{1}$$

where D is the optical density, c the concentration of the metal ion, t the crystal thickness, and ε the molar absorbance. For a typical complex of molecular weight 400 and density 2 g/ml, it is apparent that to obtain an optical density of 1 unit for values of ε of 5, 50, and 500 mol^{-1} liter cm^{-1}, crystal thicknesses of 0.4, 0.04, and 0.004 mm, respectively, will be required. This makes it clear that without a beam-concentrating device it will generally be necessary to thin down crystals when $\varepsilon > \sim 10$ mol^{-1} liter cm^{-1}. When only minor thinning is required, this can often be achieved using a suitable abrasive such as alumina, or by slicing with a scalpel if the crystal has a suitable cleavage plane. If a thinner section is required, the crystal may be mounted on the desired face in a hard epoxy resin, and ground and polished using a grinding wheel. Spectra may then be measured with the crystal still held in the resin, provided that the sample is properly masked, although for accurate work the resin should preferably be dissolved away with an organic solvent and the crystal section mounted in the usual manner. In the author's experience it is not generally possible to cut crystals of inorganic complexes with a microtome, as they are too friable.

In general, it is desirable to use a crystal with as large an area as possible. However, modern spectrophotometers, such as the Cary 17, are generally fitted with intense light sources which allow crystals with an area as small as ~ 0.05 mm^2 to be used, particularly if the spectral region of interest coincides with the maximum sensitivity of the spectrophotometer photomultiplier, which is generally ~ 500 nm. Spectrometers are normally rather insensitive in the near-infrared region, and there is an unfortunate "gap" from ~ 700 to ~ 1200 nm in which neither standard photomultiplier tubes nor lead sulfide detectors are very sensitive. This may be partly alleviated by installing a special, red-sensitive photomultiplier [15]. In order that smaller samples may be studied, some workers use optical systems to concentrate the light beam. As the focal length of a lens is wavelength dependent, such systems ideally should use reflecting optics, which are expensive and difficult to come by. However, the ability to utilize very small crystals is a big advantage if highly absorbing systems are to be studied, as it makes the problem of obtaining a very thin sample easier.

2. *Mounting and Cooling the Sample*

Before measuring the spectrum, the crystal must be placed on a suitable "mask," to ensure that all the light reaching the spectrophotometer detector passes through the crystal. In the procedure used by the author, suitable masks are prepared by cutting a hole slightly smaller than the crystal in copper sheeting, and securing the crystal to this by means of a spot of vacuum grease just above the hole. If the crystal is cooled solely by contact with the mask, and accurate knowledge of the temperature is desired, it is most important that good thermal contact be established. This cannot generally be obtained by gluing the crystal to the mask over its whole perimeter, as the thermal stresses induced by cooling then almost invariably shatter the crystal. A procedure that has been found satisfactory when it is important to know the sample temperature accurately is to hold the crystal in place by means of a very thin sheet of aluminum foil, with a hold equal in size to that in the copper mask, this being clamped to the copper block of the cryostat, as illustrated in Fig. 1. It is also essential that no light should "leak" past the crystal, as this will cause the more intense portions of the spectrum to become distorted. If circumstances permit, it is advisable to check that no light leaks are present by continuing the measurements into the ultraviolet until the onset of an intense absorption, and to follow the spectrum until an optical density significantly greater than that of the most intense d-d transition is reached. The effect of a light leak on a typical spectrum is illustrated in Fig. 2, from which it may be seen that it causes both a loss of resolution and a distortion of the relative intensities of the peaks, particularly in the near-ultraviolet (UV) region of the spectrum.

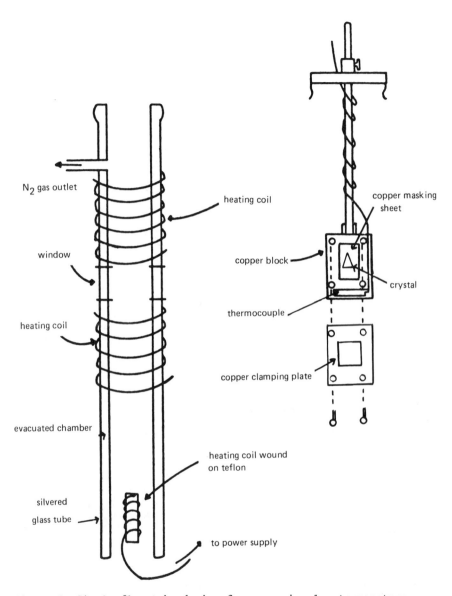

Figure 1   Simple flow-tube device for measuring low-temperature crystal spectra.

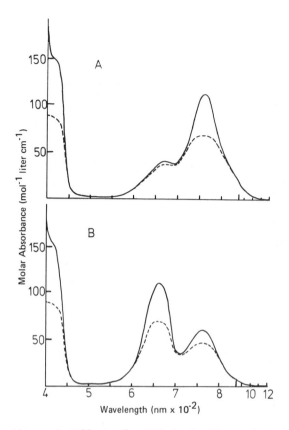

Figure 2 Effect of a "light leak" on the crystal spectrum of
bis(N-benzylpiperazinium)tetrachlorocuprate(II), dichloride measured at 7 K with the electric vector approximately parallel (B)
and perpendicular (A) to the molecular z axis of the distorted
tetrahedral complex (D_{2d} point group). The solid line is the "true"
crystal spectrum, while the dashed line is that with the crystal
moved to produce a light leak having an area ∿2-3% that of the area
of the crystal. (From Ref. 115.)

Probably the simplest method of cooling the sample is by means
of a flow tube, consisting of an evacuated double-walled cylinder,
the bottom of which is dipped into the cooling liquid. A simple device of this type by which temperatures down to ∿85 K may be obtained is shown in Fig. 1. The temperature is easily regulated by
controlling the boil-off of the cooling fluid using a heating coil.

A flow-tube also has the advantage that the sample is in good thermal contact with the cooling gas, so that there should never be any ambiguity in the crystal temperature. Although these may be operated successfully using liquid helium, they are not as convenient as modern closed-cycle cryostats which require no liquid coolant, a great advantage for workers who do not have ready access to a liquid-helium supply.

3. Baseline Corrections

Polarized light may be produced using filters. However, several of these are needed to cover the complete d-d spectral range, and it is probably better to use a calcite polarizing prism or, better still, a matched pair of prisms, one in the sample and the other in the reference light beam. It is convenient to be able to rotate these while measuring the spectrum, and also to be able to center the sample in the light beam, for instance by moving the cryostat. Because the crystal is generally much smaller than the area of the light beam, it is necessary to attenuate the reference beam with a mask similar to that surrounding the sample. Even when this is done, it will often be found that the absorption changes somewhat as a function of wavelength, even in the absence of the crystal. This effect is most pronounced for spectrophotometers in which the slit width varies with the wavelength (this is the case for most spectrophotometers currently available), particularly in the "crossover" region between the photomultiplier and the PbS detector. For this reason, it is usually necessary to measure a baseline by recording the wavelength dependence of the absorption after removing the crystal from the mask. To obtain the true crystal spectrum, this baseline must be subtracted from the initial spectrum.

B. Derivation of Molecular Spectra from Crystal Spectra

1. Measurement of Crystal Spectra

The Light Absorption Process. The intensity of light absorption by a complex is proportional to the integral

$$\langle \psi_2 | V | \psi_1 \rangle^2 \tag{2}$$

where ψ_1 represents the ground state, ψ_2 the excited state, and V
the perturbation produced by the electromagnetic radiation [16].
The electromagnetic radiation may induce a transition by either a
magnetic dipole or an electric dipole mechanism (in principle,
electric quadrupole transitions are also possible, but there are far
too weak to be important in the spectra of metal complexes [16].
The absorption intensity of a band is often expressed in terms of
the oscillator strength, f, which is close to unity for a fully
allowed electric dipole transition and $\sim 10^{-5}$ for a spin-allowed magnetic dipole transition. It is often convenient to describe band
intensities in terms of the molar extinction coefficient ε, related
to the oscillator strength by the expression

$$f = k \int_0^\infty \varepsilon_{\overline{\gamma}} \, d\overline{r} \tag{3}$$

where $\varepsilon_{\overline{\gamma}}$ is the extinction coefficient at wave number $\overline{\gamma}$ and k is a
constant [17]. An approximate guide to absorption intensity is pro-
vided by the extinction coefficient at the band maximum, this being
$\sim 1 \text{ mol}^{-1}$ liter cm^{-1} for a magnetic dipole-allowed transition. The
observed intensities of spin-allowed d-d transitions usually fall in
the range 1-500 mol^{-1} liter cm^{-1}, so that in the majority of cases
it is safe to assume that the contribution to the intensity from a
magnetic dipole mechanism is negligible. In certain situations,
notably the lowest energy transition of octahedrally coordinated
Ni(II) and Co(II) in complexes with a marked ionic character, this
is not the case, and the spectral bands can be interpreted only in
terms of a magnetic dipole interaction [18,19]. It is generally a
rather complicated procedure to distinguish experimentally between
the electric and magnetic dipole intensity mechanisms, and the
method by which this can be done has been discussed in some detail
by Ferguson [6]. However, provided that the observed bands have
values of ε_{max} greater than ~ 5 liters^{-1} mol cm^{-1}, it is safe to

assume that the intensity is derived by an electric dipole mechanism, and the following discussion will be limited to this situation.

The operator representing the electric dipole component of a photon, r, behaves like a unit vector, so that the absorption intensity of an electronic transition $\psi_2 \leftarrow \psi_1$, which is proportional to the integral

$$<\psi_2 |r|\psi_1>^2 \tag{4}$$

may be anisotropic, depending on the orientation of r within the coordinate system used to define the wave functions ψ_1 and ψ_2. One of the most important advantages of single-crystal spectroscopy is that this allows the anisotropy of a molecular spectrum to be investigated. This is achieved by using polarized light to fix the position of the electric vector with respect to the crystal. By measuring the spectrum for several different orientations of the electric vector, the anisotropy of the crystal spectrum may be studied, and if the crystal structure is known, this may be used to determine the anisotropy of the molecular spectrum.

Importance of Crystal Extinction Directions in the Spectral Measurements. The electronic spectrum of the crystal must conform to the symmetry requirements of the space group to which it belongs. The spectrum of a cubic crystal must therefore be isotropic. For uniaxial crystals, which belong to tetragonal, hexagonal, or trigonal space groups, the spectrum can be specified completely by two spectra, one with the electric dipole vector parallel, and the other perpendicular, to the crystal symmetry axis. For orthorhombic, monoclinic, and triclinic systems, the crystal spectrum will in each case have three principal components. In general, when polarized light passes through a crystal of symmetry lower than cubic, it becomes depolarized except when the electric vector is parallel to an extinction direction of the crystal face normal to the light ray [14]. (For all faces of a cubic crystal, and for the crystal faces normal to the symmetry axes of uniaxial crystals, the spectrum is,

of course, isotropic, so that there is no virtue in using polarized
light to measure the spectrum unless the crystal symmetry is to be
perturbed in some way, for instance by applying a strain to the
crystal.) This is the reason why when crystals are viewed under
crossed polarizers using a polarizing microscope, they appear dark
only for specific orientations, those where the electric vector of
light is parallel to an extinction direction. Each crystal face has
two orthogonal extinction directions. When the crystal face contains
a crystal symmetry axis, that is, a unit cell direction for systems
of orthorhombic symmetry of higher or the unique crystal axis for a
monoclinic system, the extinction directions must be parallel and
orthogonal to this axis. When the crystal face contains no crystallographic symmetry axis, which is the case for all planes of a triclinic crystal and any plane not containing the unique axis
(normally [010]) for a monoclinic crystal, the two extinction directions, although still orthogonal, may lie anywhere in the crystal
plane. Moreover, in such a case the extinction directions in principle, can vary as a function of both wavelength and temperature.
As it is essential that the direction of the electric vector within
the crystal be known in order that a polarized crystal spectrum may
be interpreted, it is clearly most important in such cases that the
dependence of the extinction directions on the foregoing factors be
known.

2. Derivation of Molecular Spectra

Molecules for Which the Coordinate System Is Not Defined by
Symmetry. The electronic spectrum of a molecule is completely defined by the absorption coefficient ellipsoid, A, a tensor having
three principal values, A_x, A_y, and A_z, and a specific orientation
in space [20]. For a molecule of such low symmetry that it belongs
to a point group in which no cartesian axis is defined by a symmetry
element, a minimum of six measurements of the spectrum, each with a
different orientation of the electric vector in the molecule, is
necessary to define the tensor completely. Because of the aforementioned restrictions imposed by the crystal symmetry, such detailed

measurements can be performed only on a triclinic crystal. Also, as each face has only two extinction directions, a total of three different crystal planes must be studied. Fortunately, most molecules are of sufficiently high symmetry that the direction of one, and often all three, molecular axes may be specified from the coordination geometry. An important class of molecules which fall into the former category is that involving unsymmetrical chelates, typical examples being $Ni(Nmesal)_2$, and $Cu(MeOac)_2 \cdot 2H_2O$, the structures of which are illustrated in Fig. 3. For these molecules, which belong to the point group C_{2h}, the z-molecular axis is defined by symmetry, being orthogonal to the metal-chelate plane. However, the x and y molecular axes are not defined by symmetry, so it is not clear how

A

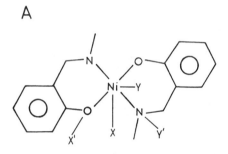

B

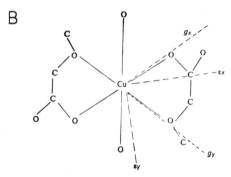

Figure 3 Schematic diagrams illustrating the molecular geometries of two complexes of C_{2h} symmetry (A) bis(N-methylsalicyclaldiminato)-nickel(II) and (B) diaquabismethoxyacetatocopper(II). For the latter complex, the in-plane orientation of the g and ε tensors is shown.

the electronic transitions will be polarized in the plane of the
molecule, and this must be deduced experimentally. A method of deriving the molecular spectra from the crystal spectra of molecules
of this type has been described by the present auther [21].

This procedure initially involves the definition of a molecular
coordinate system. While z must be coincident with the symmetry
axis of the molecule (the normal to the chelate plane), the choice
of the molecular x and y axes is arbitrary, these merely serving as
reference points with which to define the absorption tensor orientation. The molecular absorption tensor is then described in terms of
the four elements A_{zz}, A_{xx}, A_{yy}, and A_{xy}. The optical density D
measured at any wavelength for a particular orientation of the electric vector in the crystal is given by

$$D = z^2 A_{zz} + x^2 A_{xx} + y^2 A_{yy} + 2xy A_{xy} \qquad (5)$$

where x, y, and z are the projections made by the vector on the
molecular axes, where necessary averaged over the different molecules in the crystal unit cell (see the following section). To obtain the four tensor elements, A_{zz} and so on, four independent
measurements are required, meaning that the crystal symmetry must be
either monoclinic or triclinic. These may be the optical density
values for four different orientations of the electric vector in the
crystal. Alternatively, in a method described by the author [21],
three optical density values are utilized, the final piece of
information being supplied by the angle defining the position of the
extinction direction in a plane in which this is not defined by the
crystal symmetry. The latter procedure makes use of the fact that
the extinction directions of a light-absorbing crystal are likely to
coincide with the directions of maximum and minimum absorption [22].
The tensor A is then diagonalized to give principal absorption
values $\underset{\sim}{A}_x$, $\underset{\sim}{A}_y$, and $\underset{\sim}{A}_z$, with the eigenvectors yielding the angle
between the principal absorption directions, often called simply
the polarization directions, and the x and y molecular axes. To
generate the complete spectrum, this process must be carried out

over an appropriate range of wavelengths. Provided that the crystal density and the thicknesses perpendicular to the crystal faces are known, the molecular absorbances $\underline{A}$ may be converted into molar extinction coefficients ε using the Beer-Lambert relationship [Eq. (1)]. On applying the foregoing procedure to the polarized crystal spectrum of $Cu(MeOac)_2 \cdot 2H_2O$, it was found that the principal polarization directions in the xy plane apparently lie approximately midway between the bond directions and the bisector of the chelate rings [21].

To simplify the derivation of the molecular electronic spectrum, it has sometimes been assumed that the molecular polarization directions must coincide with the principal axes of the g tensor of a molecule [23-25]. However, as has been pointed out by Dawson et al. [26], there is no reason why these directions should coincide unless this is required by symmetry. This is because while the orientation of the g values is most strongly influenced by the electronic structure of the *metal* ion in the complex, the intensity of the d-d transitions is in fact dominated by the *ligand* part of the molecular orbitals (see Sec. IV.A). In fact, for $Cu(MeOAc)_2 \cdot 2H_2O$, the in-plane g axes lie close to the metal-ligand bond directions [26], while, as mentioned above, the d-d transitions are polarized along directions that lie approximately midway between the bond axes and the bisector of the angle defining the chelate ring [21].

As yet, very few studies have been made which involve determination of the polarization directions of the electronic spectra of low-symmetry metal complexes, probably because of the difficulty of obtaining sufficient experimental data. This is in marked contrast to studies of the electron paramagnetic resonance (EPR) spectra of low-symmetry metal complexes, where the orientation of the g tensor with respect to the coordination geometry has often provided a useful insight into the nature of the metal-ligand interactions [26-28]. One important reason for this is that whereas the optical spectrum of a crystal is always the sum of the spectra of the constituent molecules, it is often possible to resolve the EPR spectra of the

individual molecules within a crystal. When combined with the fact
that the EPR spectrum may be measured for any orientation of the
magnetic field, in contrast to the situation for optical spectra,
where the vector of polarized light is restricted to lie along a
crystal extinction axis, this means that the limitations on the
information that may be obtained from the crystal electronic spectra
outlined above do not apply as far as EPR spectroscopy is concerned,
except where rapid intermolecular exchange occurs [26].

It is sometimes possible to deduce the approximate molecular
polarization directions of electronic transitions without going
through the complicated procedure outlined above provided that the
packing of the molecules in the crystal is favorable. This is the
case, for instance, for several copper(II) and nickel(II) β-ketoenolate complexes of the type illustrated in Fig. 3a, studied by
Ferguson [29,30]. The crystal packing of a typical complex in the
(001) plane is illustrated in Fig. 4. If the principal in-plane
axes of the electronic spectral absorption ellipsoid approximately
bisect the chelate ring, as illustrated by x and y in Fig. 3a, these
lie approximately parallel to the a and b crystal axes. If, however,

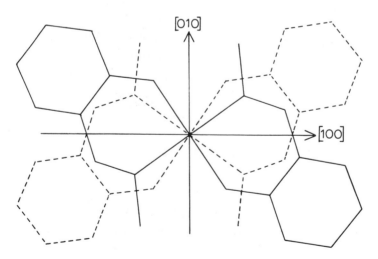

Figure 4   Molecular packing of Ni(Nmesal)$_2$ in (001) crystal plane.

the principal axes lie approximately parallel to the metal-nitrogen
and metal-oxygen bond directions, x' and y' in Fig. 3a, the packing
of the molecules means that the molecular projections on both the a
and b crystal axes are approximately equal. Experimentally, the d-d
spectra in the (001) plane are observed to be strongly polarized,
that for the electric vector parallel to the a axis being far more
intense than that for the electric vector coincident with the b
axis. Since the principal molecular absorbance values must be positive in sign, this means that x and y must lie close to the princi-
pal axes of the absorption tensor, with $\varepsilon_y \gg \varepsilon_x$. It should be noted
that these molecules also illustrate the fact that the molecular g
axes of low-symmetry molecules often do not coincide with the polarization directions of the electronic transitions, since the in-plane
principal g directions of $Cu(Nmesal)_2$ have been found to lie quite
close to the Cu-N and Cu-O bond directions, x' and y' in Fig. 3a
[31].

Molecules Having Coordinate Systems Defined by Symmetry. The
vast majority of studies of the polarized crystal spectra of metal
complexes have involved molecules for which it has been assumed,
probably not always justifiably, that the principal directions of
the molecular absorption ellipsoid are known. This greatly simplifies their interpretation, as it means that each measured crystal
spectrum can be directly transformed into the principal components of
the molecular absorbance tensor. A brief account will now be given
of the way in which this can be done [32].

Consider a monoclinic crystal having two molecules, which we
label 1 and 2, in the unit cell. It is convenient to work within an
orthogonal crystal coordinate system, a, b, c, related to the monoclinic unit cell parameters a', b', c', β, by the relationships

a = a' sin β   (6a)

b = b'   (6b)

c = c' - a' cos β   (6c)

If, in the measurement of a particular crystal spectrum, the electric

vector of polarized light makes projections E_a, E_b, E_c on the
orthogonal crystal axes, the projections on the chosen molecular
axes x, y, z, defined by the symmetry properties of the molecule,
are given by the matrix equations:

$$\begin{vmatrix} x_1 \\ y_1 \\ z_1 \end{vmatrix} = \begin{vmatrix} a_{x_1} & b_{x_1} & c_{x_1} \\ a_{y_1} & b_{y_1} & c_{y_1} \\ a_{z_1} & b_{z_1} & c_{z_1} \end{vmatrix} \begin{vmatrix} E_a \\ E_b \\ E_c \end{vmatrix} \qquad \begin{vmatrix} x_2 \\ y_2 \\ z_2 \end{vmatrix} = \begin{vmatrix} a_{x_2} & b_{x_2} & c_{x_2} \\ a_{y_2} & b_{y_2} & c_{y_2} \\ a_{z_2} & b_{z_2} & c_{z_2} \end{vmatrix} \begin{vmatrix} E_a \\ E_b \\ E_c \end{vmatrix} \qquad (7)$$

Here a_{x_1} and so on are the projections made by the indicated molecular axis on the appropriate crystal axis. The observed optical density D at any wavelength is then related to the molecular absorbances
by averaging over the two molecules:

$$D = x^2 A_x + y^2 A_y + z^2 A_z \qquad (8)$$

where $x^2 = (x_1^2 + x_2^2)/2$, $y^2 = (y_1^2 + y_2^2)/2$, and $z^2 = (z_1^2 + z_2^2)/2$.
This procedure is readily extended to take account of any number of
molecules in the unit cell. Provided that there is only one molecule in the asymmetric unit, the transformation matrices appropriate
to the different molecules in the unit cell are related to one another in a simple manner by the symmetry operations of the space
group. Bearing in mind that translational symmetry operations may
be ignored in the present context, while molecules related by an
inversion center produce identical absorption spectra, it is easily
seen, for instance, that in all monoclinic systems, just two molecular orientations are present, related by a mirror plane normal to
the crystal symmetry axis (generally, the b axis). The transformation matrices in Eq. (7) for these two "different" molecules are
thus identical except that $b_{x_1} = -b_{x_2}$, $b_{y_1} = -b_{y_2}$, and $b_{z_1} = -b_{z_2}$.
As discussed in the following section, these symmetry relationships
can in certain circumstances have a pronounced affect on the accu-

racy with which the components of a molecular spectrum may be determined.

In many studies, this is as far as the transformation of crystal to molecular spectra is taken, with each crystal spectrum merely being discussed in terms of the relative contribution expected from each molecular component. However, the desired molecular spectra (these being plots of A_x, A_y, and A_z as a function of wavelength) may, in fact, be derived from the crystal spectra in a quite straightforward manner by solving Eq. (8) for a minimum of three orientations of the electric vector in the crystal, the process being carried out over a range of wavelength values chosen so as to produce the required resolution in the final spectra. As only two sets of measurements can be made on each crystal face, a minimum of two crystal faces must be studied if the symmetry of the molecule is such that $A_x \neq A_y \neq A_z$. This adds the complicating feature that the optical densities will be affected not only by variations in the molecular projections, but also because the thicknesses normal to the two faces will not be the same. A convenient method of avoiding this problem, by taking the ratios of the optical densities of each face rather than their absolute values, has been described by Hitchman and Belford [32]. Typical crystal spectra for two crystal faces of the planar complex $Cu(benzac)_2$ are shown in Figs. 5 and 6, while the molecular components of each spectrum are given in Table 1 (the molecular coordinate system being defined assuming the complex to belong to the D_{2h} point group, with the y axis bisecting the chelate ring and z orthogonal to the plane of the complex). The molecular spectra obtained by the described above procedure [32] are shown in Fig. 7. It is important to recognize that whenever it is necessary to go through a procedure of the foregoing type to extract molecular from crystal spectra, some degradation in the quality of the spectra must occur. In certain unfavorable circumstances this may be so pronounced that it is, in fact, impossible to derive a complete molecular spectrum at all, for the reasons discussed in the following section.

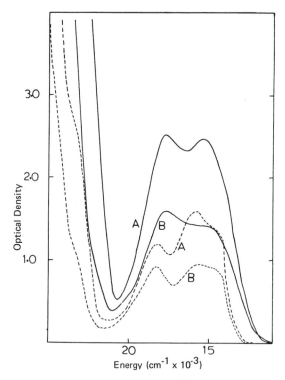

Figure 5   The room-temperature (solid line) and 8 K (dashed line)
spectra of the (011) crystal face of Cu(benzac)$_2$ with the electric
vector at A 67° and B -23° to the a crystal axis.   (From Ref. 32.)

C.   Packing Problems: Limitations in the Derivation of Molecular
     Spectra Because of the Molecular Packing in the Crystal

As outlined above, the components of the molecular absorbance spectrum of a molecule of known principal axes are obtained by solving
the set of equations for the optical density D measured for i different orientations of the electric vector of polarized light in the
crystal:

$$D(i) = x(i)^2 A_x + y(i)^2 A_y + z(i)^2 A_z \tag{9}$$

where x(i) and so on represent the molecular projections averaged
over all the molecules in the unit cell for orientation i.   The

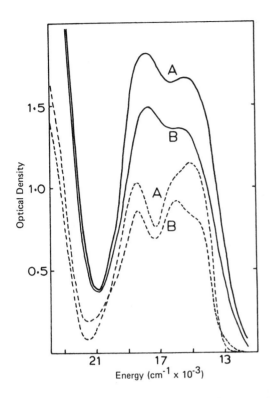

Figure 6 The room-temperature (solid line) and 8 K (dashed line)
spectra of the (001) crystal face of Cu(benzac)$_2$ with the electric
vector parallel (B) and perpendicular (A) to the b crystal axis.
(From Ref. 32.)

Table 1 Molecular Projections for a Unit Electric Vector Along the
Extinction Directions of Two Crystal Faces of Bis(benzylacetonato)-
copper(II)

| | | (Molecular projections)^2 | | |
		x^2	y^2	z^2
Extinction	Direction			
(011)	67°	0.4755	0.4543	0.0703
(011)	-23°	0.0904	0.2576	0.6520
(001)	‖b	0.6341	0.1924	0.1735
(001)	⊥b	0.0001	0.4875	0.5124

Source: Ref. 32.

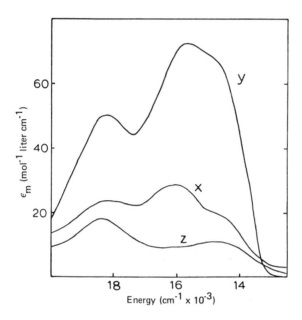

Figure 7   Molecular spectrum of Cu(benzac)$_2$.   (From Ref. 32.)

spectrum is generated by performing this calculation at appropriate
wavelength increments, and it is apparent that the equations will
provide a unique set of $A_{(x)}$ and so on when $i = 1$-3.   (When more
than three independent spectra can be measured, the problem is over-
determined, and a least-squares procedure may be used to determine
the "best-fit" molecular absorbances; however, the present discussions will be limited to the case where just the minimum data are
available.)   A point which has not always been properly appreciated
is that the accuracy with which the polarized molecular spectrum may
be determined depends not only on the normal experimental errors
inherent in measuring the crystal spectra, but also on the relative
magnitudes of $x(i)^2$, $y(i)^2$, and $z(i)^2$ for the three equations to be
solved.   Except in the ideal case in which the three molecular axes
of all the molecules coincide with the three extinction directions
used for the crystal measurements (corresponding to $x = 1$, $y = 0$,
$z = 0$ for $i = 1$, $x = 0$, $y = 1$, $z = 0$ for $i = 2$ and $x = 0$, $y = 0$,

$z = 1$ for $i = 3$), the effect of the transformation from crystal to molecular coordinates must always be to increase the uncertainty in the molecular spectra. The precise way in which the errors are amplified depends on how much the ratio $x^2 : y^2 : z^2$ differs over the three crystal spectra, with a greater variation producing a better defined set of molecular spectra. Uncertainties due to simple instrumental factors may be controlled by making the wavelength increments at which measurements are made small enough to give molecular spectra of the desired "resolution." However, this does not take into account possible errors in baseline corrections, or factors such as unevenness in the crystal faces. For this reason, in the view of the present author, it is generally best to check the reliability of the molecular spectra by comparing the spectra obtained from measurements made on at least two separate sets of data.

For triclinic crystals, it is always possible, at least in principle, to obtain two crystal faces giving a well-defined set of equations for the calculation of the molecular spectra. However, for higher-symmetry space groups, this is no longer the case, as the molecular projections $x^2(i)$, $y^2(i)$, $z^2(i)$ are now the averages for the symmetry-related molecules in the unit cell. This provides a fundamental limitation to the precision with which molecular spectra may be derived, and in certain unfavorable situations it is in fact impossible to deduce all the components of a molecular spectrum. This is often called the "packing problem" of polarized crystal spectroscopy and occurs when a molecular axis of one molecule in the unit is approximately parallel to a different axis of the second molecule. A much studied example of a complex having a packing problem of this kind is $Cu(acac)_2$ [33-37]. The crystal spectrum of this compound was first studied by Ferguson [33], who concluded from the molecular projections associated with each spectrum that the d-d transitions were polarized in a manner which implied a most unusual ground state for the compound, with the unpaired electron residing in the d_{yz} orbital. Subsequent work found that the crystal structure reported [38] for $Cu(acac)_2$ was in error, and the revised

structure determination showed [35] that the y and z molecular axes
of the two molecules in the monoclinic unit cell are almost exactly
parallel. This means that a set of equations [Eqs. (9)] in which
the coefficients $y(i)^2$ and $z(i)^2$ are linearly independent cannot be
obtained, so that it is physically impossible to distinguish between
the z and y molecular spectra of the complex. When this is taken
into account, the spectrum of $Cu(acac)_2$ is quite consistent with
those of other similar β-ketoenolate complexes, the predominant feature of these being the strong y polarization of all the d-d transitions [9] (see Sec. IV.A.2). Other examples are known in which the
crystal packing induces a significant degradation in the quality of
the molecular spectrum [39]. It is therefore always advisable to
look for problems of this kind before undertaking a time-consuming
study of crystal spectra. A rapid check may be made by noting that
a packing problem is to be expected whenever two of the molecular
axes of a complex make angles of ∿45° with a crystal axis that is
perpendicular to a mirror plane in the unit cell.

III. BRIEF SUMMARY OF THE NATURE OF ELECTRONIC SPECTRA

A description of the theory of molecular electronic spectra as
applied to transition metal complexes is to be found in several
general texts [4,5,40,41]. However, a brief summary of those aspects which are of special relevance to the present discussion is in
order.

Many of the important features of electronic spectra are
conveniently represented in terms of an energy diagram showing the
potential surfaces of the ground and excited electronic states
drawn as a function of one of the normal modes of the molecule. A
typical schematic diagram of this kind is shown in Fig. 8. In the
simple case illustrated, transitions are observed from the lowest
vibrational state of the ground electronic state to several vibrational members of the excited electronic state (the relative intensities of these may, in fact, be used to provide a measure of the
displacement in the normal-mode Q between the equilibrium geometries

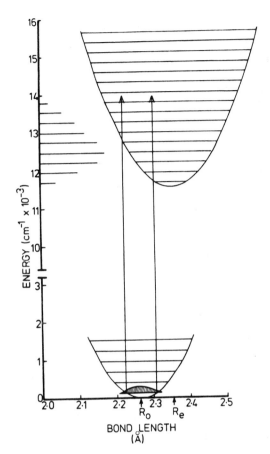

Figure 8   Illustration of the way in which the vibrational components
of an electronic transition depend on the displacement between the
ground- and excited-state potential surfaces. The diagram, which is
drawn approximately to scale, is for the $^2B_g(d_{xy}) \leftarrow {}^2B_{1g}(d_{x^2-y^2})$
transition of the planar $CuCl_4^{2-}$ in $(nmph)_2CuCl_4$ which is accompanied by an elongation of ∿0.18 Å in the α_{1g} totally symmetric Cu-Cl
stretching mode, corresponding to an elongation of ∿0.09 Å of each
Cu-Cl bond.

of the ground and excited electronic states; this aspect is considered further in Sec. IV.C). In general, spectra are complicated by
two things. The first is by the population of excited vibrational

levels of the ground electronic state, which means that at higher
temperatures the spectrum is always a superposition of the spectra
of molecules in several vibrational levels. While the variation of
the spectrum as a function of temperature can occasionally give
valuable information on the nature of the vibrations coupled to the
electronic transitions (see Sec. IV.B.1), this does mean that above
∿150 K the overlapping of the various bands usually blurs out all
structure in the electronic spectra of metal complexes. This
particular problem may always be remedied by cooling the sample,
preferably to ∿4 K. The second complicating feature, however, arises
because a complex always has a large number of normal modes. If the
electronic transition is coupled to several of these, the spectrum
will consist of a superposition of bands built on a number of different origins, and these may well overlap to produce a featureless
composite spectrum. As each of the individual bands is likely to be
polarized along a particular molecular axis, the chance of resolving
structure is greatly increased if the molecules are packed in the
crystal in such a manner that relatively "pure" molecular spectra
can be observed (see Sec. II.B). Clearly, a major requirement for
the observation of structure in an electronic transition is that the
complex should have as few normal modes as possible, and since the
number of these increases sharply with the number of atoms in a
molecule, this is probably the reason why structure is seldom observed in complexes involving large polyatomic ligands. It is also
not yet clear to what extent the oriented gas model is obeyed as far
as the coupling of vibrational and electronic transitions in metal
complexes is concerned. Recent evidence suggests that in several
planar tetrahalo complexes [39,42,43] the electronic transitions are
coupled not only to metal-ligand vibrations, but also to what are,
formally, lattice modes. This aspect is considered further in Sec.
IV.F.2, but it may also be an important factor which generally tends
to blur out the vibrational fine structure in the low-temperature
spectra of metal complexes.

IV. CHEMICAL INFORMATION FROM CRYSTAL SPECTRA

A. Mechanisms Inducing Intensity into d-d Transitions

1. *Noncentrosymmetric Complexes*

A molecule having a ground state characterized by wave function ψ_g is able to absorb a photon to undergo a transition to an excited state ψ_e if the integral $<\psi_e|r|\psi_g>$ is nonzero. Here r represents the electric vector of light. Whether such a process is "allowed" or "forbidden" may conveniently be determined from the character table appropriate to the symmetry of the molecule [44]. For the d-d excitations of transition metal complexes, the wave functions represent states in which the electrons occupy molecular orbitals which are largely d in composition. For a noncentrosymmetric complex belonging to a clearly defined point group, it is a quite straightforward procedure to derive selection rules showing which transitions are "allowed" when the electric vector of light is along each of the cartesian axes in the complex. For instance, the compound $(bzpipzn)_2$-$CuCl_6$ contains $CuCl_4^{2-}$ ions which are slightly distorted away from square planar towards a tetrahedral geometry [44a]. In the D_{2d} point group of the complex the transitions $^2E(d_{xz},d_{yz}) \leftarrow {}^2B_2(d_{xy})$ and $^2A_1(d_z^2) \leftarrow {}^2B_2(d_{xy})$ are allowed in (xy) and z polarization, respectively. The crystal spectrum (Fig. 2) shows peaks at 13,200 and 15,200 cm^{-1}, the former being stronger in (xy) and the latter in z polarization, suggesting the foregoing assignments for the transitions. As expected, the bands are 5-10 times more intense than the corresponding peaks in the spectrum of the corresponding, centrosymmetric planar $CuCl_4^{2-}$ ion (Fig. 12).

As a further example we may consider the complex $Cu(acac)_2 \cdot$quinoline, the geometry of which is illustrated in Fig. 9. To a good approximation, this molecule belongs to the point group $C_{2v}(z)$, and from the symmetry properties shown in Table 2 it is easily found that the transitions $^2B_2(d_{yz}) \leftarrow {}^2A_2(d_{xy})$ and $^2B_1(d_{xz}) \leftarrow {}^2A_2(d_{xy})$ are allowed in x and y polarization, respectively. From this it might be

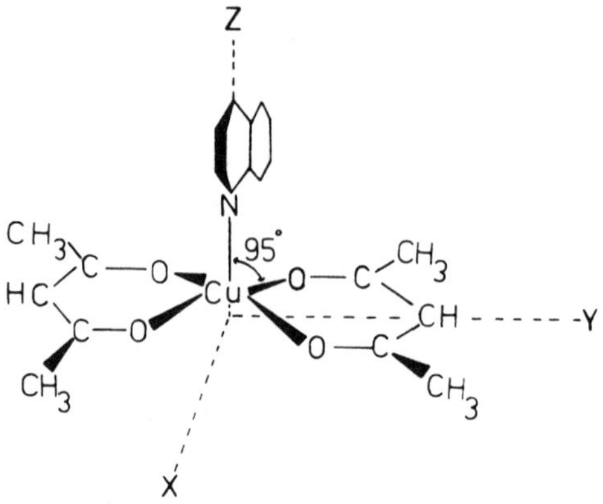

Figure 9   Molecular geometry and coordinate system of Cu(acac)$_2$·quinoline.

Table 2   Character Table for Point Group $C_{2v}(z)$

$C_{2v}(z)$	E	C_2	$\sigma_v(xz)$	$\sigma'_v(yz)$		
A_1	1	1	1	1	z	x^2, y^2, z^2
A_2	1	1	-1	-1		xy
B_1	1	-1	1	-1	x	xz
B_2	1	-1	-1	1	y	yz

thought that the molecular spectrum should show two relatively intense peaks, one being present in x and the other in y polarization.
The polarized crystal spectrum reported for Cu(acac)$_2$·quinoline [45]
is shown in Fig. 10.   From this it may be seen that while the y
spectrum is indeed dominated by one intense peak, the x spectrum is
quite weak.   This illustrates the important point that although
group theory is a powerful tool for determining which electronic
transitions are formally allowed, it says nothing about their actual
intensity.   In the case of Cu(acac)$_2$·quinoline the fact that the
formally allowed transition $^2B_2(d_{yz}) \leftarrow {}^2A_2(d_{xy})$ is of only very
weak intensity was shown [45] to be in good agreement with a

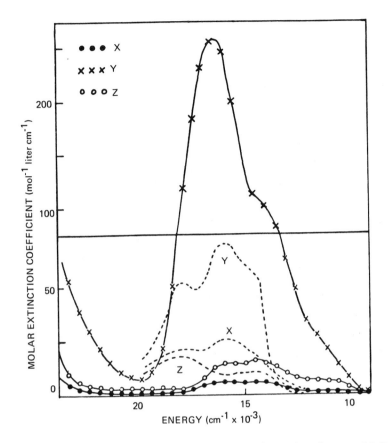

Figure 10 Molecular spectra of Cu(acac)$_2$·quinoline at 80 K (solid lines). The spectrum of Cu(benzac)$_2$ at 8 K is shown for comparison (dashed lines). (From Ref. 45.)

proposed mechanism for the way in which the d-d transitions in centrosymmetry copper β-ketoenolate complexes gain their intensity (see Sec. IV.A.2). In general, it is usually not possible to interpret the absolute intensities of d-d transitions quantitatively. For this reason, whenever possible it is helpful to be able to compare the spectra of noncentrosymmetric complexes with those of closely analogous centrosymmetric molecules, in which the d-d transitions are all formally forbidden by the selection rules above (see the following section). When the spectrum of Cu(acac)$_2$·quinoline is compared with that of an analogous planar, centrosymmetric complex, Cu(benzac)$_2$, also shown in Fig. 10, it is readily apparent that it is just the spectrum in y polarization which increases in intensity on adduct formation. Similarly, comparison of the intensities of the d-d bands in the complexes Cu(acac$_2$en) and Cu(acac$_2$en)·H$_2$O with those in the analogous centrosymmetric trans Schiff-base complexes has provided a valuable insight into the intensity mechanisms operating in this type of complex [46].

Another example of the importance of comparing the spectra of formally noncentrosymmetric compounds with those of centrosymmetric analogs is provided by the extensive work carried out on crystals of the tris-ethylenediamine complexes of Co^{3+} [47], Cr^{3+} [48], and Ni^{2+} [49], in which it has been observed that the band intensities are quite similar to those of the corresponding centrosymmetric hexamine complexes. Although the former complexes formally belong to the noncentrosymmetric point group D$_3$, the effective departure from O$_h$ symmetry is quite small, and detailed studies backed by theoretical calculations suggest that in the case of the Co(en)$_3^{3+}$ ion the intensity due to this "static" distortion contributes only $\sim$20% to the total band intensity, the remainder being due to coupling with noncentrosymmetric vibrations [47].

The examples above all concern molecules in which the geometry can be regarded as a comparatively minor asymmetric perturbation superimposed on a dominant centrosymmetric ligand arrangement. A number of studies of the crystal spectra of complexes having fairly regular, noncentrosymmetric geometries have also appeared. Several trigonal bipyramidal cobalt(II) [50] and nickel(II) [51,52] complexes have been investigated, as have a number of nickel(II) compounds with square-pyramidal geometries [53-55], although as yet no detailed interpretation of the intensity mechanisms operating in these types of complex has been made. The crystal spectra of a large number of copper(II) complexes with a range of highly distorted coordination geometries have also been reported by Hathaway and co-workers [28,56].

Probably the most detailed spectral studies of noncentrosymmetric complexes have involved the tetrahedral ions $CoCl_4^{2-}$ [57-59] and $NiCl_4^{2-}$ [60-63] and the distorted $CuCl_4^{2-}$ ion [64]. Because of the high intensity of the bands, each of these species has been studied when doped into a transparent host lattice. The spectrum of the flattened tetrahedral $CuCl_4^{2-}$ ion has been of particular interest, as this has been the subject of several detailed theoretical treatments [65-67]. The observed band energies and intensities are in reasonable agreement with the calculations of Ros and Schuit [65], and the general conclusion to be drawn from the theoretical results is that the bulk of the intensity in the spectra of this kind of complex derives from integrals involving the ligand portions of the molecular orbitals, with a somewhat smaller contribution coming from cross-terms involving the metal d and ligand p orbitals; the metal s and p portions of the orbitals apparently have little effect on the intensities of the d-d transitions.

2. Centrosymmetric Complexes

Simple Vibronic Selection Rules. Application of the simple group-theoretical selection rules described in the preceding section to the d-d transitions in centrosymmetric complexes implies that these are always formally forbidden, since the components of the electric vector transform according to ungerade representations, while the molecular orbitals involving the d functions belong to gerade representations. In agreement with this, the d-d transitions in centrosymmetric complexes are normally rather weak, with molar extinction coefficients typically lying in the range 5-100 liters mol^{-1} cm^{-1}. It has long been realized that to explain the intensities observed for the spectra of this class of compound, it is necessary to consider not the time-averaged geometry of the complex, but the way in which the geometry changes as a function of time. This is described by the normal vibrational modes of the molecule, and since, as stated by the Franck-Condon principle [68], electronic transitions occur much more rapidly than vibrational motion, this means that at any instant the observed electronic spectrum will be the superposition of the spectra

of complexes having the complete range of geometries defined by the
normal modes.   These are illustrated for a planar tetrahalide complex
in Fig. 11.   Selection rules for each d-d transition may, in fact,

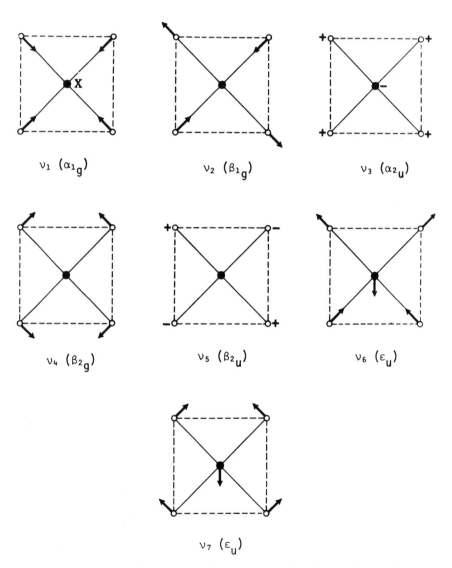

Figure 11   Normal vibrations of a planar molecule complex such as
$CuCl_4^{2-}$.

therefore be derived simply by applying the group-theoretical criteria considered in the preceding section to the particular geometry produced by each ungerade vibration. Table 3 shows the way in which the d-d transitions are activated by each mode for a planar complex such as $CuCl_4^{2-}$. Electronic transitions activated by vibrations in this way are said to be "vibronically" allowed.

Although these considerations allow a simple understanding of the reason d-d transitions are expected to have nonzero intensity even in centrosymmetric complexes, the foregoing procedure for deducing selection rules is cumbersome, and historically the theoretical treatment of the vibronic intensity mechanism has proceeded along rather different lines. The generally accepted perturbation model for the way in which intensity is induced in parity-forbidden d-d transitions has been described in several recent reviews [69-71], but is relevant to the subsequent discussion to summarize briefly the way in which the vibronic selection rules are derived.

Table 3 Activation of the d-d Transitions by the u Vibrational Modes of a Copper(II) Complex Belonging to the D_{4h} Point Group

Vibrational mode	"Instantaneous" point group[a]	Allowed electronic transitions[b]	
		xy	z
β_{2u}	C_{2v}	$d_{xz}, d_{yz} \rightarrow d_{x^2-y^2}$	$d_{z^2} \rightarrow d_{x^2-y^2}$
α_{2u}	C_{4v}	$d_{xz}, d_{yz} \rightarrow d_{x^2-y^2}$	-
ε_u(stretch)	C_{2v}	$d_{xy}, d_{z^2} \rightarrow d_{x^2-y^2}$	$d_{xz}, d_{yz} \rightarrow d_{x^2-y^2}$
ε_u(bend)	C_{2v}	$d_{xy}, d_{z^2} \rightarrow d_{x^2-y^2}$	$d_{xz}, d_{yz} \rightarrow d_{x^2-y^2}$

[a]Point group of molecule with atoms displaced along the normal mode as illustrated in Fig. 11.

[b]Coordinate system defined as for the time-averaged nuclear geometry of D_{4h} symmetry.

Consider the formally forbidden transition $\psi_{2g} \leftarrow \psi_{1g}$ in r polarization. The u normal modes of the complex Q_u, are considered to act as perturbations that mix all available u excited states ψ_{iu} into the g wave functions, to yield the new functions ψ_1 and ψ_2:

$$\psi_1 = \psi_{1g} + \overset{i}{\sum} C_{1i}\psi_{iu} \tag{10a}$$

$$\psi_2 = \psi_{2g} + \overset{i}{\sum} C_{2i}\psi_{iu} \tag{10b}$$

To the first order, each mixing coefficient is obtained by summing over all the u modes:

$$C_{1i} = \frac{\overset{Q}{\sum} Q{<}\psi_{1g}|\partial V/\partial Q|\psi_{iu}{>}}{E(\psi_{iu} - \psi_{1g})} \tag{11}$$

$$C_{2i} = \frac{\overset{Q}{\sum} Q{<}\psi_{2g}|\partial V/\partial Q|\psi_{iu}{>}}{E(\psi_{iu} - \psi_{2g})} \tag{12}$$

The relevant integral of the electronic transition now becomes $<\psi_2|r|\psi_1>$, and substitution of the expanded forms of the wave functions (10a) and (10b), to first order, yields the nonzero terms:

$$\overset{i}{\sum} C_{1i}{<}\psi_{2g}|r|\psi_{iu}{>} + \overset{i}{\sum} C_{2i}{<}\psi_{iu}|r|\psi_{1g}{>} \tag{13}$$

The integral $<\psi_{2g}|r|\psi_{iu}>$ is nonzero if $\Gamma_{2g} \times \Gamma r \times \Gamma_{1u} \in A_{1g}$. As the operator $\partial V/\partial Q$ transforms in the same representation as Q, the coefficient C_{1i} is nonzero when $\Gamma_{1g} \times \Gamma_Q \times \Gamma_{iu} \in A_{1g}$, that is, when $\Gamma_{iu} = \Gamma_{1g} \times \Gamma_Q$. Both these conditions must be satisfied in order for the transition to be vibronically allowed, and combining the expressions above yields the requirement

$$\Gamma_{2g} \times \Gamma_r \times \Gamma_{1g} \times \Gamma_Q \in A_{1g} \tag{14}$$

The same requirement is obtained for the second term in Eq. (13). This means that the representation of the normal mode (or modes) that induces intensity into the electronic transition is given by the expression

$$\Gamma(Q) = \Gamma(\psi_{2g}) \times \Gamma(\psi_{1g}) \times \Gamma(r) \qquad (15)$$

If the molecule has at least one vibration of this symmetry type, the transition is vibronically allowed, while if none of the normal modes transforms in that symmetry representation, the transition is vibronically forbidden. As the normal-mode symmetries are tabulated for all likely stereochemistries [72], it is therefore a fairly straightforward procedure to derive simple "yes or no" selection rules for the vibronic transitions of any metal complex. When doing this, however, it is important to ensure that the same symmetry axes have been used to describe the electronic and vibrational wave functions. It should be noted that the coefficients C_{2i} are usually expected to be significantly larger than C_{1i} in Eq. (13), as the excited electronic states of u symmetry are closer in energy to the excited d states than they are to the ground state; that is, $E(\psi_{iu} - \psi_{1g}) > E(\psi_{iu} - \psi_{2g})$ in Eqs. (11) and (12). This means that the vibronic intensity mechanism essentially operates by the "stealing" of intensity from the parity allowed transitions $\langle\psi_{iu}|r|\psi_{1g}\rangle$, via the vibrational coupling of the excited d states with states of u symmetry:

$$\langle\psi_{2g}|\partial V/\partial Q|\psi_{iu}\rangle$$

The most common application of the vibronic selection rules is as an aid to the assignment of electronic spectral transitions. For instance, the ordering of the d orbitals in the planar $CuCl_4^{2-}$ ion has long been the subject of controversy [65-67,73] and probably the most direct experimental evidence on this question is provided by polarized crystal spectroscopy. To a good approximation, this ion belongs to the point group D_{4h}, and the normal vibrations allowing each d-d transition in (xy) and z polarization are listed in Table 4. From this it may be seen that just one transition is forbidden, $^2B_{2g}(d_{xy}) \leftarrow {}^2B_{1g}(d_{x^2-y^2})$ in z polarization. The spectrum of the (100) crystal face of a typical complex containing planar

Table 4   Vibronic Selection Rules for a Copper(II) Complex of D_{4h} Symmetry

Electronic transition	Active vibrations	
	xy	z
$^2B_{2g}(xy) \leftarrow {}^2B_{1g}(x^2 - y^2)$	ε_u	-
$^2E_g(yz,yz) \leftarrow {}^2B_{1g}(x^2 - y^2)$	α_{2u}, β_{2u}	ε_u
$^2A_{1g}(z^2) \leftarrow {}^2B_{1g}(x^2 - y^2)$	ε_u	β_{2u}

$CuCl_4{}^{2-}$, (methadonium)$_2CuCl_4$, is shown in Fig. 12 measured at $\sim$6 K [74]. Here, when the electric vector lies along [001] it is almost parallel to the z molecular axis, whereas when it is along [010] it is almost in the xy plane of the $CuCl_4{}^{2-}$ group. Ignoring at this stage the vibrational fine structure observed on two of the peaks, the spectrum consists of three bands, centered at $\sim$12,500, 14,500, and 17,000 cm^{-1}, and the first of these is almost absent in z polarization, so that this may confidently be assigned to the transition $^2B_{2g}(d_{xy}) \leftarrow {}^2B_{1g}(d_{x^2-y^2})$. The assignment of the other two peaks cannot be deduced from the selection rules of the D_{4h} point group. However, when the slight difference between the two independent Cu-Cl bond distances in the complex is taken into account, the point group symmetry is lowered to D_{2h}, the result being that the $^2E(d_{xz},d_{yz})$ state is split into two components, $^2B_{2g}(d_{xz})$ and $^2B_{3g}(d_{yz})$, with the transition to the former level being vibronically forbidden in y polarization, and that to the latter in x polarization. In the crystal spectrum of the analogous complex (Nmph)$_2CuCl_4$, the x and y molecular spectra can be resolved [39], and the band at 14,500 cm^{-1} is indeed observed to be split into two components separated by $\sim$400 cm^{-1} and with the predicted polarization properties, allowing this to be assigned to the transition to the $^2E(d_{xz},d_{yz})$ excited state. By default the band at 17,000 cm^{-1}, which occurs in

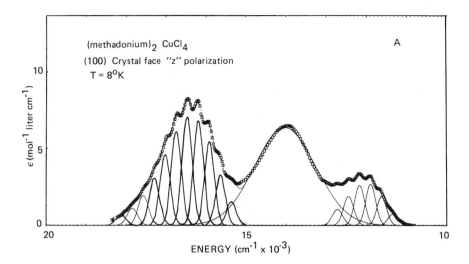

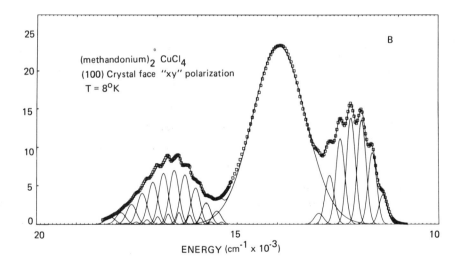

Figure 12   Spectrum of the (100) crystal face of (methadonium$_2$CuCl$_4$
at 8 K resolved into Gaussian components with the electric vector
approximately parallel (A) and perpendicular (B) to the z molecular
axis of the planar CuCl$_4{}^{2-}$ ion.

all three polarization directions, is assigned to the transition $^2A_{1g}(d_{z^2}) \leftarrow {}^2B_{1g}(_{x^2-y^2})$. Vibronic selection rules have been used in a similar fashion to aid in the assignment of the spectra of several other planar complexes, including the isomorphous minerals gilles-pite, $BaSi_4FeO_{10}$ [75], and egyptian blue, $CaSi_4CuO_{10}$ [76], the com-plex $[Ni(DACO)_2](ClO_4)_2 \cdot 2H_2O$ [77], where DACO represents a saturated diamine, and a range of platinum(II) and palladium(II) tetrahalide complexes [42,43,78-80]. These spectral studies have been largely instrumental in uncovering the unusual bonding characteristics of this class of complex [81] discussed in Sec. IV.E.2.

The crystal spectra of various complexes of general formula trans-NiL_4X_2 have also been discussed within the framework of the D_{4h} point group, where L is an aromatic amine such as pyridine and imidazole [82] or pyrazole [83] and X is a halide ion or water mole-cule, as have those of the complexes $Ni(NH_3)_4X_2$, X = NO_2 and NCS [84], and $Ni(en)_2X_2$, X = NO_2 and NCS [85]. The spectra of the nitro-complexes have recently been remeasured, however, and it has been found [86,87] that the band is probably a weak metal $\rightarrow$ ligand charge transfer transition rather than a d-d excitation (see Sec. IV.F.3). The crystal spectrum of $Ni(thiourea)_4Cl_2$ has also been described [88], as have the spectra of two six-coordinate histidine complexes of nickel(II) [89]. The crystal spectra of a wide range of centro-symmetric copper(II) complexes having tetragonally distorted octa-hedral geometries have been interpreted in terms of the appropriate vibronic selection rules by Hathaway and co-workers and the results of these studies are summarized in several review articles [28,56, 90]. A detailed study of the crystal spectra of $CoCl_2 \cdot 6H_2O$ [91] and $CoCl_2 \cdot 2H_2O$ [92] and their deuterated analogs has also been reported, as have the polarized spectra of crystals containing the trans-$Co(en)_2X_2^+$ [93,94] and trans-$Cr(en)_2X_2^+$ [95,96] ions, where X = Cl^- and Br^-.

It is sometimes possible to use the vibronic selection rules to aid in the assignment of spectra even when the crystal structure of the complex has not been determined. This is the case, for instance,

when the molecular point group is known, and the selection rules
suggest that just one of two transitions should be strongly polarized. The crystal spectrum of the complex trans-$[Cr(en)_2F_2]ClO_4$ was
used in this way [97] to resolve a long-standing controversy [98]
concerning the band assignments of the trans-$[Cr(en)_2F_2]^+$ ion.
Similarly, the crystal spectra of a range of nickel(II) and cobalt-
(II) carboxylate, nitrate, and nitrite complexes of various substituted diamines have been reported by Lever and co-workers [13,
99-101] and used to deduce both the energy levels and probably
stereochemistries of the compounds, even in the absence of crystal
structure data. It must be remembered, however, that these experiments rely first, on the compounds having favorable packing of the
molecules within the crystal lattice, and second, on the vibronic
selection rules being obeyed in a straightforward manner. Since it
is known that in some cases the latter condition is not met (see the
following section), it is always better to use samples of known
crystal structure whenever possible, so that the observed polarization properties may be related directly to the molecular geometry.

Deviations from the Simple Vibronic Selection Rules. The
validity of the simple "yes or no" vibronic selection rules, derived
as outlined above, depends on two important assumptions: First,
that for each polarization an ungerade excited state is available
from which intensity may be "borrowed," and second, that of the u
vibrational modes of the molecule, at least one of each symmetry
type is active in inducing intensity. If either of these conditions
is not met, at least approximately, the simple selection rules will
be complicated by the fact that significant differences in intensity
will be observed between the formally vibronically allowed transitions.

If a particular vibration dominates in the intensity-stealing
process, the bands activated by this mode will dominate each polarized spectrum. It has been suggested [102] that this is the case
in the crystal spectrum of Ni(diethylcarbamate)$_2$ with the β_{2u} vibration of this planar molecule of D_{2h} symmetry being the active mode.

It has also been proposed, on the basis of the relative intensities
of the bands in the (xy) and (z) polarized spectra of a number of
tetragonally distorted copper(II) complexes of D_{4h} symmetry, that
the out-of-plane bending vibration of β_{2u} symmetry is particularly
active in inducing intensity in this type of complex [38,56]. It
may be seen from the selection rules shown in Table 3 that this im-
plies that the transition $^2E_g(d_{xz}, d_{yz}) \leftarrow {}^2B_{1g}(d_{x^2-y^2})$ should be the
most intense band in (xy) polarization, while the band due to
$^2A_{1g}(d_{z^2}) \leftarrow {}^2B_{1g}(d_{x^2-y^2})$ should dominate the (z) spectra. It may be
seen from the spectra in Fig. 12 that this pattern is indeed observed
experimentally for the planar $CuCl_4^{2-}$ ion in $(methadonium)_2CuCl_4$.

A class of compounds for which the simple vibronic selection
rules are clearly inadequate is the range of planar β-ketoenolate
complexes formed by copper(II). The simplest of these, $Cu(acac)_2$,
has already been discussed in connection with the problems that can
occur in deriving molecular spectra from crystal spectra (Sec. II.C).
The crystal spectra of some five complexes of this type have now been
measured [9,32,33,103,104] and these all show the same general pattern, with the spectrum being much more intense in y than in x or z
polarization (the y axis bisects the chelate ring). An example of a
typical spectrum of a molecule of this kind is shown in Fig. 7.
Similar polarization behavior has also been observed for a number of
planar copper(II) and nickel(II) Schiff-base complexes [29,30], suggesting that this is a quite general feature of the spectra of such
molecules. The vibronic selection rules for a copper(II) complex of
D_{2h} symmetry in which the axes bisect the metal-ligand bond directions suggest that all the d-d transitions are formally allowed in
every polarization. Clearly, the dominance of a single polarization
in the molecular spectrum cannot be caused by the activity of particular ungerade vibrational mode, as this would intensify one or more
peaks in all three polarizations. It has been suggested by Belford
and co-workers [9,32] that a single polarization is expected to
dominate the spectrum if all u modes are effectively active, and the

bulk of the intensity is borrowed from just one ungerade excited
state. That is, the summation in Eq. (12) is carried out over all
Q, but just one excited state ψ_i dominates in the intensity-stealing
process. To produce the observed y polarized spectra, this state
must be of B_{3u} symmetry. Because it must differ from both the
ground and excited d states by just a single electron, as the integrals in Eqs. (12) and (13) both involve one-electron operators,
Belford was further able to show that it is likely that the B_{3u}
state is produced by a y polarized ligand → metal electron transfer
transition in which the electron originates in the molecular orbital
of b_{3u} symmetry derived from the appropriate combination of nonbonding "lone-pair" electrons of the ligand oxygen atoms. This hypothesis is in agreement with molecular orbital calculations on a model
copper(II) acetylacetonato complex [105], which suggests that this
transition occurs at rather low energy, and with the limited data
that are available on the polarization properties of the charge
transfer spectra of compounds of this type [106]. Further support
for the correctness of the proposed mechanism is provided by the
apparently anomalous crystal spectrum (Fig. 10) of the five-coordinate adduct $Cu(acac)_2 \cdot$quinoline discussed in Sec. IV.A.1. This complex is obtained by adding a quinoline molecule along the z axis of
$Cu(acac)_2$, with the metal ion moving slightly out of the plane of
the acetylacetonate oxygen atoms toward the nitrogen ligand atom
(Fig. 9). This lowers the symmetry of the complex from D_{2h} to C_{2v},
and in the latter point group the transitions $^2B_1(d_{xz}) \leftarrow$
$^2A_2(d_{xy})$ and $^2B_2(d_{yz}) \leftarrow {}^2A_2(d_{xy})$ become formally electric dipole
allowed in y and x polarization, respectively. In agreement with
this, one peak in the spectrum $Cu(acac)_2 \cdot$quinoline is much more intense in y polarization than any in the spectrum of the analogous
centrosymmetric complex, and this may confidently be assigned to the
transition $^2B_1(d_{xz}) \leftarrow {}^2A_2(d_{xy})$. The x spectrum is anomalous in that
all bands are relatively weak; that is, no measurable intensifica-
tion of the formally allowed $^2B_2(d_{yz}) \leftarrow {}^2A_2(d_{xy})$ transition has taken
place. This anomaly can, however, be rationalized by the intensity

mechanism above when it is recognized that the d_{yz} orbital is, in fact, orthogonal to the ligand lone-pair orbitals involved in the excited state from which intensity is borrowed [45].

Several other complexes are known for which the overall intensity of all peaks is considerably greater in one polarization than in another. For instance, in the planar complexes $CaSi_4CuO_{10}$ [76] and $Ni(DACO)_2(ClO_4)_2$ [77] the spectra in xy polarization are much more intense than in z polarization; to a lesser extent this would seem to be true of all tetragonally distorted copper complexes [28,56] (see, e.g., the spectrum of planar $CuCl_4^{2-}$ in Fig. 12). It has been suggested [39] that this may possibly reflect the fact that the bulk of the intensity in this type of complex is borrowed from the xy polarized ligand → metal charge transfer transition, in which the electron originates in the σ bonding orbital of e_u symmetry.

B. Effects of Temperature on d-d Spectra

1. *Variation of Intensity: The* coth^{-1} *Rule*

Although the extinction coefficients of parity-allowed transitions often decrease substantially when the temperature is raised, this is normally approximately balanced by an increase in the band widths (see Sec. IV.B.2), so that the oscillator strengths stay approximately constant. A slight decrease in the integrated intensity of the $^4T_1 \leftarrow {}^4A_2$ transition of the tetrahedral $CoCl_4^{2-}$ ion has been observed to accompany an increase in temperature from 4 K to 290 K, and this was interpreted [107] in terms of coupling with vibrational modes that destroy the formal T_d symmetry of the complex.

In the case of centrosymmetric complexes, where the intensity is induced by coupling with u vibrations as outlined in the preceding sections, it is clear that the thermal population of excited vibrational levels of the ground electronic state is expected to produce an increase in intensity, since the vibrational amplitudes will be greater. For each u mode that is active, the increase in intensity at any temperature, compared with that induced by the zero-point motion present even at 0 K, will depend on the energy of the vibration. The mathematical relationship between intensity and temperature for a vibronically allowed d-d transition was originally formulated by Liehr and Ballhausen [108] and later developed by Englman [109]. This approach assumes a Boltzmann distribution over the vibrational levels of the ground electronic state, these behaving as simple harmonic oscillators. The intensity of a band, f_i, at temperature T induced by coupling with the ith normal mode of energy $\overline{\gamma}_i$ is given by

$$f_{iT} = f_{i0} \frac{[1 + \exp(-\overline{\gamma}_i/kT)}{1 - \exp(-\overline{\gamma}_i/kT)]} \tag{16}$$

where f_{i0} is the zero-point intensity and k is the Boltzmann constant.

Equation (16) may conveniently be rearranged to give the well-known "coth^{-1} rule" for the variation of vibronically induced intensity as a function of temperature:

$$\coth^{-1} \frac{f_{iT}}{f_{i0}} = \frac{\overline{\gamma}_i}{2kT} \tag{17}$$

The original derivation of this relationship included as a restriction the assumption that the equilibrium nuclear geometries of the ground and excited electronic states must belong to the same point group, a situation that for d-d transitions may not be realized (see Sec. IV.C). However, more recent work by Lohr [110] has suggested that this restriction is in fact unnecessary, and that Eq. (17) should be obeyed irrespective of the geometry of the excited electronic state. This seems reasonable if the electronic excitations are viewed simply as Franck-Condon transitions summed over the nuclear geometries appropriate to the various u modes, as outlined at the start of the preceding section. At any particular temperature, the relative intensity compared with that at absolute zero should then depend only on the magnitudes of Q for the different vibrational levels of the ground electronic state [or rather Q^2, since the transition moment involves the square of the integrals given in Eqs. (11) and (12)], summed over the populations of these at that temperature.

Qualitatively speaking, considerable experimental evidence is available to show that the intensities of d-d transitions of centrosymmetric complexes generally do increase, often quite substantially, when the temperature is raised. Indeed, the absence of such a temperature dependence has sometimes been used as evidence that a particular transition is allowed by a static rather than a vibronic mechanism. It should be remembered, however, that a change in intensity with temperature is to be expected for a vibronically allowed transition only if the active vibration is of low enough energy to have the first excited state thermally populated within the temperature range of the experiment (normally 4-300 K). For most metal-ligand vibrations this will be the case, but where the stretching modes of light and strongly bound ligands are involved, these may have such high frequencies that only a slight temperature dependence is observed. This is the case for some of the bands observed in the crystal spectrum of egyptian blue, $CaCuSi_4O_{10}$ [76]. It may be noted in this context that for a peak coupled to an active mode of energy 500 cm^{-1} the $coth^{-1}$ rule predicts an increase in intensity of $\sim$20% on warming from 0 K to room temperature.

Comparatively little work has yet been carried out on the quantitative interpretation of the way in which the intensities of vibronically allowed d-d transitions vary as a function of temperature. When just one u mode is active in inducing intensity, the model above predicts that a plot of $coth^{-1}(f_T/f_0)$ against 1/T should produce a straight line of slope $\bar{\gamma}/2kT$ passing through the origin. When more than one mode is active, however, the situation is more complex, since while the *components* of the intensity induced by each u vibration should obey the $coth^{-1}$ relationship above, their sum, which is what is measured experimentally, will not. This is clearly illustrated by the plots shown in Figs. 13 and 14, which show how

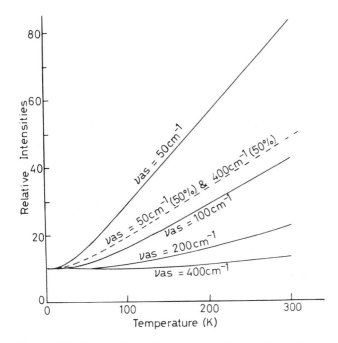

Figure 13 Variation of the total intensity of a vibronically allowed electronic transition as predicted by the coth^{-1} rule for different energies of the active u mode.

the total intensity of f_T and the function coth^{-1}(f_T/f_0) are predicted to vary as a function of temperature when f is composed of two contributions activated by different u modes. The plots are shown for the ratio f_1/f_2 varying from 0 to 1, for pairs of u modes of energy 50 and 200 cm^{-1}, and it can be seen that quite a small contribution to the zero-point intensity by a low-energy mode is predicted to cause a substantial deviation in the coth^{-1}(f_T/f_0) plot of the total intensity observed. Moreover, when more than one mode is active in inducing intensity, it is virtually impossible to pinpoint both the energy and effectiveness of the active modes with any accuracy, particularly as the experimental uncertainty in the ratio f_T/f_0 may well be ∿10%. However, when the likely energy of each u mode is known, considerable information may be inferred from a study of the temperature dependence of d-d transitions. This may be

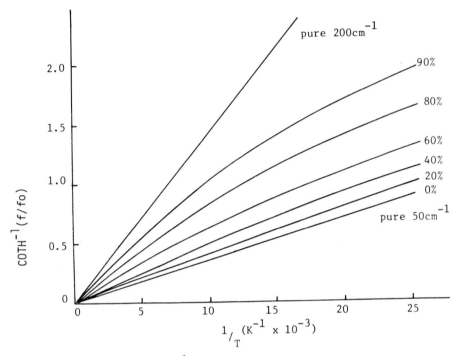

Figure 14   Plots of $\coth^{-1}(f/f_0)$ versus $1/T$, where f is the total intensity induced by coupling with u modes of 50 and 200 cm^{-1}, these being active in various proportions.

illustrated by considering the spectrum of the planar $CuCl_4^{2-}$ ion, the temperature dependence of which is shown in Fig. 15 [74]. Qualitatively speaking, it is apparent that one or more u modes of very low energy are active in inducing intensity in this complex, first, because of the dramatic increase in overall intensity that occurs on raising the temperature from 7 K to 295 K, and second, because the intensity increase begins at a very low temperature.

The vibronic selection rules for a planar complex such as $CuCl_4^{2-}$ have been given in Table 3, and the overall band polarizations suggest the assignments $^2B_{2g}$, ^2E_g, $^2A_{1g} \leftarrow {}^2B_{1g}$ at 12,200, 14,000, and 16,500 cm^{-1}, respectively, for (methadonium)$_2CuCl_4$ (see Sec. IV.A.2). The symmetries of the active normal modes in each

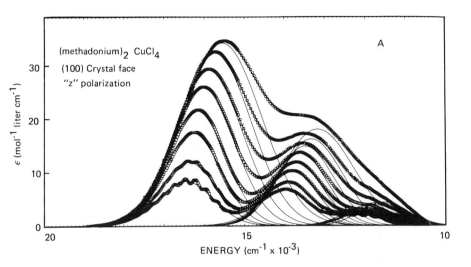

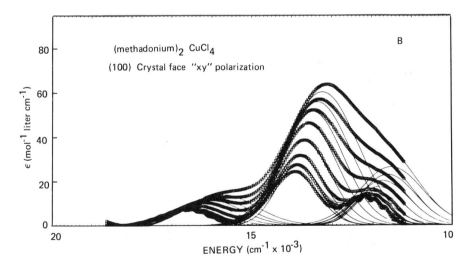

Figure 15   Temperature dependence of the spectrum of the (100) crystal face of (methadonium)$_2$CuCl$_4$ with the electric vector approximately parallel (A) and perpendicular (B) to the z molecular axis of the planar CuCl$_4{}^{2-}$ ion. Experimental points are shown by squares, "best-fit" gaussian curves, and their sums are shown as solid lines.

polarization are shown in Table 4, the energies of various modes as
suggested by infrared and Raman spectroscopy being given in Table
5. The function $\coth^{-1}(f_T/f_0)$ plotted against $1/T$ is shown for
each transition in Fig. 16. Inspection of Tables 4 and 5 shows
that for the transition $^2A_{1g}(d_{z^2}) \leftarrow {}^2B_{1g}(d_{x^2-y^2})$ in z polarization,
just a single vibration is predicted to be active in inducing
intensity, that of β_{2u} symmetry. In agreement with this, the plot
of $\coth^{-1}(f_T/f_0)$ versus $1/T$ yields a straight line passing through
the origin (Fig. 16a), the slope of this suggesting an energy of
~ 50 cm^{-1} for the β_{2u} vibration. As this mode is both Raman and
infrared inactive (Table 5), the energy cannot be deduced directly
from vibrational spectroscopy; however, a normal coordinate analysis
suggests that it should be of low energy (~ 75 cm^{-1}) [111]. The
transition $^2E(d_{xz}, d_{yz}) \leftarrow {}^2B_{1g}(d_{x^2-y^2})$ in xy polarization is allowed
by vibrations of both α_{2u} and β_{2u} symmetry and the plot of
$\coth^{-1}(f_T/f_0)$ versus $1/T$ is nonlinear, suggesting that both these

Table 5 Vibrational Energies of the Planar CuCl$_4^{2-}$ Ion, Point
Group D$_{4h}$

Mode	Activity	Motion	Energy (cm^{-1})
$\nu_1(\alpha_{1g})$	Raman	Symmetric Stretching	276
$\nu_2(\beta_{1g})$	Raman	Stretching	210
$\nu_3(\alpha_{2u})$	IR	Out-of plane bending	152
$\nu_4(\beta_{2g})$	Raman	In-plane bending	182
$\nu_5(\beta_{2u})$	Inactive	Out-of-plane bending	$-^a$
$\nu_6(\varepsilon_u)$	IR	Stretching	~ 300
$\nu_7(\varepsilon_u)$	IR	In-plane bending	188

^{a}Not observed experimentally.
Source: Ref. 39.

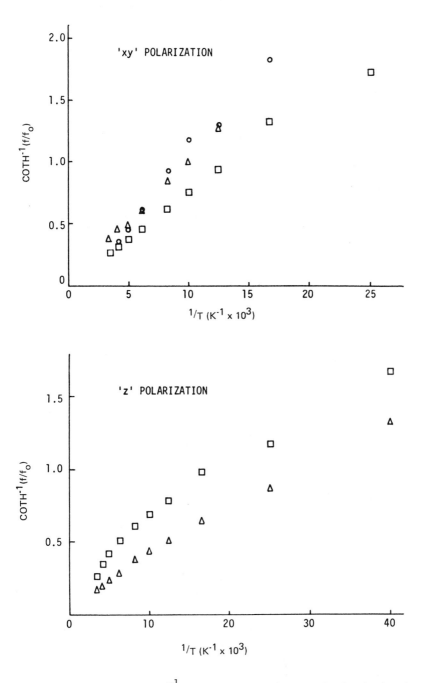

Figure 16 Plots of $\coth^{-1}(f/f_0)$ versus $1/T$ for the bands in the spectrum of (methadonium)$_2$CuCl$_4$, circles represent band 1; squares, band 2; and triangles, band 3, in order of increasing energy.

vibrations are active (Fig. 16b). The bands due to the transitions $^2E_g(d_{xz},d_{yz}) \leftarrow {}^2B_{1g}(d_{x^2-y^2})$ in z polarization, and $^2A_{1g}(d_{z^2}) \leftarrow$ $^2B_{1g}(d_{x^2-y^2})$ and $^2B_{2g}(d_{xy}) \leftarrow {}^2B_{1g}(d_{x^2-y^2})$ in xy polarization, are each allowed by vibrations of ε_u symmetry. The $CuCl_4^{2-}$ has two modes of this symmetry type, an in-plane bend of energy ~190 cm^{-1} and a stretching vibration of ~300 cm^{-1} (Fig. 11). The transition $^2B_{2g}(d_{xy}) \xleftarrow{xy} (d_{x^2-y^2})$ shows a single vibrational progression at low temperature (Fig. 12b), implying that a single u mode dominates in the intensity mechanism. The slope of the coth^{-1} plot suggests an energy of ~150 cm^{-1} for this vibration, implying that it is the in-plane bend of ε_u symmetry that is the active mode. In the case of the band due to the $^2A_{1g}(d_{z^2}) \xleftarrow{xy} {}^2B_1(d_{x^2-y^2})$ transition, at low temperature this is resolved into two vibrational progressions (Fig. 12b), suggesting that in this case two u modes are active in inducing intensity. A comparison of the energies of the origins of the progressions with that in z polarization suggests energies of the active modes of ~70 cm^{-1} and ~190 cm^{-1} if the simple vibronic intensity mechanism is obeyed (Sec. IV.D), while the overall intensities of the progressions suggest that $\sim15\%$ of the total band area is due to coupling with the lower-energy mode, and $\sim85\%$ to the higher-energy mode. In agreement with this, the change of total band intensity as a function of temperature is well reproduced by Eq. (16), assuming the foregoing values for $\bar{\gamma}_1$ and $\bar{\gamma}_2$, and f_{10}/f_{20}, as may be seen from the plot shown in Fig. 17. The energy of the mode $\bar{\gamma}_2$, ~190 cm^{-1}, agrees well with that estimated by infrared spectroscopy for the in-plane ε_u stretching vibration (Table 5). The mode of energy ~70 cm^{-1} is presumably formally a lattice vibration or the inactive β_{2u} mode, so that in this case the induced intensity represents a breakdown in the simply oriented gas vibronic model. In the case of the transition $^2E_g(d_{xz},d_{yz}) \xleftarrow{z} {}^2B_1(d_{x^2-y^2})$, as no vibrational fine structure is resolved it is impossible to tell how many vibrational modes are active in producing intensity.

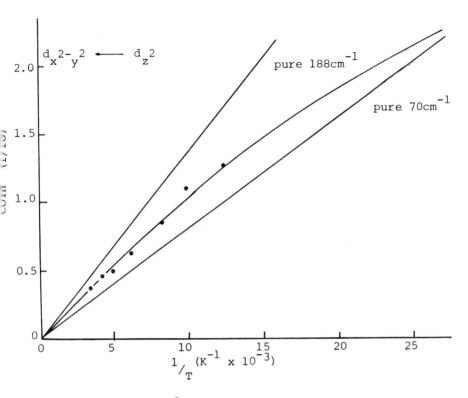

Figure 17 Plot of $\coth^{-1}(f/f_0)$ versus $1/T$ for the band due to the $d_{x^2-y^2}) \leftarrow d_{z^2}$ transition of the planar $CuCl_4^{2-}$ ion in (methadonium)$_2$-$CuCl_4$ with the electric vector approximately perpendicular to the z molecular axis (solid circles). The variations predicted by the $\coth^{-1}$ rule assuming an active u mode of energy 188 cm^{-1}, 70 cm^{-1}, and the proportion 85% of the former and 15% of the latter, as suggested by the areas of the vibrational progressions, are also shown as full lines.

However, the fact that the temperature dependence suggests an "average" effective mode of energy $\sim$100 cm^{-1} implies that here also low-energy lattice modes make a significant contribution to the intensity (or that the low-energy metal-ligand vibration of β_{2u} symmetry is active, despite the fact that coupling with that mode is formally disallowed in this polarization).

Comparatively few quantitative studies of the temperature dependence of d-d spectra have yet been reported. In a pioneering investigation of the spectra of the hexahydrate complex of various divalent and trivalent metal ions, Holmes and McClure [112] derived energies for the active u vibrational modes using a relationship of the form

$$f_T = f_0 \left[1 + \exp\left(\frac{-\theta}{T}\right) \right] \tag{18}$$

where θ is a constant that may be related to the energy of the active mode. However, as pointed out by Harding et al. [113], the neglect of the term $1/[1 - \exp(-\bar{v}/kT)]$ in Eq. (16) is likely to introduce quite large inaccuracies into the estimated vibrational energies. The latter workers reported [113] a detailed study of the temperature dependence of the $^3T_{2g} \leftarrow {}^3A_{2g}$ band of the $Ni(H_2O)_6^{2+}$ ion in $Ni(H_2O)_6(BrO_3)_2$, and were able to simulate successfully the nonlinear plot of $\coth^{-1}(f_T/f_0)$ against $1/T$ by assuming that 30% of the zero-point intensity is induced by the t_{1u} metal-ligand mode of energy 320 cm^{-1}, with the remaining intensity being derived from the t_{1u} mode of energy 190 cm^{-1}. The temperature dependence of the d-d spectrum of the octahedral $NiCl_6^{4-}$ chromaphore obtained by "doping" Ni^{2+} into $KMgCl_3$ has been studied over the temperature range 80 K-763 K by Brynstead et al. [114]. These workers observed a large temperature dependence for the bands, which could not be explained satisfactorily using a simple $\coth^{-1}$ relationship, particularly at high temperatures. An attempt was made to fit the experimental data to a vibronic model including anharmonic corrections, developed by Englman [109], but this also proved unsuccessful. As recognized by the authors, an important limitation in the treatment was the fact that the nature and energies of the u modes active in inducing intensity was unknown. In a detailed study of the spectrum of the $Co(en)_3^{3+}$ ion, however, Ballhausen and Dingle [47] noted that the intensity increase in the $^1T_{2g} \leftarrow {}^1A_{1g}$ transition on going from 20 K to 298 K was in good agreement with the simple vibronic intensity rules, assuming that the τ_{1u} vibration of energy 350 cm^{-1} is active in inducing intensity. The temperature dependence of the d-d bands of the planar $CuCl_4^{2-}$ ion in $(Nmph)_2CuCl_4$ has been analyzed by Hitchman and Cassidy [39], the conclusions being rather similar to those outlined above for this ion in $(methadonium)_2CuCl_4$, with the out-of-plane mode of β_{2u} symmetry being particularly active in inducing intensity, and coupling with low-energy lattice modes also having a significant effect for certain transitions.

Occasionally, useful information may be derived from temperature-dependence measurements, even in the absence of a detailed analysis. Thus Belford and co-workers [9,32] have used the fact that in copper(II) acetylacetanato complexes the d_{xz}, $d_{yz} \leftarrow d_{xy}$ transitions are allowed by out-of-plane bending vibrations in xy polarization, but by in-plane stretches and bends in z polarization, whereas the reverse is true for the d_{z^2}, $d_{x^2-y^2} \leftarrow d_{xy}$ transitions, to help clear up the long-standing controversy which has surrounded the assignment of the d-d transitions in this class of complex. As vibrations of the former type are expected to be of considerably lower energy than those of the latter, the bands allowed by out-of-plane bending modes might be expected to exhibit a significantly greater temperature dependence than those activated by in-plane stretches and bends. The behavior observed was thus consistent with the transitions to the d_{xz}, d_{yz} orbitals occurring at higher energy than those to the $d_{x^2-y^2}$ and d_{z^2} orbitals. Although these arguments provide useful corroborative evidence, it must be remembered that they neglect the possibility of coupling with low-energy lattice modes, which as we have seen in the example of the planar $CuCl_4^{2-}$ ion, can sometimes substantially affect the temperature dependence of vibronically allowed d-d transitions.

2. Variation of Band Position and Width

To a first approximation, the energy of the band maximum of a parity-allowed d-d transition of an isolated transition metal complex is not expected to vary as a function of temperature. For any particular complex the precise behavior will depend on the way in

which the Franck-Condon factors associated with the thermally
excited vibrational states of the molecule differ from those of the
ground vibrational state. So far, few experimental data are available to provide information on this question. It has been observed
[115] that for the distorted tetrahedral $CuCl_4^{2-}$ ion, the $d_{xy} \leftarrow$
$d_{x^2-y^2}$ transition shifts significantly to lower energy as the
temperature is raised from 7 K to 300 K, and it seems possible that
this is due to the thermal population of higher levels of vibrational modes which carry the complex toward a more regular tetrahedral geometry, as discussed below for the planar $CuCl_4^{2-}$ ion.
In general, metal-ligand interactions are expected to decrease as
the temperature is raised, owing to a lengthening of the metal-
ligand bond, and this should cause a decrease in d-orbital splittings. However, for an isolated metal complex this change in bond
length is associated with the anharmonicity of the totally symmetric
metal-ligand stretching vibration, and as this mode is normally of
quite high energy (250-500 cm^{-1}), it should not have a significant
effect except at quite high temperatures. For a continuous lattice
involving bridging ligands the situation is more complicated, and
it is likely that the mean metal-ligand distance will be more
directly dependent on temperature.

For a centrosymmetric complex, the simple vibronic model
developed using a perturbation approach outlined in Sec. IV.A.2
predicts that each d-d electronic transition of energy E must be
accompanied by a transition of an active u normal mode, with the
latter obeying the selection rule that the vibrational quantum number must change by one unit [108,109]. This means that when the
complex is in the ground vibrational state, the d-d band will be
built on an origin of energy $E + \bar{\gamma}_{u'}$, where $\bar{\gamma}_{u'}$ is the energy of the
u mode in the excited electronic state. When the complex is therm-
ally promoted into the first vibrational state of the active u mode
(of energy $\bar{\gamma}_u$) a "hot" band will occur, built on an origin of
energy $E - \bar{\gamma}_u - \bar{\gamma}_{u'}$. This should produce a shift to lower energy
of the overall band maximum as the temperature is raised, although

it should be noted that from this effect alone the shift should be significantly less than $\sim 2\bar{\gamma}_u$. Again, little experimental work on the variation of band maxima with temperature has been reported, although what information is available, for instance on metal hydrate complexes [112], suggests that shifts may be considerably greater than predicted by the simple explanation above. For example, the band maxima of the planar $CuCl_4^{2-}$ ion shift to lower energy by ~ 900 cm^{-1} on warming from 6 K to 295 K (Fig. 15) [39,74,116], and this cannot be rationalized solely in terms of hot-band excitations. A possible explanation might be an effective increase in the Cu-Cl bond length as the temperature is raised. Assuming that the oriented gas model holds, this corresponds to the thermal population of higher states of the totally symmetric a_{1g} stretching mode, with this being substantially anharmonic. A mechanism of this kind has been suggested by Englman [109]. In the present case this explanation is clearly inadequate, as the shift in band maximum begins at far too low a temperature to be associated with such a high-energy vibrational mode (~ 270 cm^{-1}). Instead, it seems more probable that the β_{2u} out-of-plane bending mode is involved, and that it is changes in the Franck-Condon factors accompanying the thermal population of higher states of this vibration that cause the overall band maximum to shift to lower energy as the temperature is raised. It is noteworthy that the β_{2u} vibration carries the $CuCl_4^{2-}$ ion toward a tetrahedral geometry, and the low energy (~ 50 cm^{-1}) and large amplitude of the mode mean that, in effect, as the temperature is raised, the average ligand arrangement at any instant of time tends more and more toward this stereochemistry, so that the energy states of the molecule cannot be treated adequately in terms of the *time-averaged* square-planar nuclear geometry. This situation is quite similar to that which occurs for molecules exhibiting dynamic Jahn-Teller effects, where again the time-averaged geometry, as indicated, for instance, by x-ray crystallography, may suggest a regular octahedral ligand arrangement, while the electronic properties show that at any instant of time the nuclear geometry is likely to be

substantially distorted along the Jahn-Teller active vibrational
modes [117]. The value of Dq was also observed [114] to decrease
quite substantially (by ∿12%) on heating from 80 K to 763 K for the
$NiCl_6^{4-}$ chromaphore in Ni^{2+}-doped $KMgCl_3$, but this was not interpreted quantitatively.

Qualitatively speaking, it is well established that as the
temperature is raised, electronic spectral bands generally broaden.
When the energies of the transitions originating from higher vibrational levels of the ground electronic state differ from those from
the zero vibrational state, as is the case for the hot bands of
vibronically allowed transitions, this will contribute to the overall band width at higher temperatures, and any quantitative interpretation of the broadening will be difficult. However, if the energy
of the band maximum does not shift significantly as a function of
temperature, the broadening is likely to be due simply to the fact
that the excited vibrational levels of the ground state overlap with
a greater range of the excited-state vibrational levels than does
the zero vibrational state of the ground state. This is illustrated
in Fig. 18. The band envelopes of spin-allowed d-d transitions are
normally dominated by progressions in the totally symmetric mode
(see the following section), so that the band width at any temperature is expected to be decided by the thermal distribution over the
various levels of this vibration. In the case of charge transfer
transitions it has been observed [118,119] that the band half-width
H_T obeys the relationship

$$H_T^2 = H_0^2 \coth \frac{\bar{\gamma}}{2kT} \tag{19}$$

where H_0 is the half-width at absolute zero and $\bar{\gamma}$ is the energy of
the α_{1g} stretching mode. As expected, the form of this equation is
closely analogous to that used to describe the temperature dependence of the intensity of vibronically allowed electronic transitions [Eq. (17)]. Although Eq. (19) has apparently not yet been
used to investigate the behavior of Laport-allowed d-d transitions,

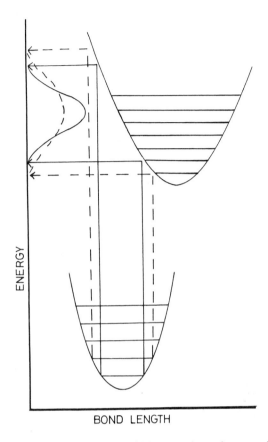

ENERGY

BOND LENGTH

Figure 18   Diagram illustrating the way in which the band width of
an electronic transition is expected to depend on the thermal population of the α_{1g} vibrational levels of the ground electronic state.

a quite similar behavior to that observed for charge transfer transitions is expected.

The considerations above apply to the situation expected for
most spin-allowed d-d transitions, where comparatively broad bands
composed of vibrational progressions are observed, as illustrated in
Fig. 8.   The line width is then dominated by the number of vibrational levels of the excited state which overlap with the ground-
state vibrational wave function.   When the observed peak consists of

just one, or a few, vibronic transitions, which for d-d transitions
will generally only be the case for spin-forbidden transitions (see
the following section), the variation in peak width as a function
of temperature will depend on the way in which the line shape of
the individual vibronic transitions is influenced by temperature.
Although it is clear that the individual vibronic peaks often
broaden quite dramatically when the temperature is raised, for instance in the case of the spin-forbidden transitions of the $NiCl_4^{2-}$
[62] and $CoCl_4^{2-}$ [59] ions, the actual mechanism by which this
occurs has not yet been investigated.

C. Geometries of Complexes in Excited Electronic States

It has long been recognized that the band shape of d-d transitions
is related to the difference between the equilibrium nuclear geometry of the ground and excited electronic states [4,5]. When this
difference is small, a sharp peak occurs; whereas when it is large,
a broad band results. These effects arise because if the ground and
excited states have identical geometry and vibrational force constants, the overlap between the vibrational wave functions requires
that for a Laporte-allowed transition no change in the vibrational
quantum number occurs. For a vibronically allowed transition the
same applies except that the electronic transition is accompanied
by a change in one quantum of the active u mode. The net result is
that a single, sharp peak is expected at 0 K, with in the latter
case an additional hot peak occurring at higher temperatures. However, if in the excited electronic state the complex is displaced
in its equilibrium geometry along a normal coordinate Q by an amount
δ, the overlaps with higher vibrational levels of the upper state
will no longer be zero, and the electronic transition will occur as
a band (see Sec. III and Fig. 8). If the vibrational quantum numbers of the band components can be assigned, their relative intensities can be used, together with the change in vibrational frequence
of the mode associated with the band, to estimate the magnitude of

the displacement δ. A convenient procedure by which this may be
done has been described by Henderson et al. [120] and published as
a series of tables listing the way in which the relative overlap
integrals involving each vibrational member of the excited electronic state are expected to vary as a function of the displacement in
normal coordinates and the ratio of the vibrational frequencies in
the ground and excited states [121]. The relative importance of
these factors has been considered by Yersin et al. [122], who have
given numerical expressions for calculating the intensities of the
band components for both absorption and emission spectra. The absorption intensity of the transition to the nth vibrational level
of the excited state, I_n, relative to that of the zeroth level, is
given by

$$\frac{I_n}{I_0} = \frac{E_n}{E_0}\left(\frac{R_n}{R_0}\right)^2 \tag{20}$$

where E is the energy of the relevant state and R is the vibrational
overlap integral. The vibrational overlap integrals are given by

$$R_0 = [2\delta(1 + \delta^2)]^{1/2} \exp\left[-\frac{1}{2}\rho^2\right] \tag{21}$$

$$R_{n+1} = \frac{-2\delta^2 D R_n - (2n)^{1/2}(\delta^2 - 1)R_{n-1}}{(\delta^2 + 1)[2(n + 1)]^{1/2}} \tag{22}$$

where $\delta = (\gamma_1/\gamma_2)^{1/2}$, $D = C\sqrt{m\gamma_2}\Delta S$, and $\rho = D/(1 + \delta^2)^{1/2}$. Here γ_1
and γ_2 are the vibrational frequencies in the ground and excited
states, m the reduced mass of the ligands, ΔS the displacement along
the normal coordinate, and C is a constant. When the displacement
occurs in the α_{1g} totally symmetric stretching mode, as is usually
the case for transition metal complexes, if m, the mass of one li-
gand, is in atomic mass units, γ_1 and γ_2 are in cm^{-1}, and ΔS is in
angstrom units, the constant C takes the value 0.1722 [123]. The
normal way of estimating the change in normal coordinate is to vary
ΔS until optimum agreement with experiment is obtained. The component intensities are quite sensitive to this parameter, as may be

seen from the fits to the absorption spectra of the $^1A_{2g} \leftarrow \ ^1A_{1g}$
transition of the $PdCl_4{}^{2-}$ ion reported by Patterson et al. [79] and
the $^3A_2 \leftarrow \ ^3T_1$ transition of the tetrahedral $NiCl_4{}^{2-}$ ion reported by
Couch and Pedro-Smith [61] shown in Fig. 19. A point not always
fully appreciated is that the change in normal coordinate is not
equal to the change in bond length r. For the α_{1g} mode these are
related by the expression

$$\delta r = \frac{1}{\sqrt{N}} \Delta S \tag{23}$$

where N is the number of ligands bound to the metal [122]. Similar
analyses of the vibrational progressional members have been made
for the crystal spectra of several other complexes, and the results
are included in Table 6. In addition to these, it has been estimated [124] that a displacement of $\Delta S = 0.29$ Å (corresponding to

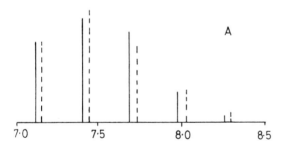

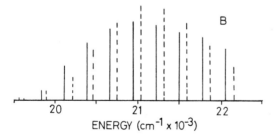

ENERGY (cm^{-1} x 10^{-3})

Figure 19   Calculated intensities of the progressional members of
the $^3A_2 \leftarrow \ ^3T_1$ transition of $Cs_2NiCl_4 \cdot CsCl$ (A) and the $^1A_{2g} \leftarrow \ ^1A_{1g}$
transition of K_2PdCl_4 (B) (dashed lines) assuming changes in each
metal-ligand bond length of 0.045 and 0.103 Å, respectively. The
experimental values are shown by solid lines. (Data from Ref. 61
and 79.)

$r = 0.12$ Å) occurs between the $^3T_{1g}$ and $^1A_{1g}$ states of the $Co(CN)_6^{3-}$ ion.

Usually, spin-allowed d-d transitions are accompanied by a substantial overall change in the equilibrium metal-ligand bond length, so that, as in the cases above, progressions are observed in the α_{1g} mode. When transitions occur to orbitally degenerate electronic excited states, distortions along a Jahn-Teller active normal mode are also to be expected. In a detailed study of the crystal spectrum of $[Cr(NH_3)_6](ClO_4)_2Cl\cdot KCl$, Wilson and Solomon [125] were able to deduce the displacement along the ε_g Jahn-Teller active vibrational mode in the $^4T_{2g}$ excited state by measuring the splitting of the magnetic-dipole-allowed origins of the band. However, the magnitude of this ($\Delta Q_{\varepsilon g} = 0.15 \pm 0.01$ Å) is not sufficient to explain the observed intensities of the vibronic components of the band, as may be seen from Fig. 20. Reasonable agreement with the observed spectrum can be obtained if it is assumed that a displacement along the α_{1g} normal mode of $\Delta Q_{\alpha_{1g}} = 0.16 \pm 0.02$ Å also occurs (Fig. 20). Taken together, these suggest the equilibrium nuclear geometry shown in Fig. 21 for the $^4T_{2g}$ excited state, in which four ammonia molecules are substantially displaced away from the Cr^{3+} ion, while the other two move slightly toward the metal, compared with the ground state (the sign of the displacement in the ε_g mode is chosen to be consistent with the fact that an electron is excited predominantly into the $d_{x^2-y^2}$ orbital). The same workers have described similar studies on the spectrum of the $Co(NH_3)_6^{3+}$ ion, and were able to show that this undergoes a rather similar distortion to the chromium(III) complex in both the $^1T_{1g}$ and $^3T_{1g}$ excited states [124]. Similarly, the $^4T_{2g} \leftarrow {}^6A_{2g}$ transition in Cs_2MnF_6 has been observed to exhibit progressions in both the α_{1g} and ε_g modes, suggesting a displacement along both these normal coordinates in the excited electronic state [126], although the magnitudes of these were not estimated. Distortions along Jahn-Teller active modes of both ε_g and τ_{2g} were estimated quantitatively by Solomon and McClure for four excited states from the crystal

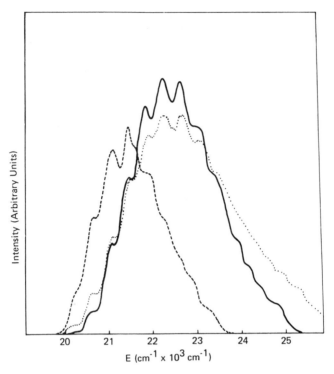

Figure 20   Band shape predicted for the $^4T_{2g} \leftarrow\, ^4A_{2g}$ transition of the $Cr(NH_3)_6{}^{3+}$ ion assuming distortions $\Delta Q_{\varepsilon g} = 0.15$ Å (dashed line) and $\Delta Q_{\varepsilon g} = 0.15$ Å plus $\Delta Q_{\alpha_{1g}} = 0.16$ Å (full line). The dashed line has been scaled down by a factor of 3/5. The experimentally observed band is shown by the dotted curve. (From Ref. 125.)

spectra of $RbMnF_3$ [127]. All in all, the results above suggest that care must be taken in deducing excited-state geometries from an analysis of the intensities of band components when it is possible that the distortion may occur along more than one vibrational mode and these are close enough in energy that they cannot be identified unambiguously from the spacings of the progressional members. Thus the band structure associated with the $(t_{2g})^6 \rightarrow (t_{2g})^5 (e_g)^1$ electronic excitation observed for the $PtF_6{}^{2-}$ ion doped into Cs_2GeF_6

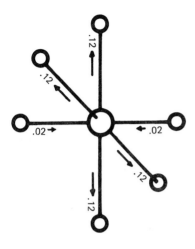

Figure 21   Equilibrium geometry of $Cr(NH_3)_6^{3+}$ in the $^4T_{2g}$ excited state.   The bond-length changes (Å) from the ground-state values of 2.06 Å occur in the directions indicated by the arrows.   (From Ref. 125.)

was initially interpreted [128] in terms of a distortion along the α_{1g} normal mode, while more recent measurements of the luminescence spectrum [129] suggest that a displacement along the ϵ_g vibration is more likely.   Judging by the behavior of the Co^{3+} complexes above, it seems possible that distortions along both these normal coordinates occur in the PtF_6^{2-} excited states.   Studies of the type described above are of particular importance because of their implications on the photoreactivity of metal complexes [124,125].

Although it has long been recognized that the increase in the equilibrium metal-ligand bond distance which accompanies the promotion of an electron from the t_{2g} to the e_g orbitals of an octahedral complex is related to the greater repulsion experienced by the ligands in the excited state, it is only recently that attempts have been made to rationalize the bond length changes theoretically.   Using an electrostatic model, Solomon et al. [125] estimated the over-all change in the α_{1g} normal coordinate expected to accompany the

$^4T_{2g} \leftarrow {}^4A_{2g}$ transition of the $Cr(NH_3)_6{}^{3+}$ ion, and obtained a value
about twice that estimated from the electronic spectrum. Recently,
the present author derived a general relationship between the bond-
length change δr expected to accompany a change of m electrons between two d orbitals separated in energy by an amount Δ [130]:

$$\delta r \cong \frac{mn\Delta}{Nf_{\alpha_g} r_0} \qquad (24)$$

Here N is the number of ligand atoms bound to the metal, f is the
force constant of the α_{1g} mode in the ground state, and r_0 is the
initial bond distance. This approach assumes that the d-orbital
separation   depends inversely on some power, n, of the bond distance. Both theory and experiment suggest that for the interaction
between a ligand and the d orbitals, $n \approx 5$ [130]. Substitution of
this into Eq. (24), together with the appropriate values of the
other parameters, yields the estimated bond-length changes listed
in Table 6 for various electronic transitions of a range of complexes of different stereochemistries. The values estimated from
the analysis of the relative intensities of the band components are
also shown, and these agree well with those calculated using Eq.
(24). It may be noted that the model predicts that for a two-electron transition, the bond-length change should be twice that when a
single electron is involved, in agreement with the analysis of the
$^5T_{1g} \leftarrow {}^1A_{1g}$ transition of the $Co(NH_3)_6{}^{3+}$ ion by Wilson and Solomon
[124]. It also suggests that the change in bond distance accompany-
ing a d-d transition of a tetrahedral complex should be much less
than those for a planar or octahedral complex, because although the
α_{1g} force constants are comparable, the ligand field splitting Δ is
much smaller for the former stereochemistry; again, this agrees with
the limited spectral data available. A similar expression may be
derived for the displacement along the Jahn-Teller active normal
mode accompanying an excitation of an electron to an orbitally
degenerate excited state [131].

Table 6   Calculated and Observed Changes in Overall Metal-Ligand
Bond Lengths Accompanying d-d Excitations

Complex	Stereochemistry	δr (Å) Spectra	Ref.	Calculated
$[Co(NH_3)_6](ClO_4)_2Cl \cdot 2KCl$	Octahedral	0.07	124	0.08
$[Cr(NH_3)_6](ClO_4)_2Cl \cdot 2KCl$	Octahedral	0.07	125	0.08
K_2PtCl_4	Planar	0.10	122	0.12
K_2PdCl_4	Planar	0.11	79	0.12
K_2PtBr_4	Planar	0.10	122	0.12
K_2PdBr_4	Planar	0.10	235	0.12
$(C_6H_5C_2H_4NH_2CH_3)_2CuCl_4$	Planar	0.07	236	0.09
$[Cs_2NiCl_4]CsCl$	Tetrahedral	0.04	237	0.03

D.   Vibrational Properties of Complexes

As already mentioned (Sec. IV.B.1), the temperature dependence of
the intensity of a vibronically allowed transition may be used to
estimate the approximate energy of the active u mode if a single
mode dominates in the process.   Generally, this is not of interest
in its own right, as the energies of such vibrations may be obtained
directly from the infrared spectrum of the complex.   However,
occasionally, a mode may be both Raman and infrared inactive, and in
this situation the temperature dependence of the electronic spectrum
provides a useful method of determining the energy of the vibration.
This is the case for the β_{2u} vibration of planar MX_4^{2-} ions, and the
temperature dependence of transitions allowed by this mode suggests
an energy of between 50 and 90 cm^{-1} for this vibration for planar
$CuCl_4^{2-}$ in complexes with several different countercations [39,74],
in good agreement with the energy of ~ 75 cm^{-1} estimated [111] by a
normal coordinate analysis of this species.   This is somewhat lower
in energy than the value between 120 and 170 cm^{-1} estimated for this
mode in $PtCl_4^{2-}$ and $PdCl_4^{2-}$ by force field calculations [79,132].
It would clearly be of interest to obtain an experimental estimate

of the vibrational energy from the temperature dependence of d-d
transitions activated by the β_{2u} mode in the latter complexes.

When the band structure can be resolved in a low-temperature
crystal spectrum, this provides a means of determining the vibrational frequencies in the excited electron state. If the change in
bond distances accompanying the electronic excitation is known,
this allows the way in which the force constant varies as a function of bond length to be investigated. Data for the α_{1g} totally
symmetric stretching mode obtained from the crystal spectra of a
range of complexes are shown in Table 7. This shows that, as expected, the vibrational energy decreases as the bonds lengthen in
every case. Various empirical relationships between bond distance
and force constant have been proposed, perhaps the best known being
due to Badger [133], who suggested a relationship of the form

$$f \propto (r - d)^{-3} \tag{25}$$

where f is the force constant, r the equilibrium bond distance, and
d is a constant depending on the position of the relevant atoms in
the periodic table. For a change in bond distance δr, this implies
a relationship of the form

$$r = c(\bar{\gamma}_1^{-2/3} - \bar{\gamma}_2^{-2/3}) \tag{26}$$

where $\bar{\gamma}_1$ and $\bar{\gamma}_2$ are the vibrational energies associated with the two
geometries [39] and c is a constant. Although it should be remem-
bered that the data in Table 7 are subject to rather large experimental error, it is interesting to note that the change in
vibrational energies observed for the palladium(II) and platinum(II)
tetrahalide ions is significantly greater than that seen for the
complexes of the first-row transition ions.

It is often possible to observe transitions to a large number
of vibrational levels of an excited electronic state, and it has almost always been found that the vibration is completely harmonic to
the accuracy to which the measurements can be made [39,42,43,124,

Table 7   Totally Symmetric Stretching Frequencies in the Ground and
Excited Electronic States of Various Complexes

Complex	$\bar{\nu}(\alpha_{1g})$ (cm^{-1})		Bond-length difference $(\mathring{A})^a$	c^b	Ref.
	Ground state	Excited state			
$Co(NH_3)_6^{3+}$	498	480	0.07	170	124
$CuCl_4^{2-}$	276	270	0.07	200	39
$NiCl_4^{2-}$	292	285	0.04	110	61
$PtCl_4^{2-}$	329	290	0.10	54	43
$PdCl_4^{2-}$	310	271	0.10	54	76
$PtBr_4^{2-}$	205	170	0.10	26	235
$PdBr_4^{2-}$	190	166	0.10	35	235

[a]Estimated from the relative intensities of the members of the
vibrational progressions.

[b]Proportionality constant relating the change in vibrational frequency to the change in bond length defined as in Eq. (26) with δr
in angstroms and $\bar{\nu}$ in cm^{-1}.

125]. An exception is the PtF_6^{2-} ion, in which it is thought that
the observed progression is in the ε_g mode, with this being slightly anharmonic [129]. The highly harmonic nature of these α_{1g}
vibrations is rather surprising, considering the fact that the
force constants are known to vary substantially as a function of
bond distance (Table 7). Possibly, this is because the constraining
effect of the surrounding lattice tends to modify the potential surface of the molecules at the larger amplitudes associated with high
vibrational quantum numbers.

The fact that transitions to highly excited vibrational levels
can sometimes be observed in the crystal spectra of metal complexes
means that it is occasionally possible to observe isotopic splittings in the vibrational structure. For a tetrachlorocomplex

containing chlorine in natural abundance (75% ^{35}Cl and 25% ^{37}Cl)
distributed randomly, it is predicted that the transition to the
nth vibrational level of the excited state should be split into
five lines of relative intensity in order of increasing energy
1:12:54:108:81, the separation between each pair of adjacent peaks
being $n\bar{\gamma}(1 - (35/37)^{1/2}]/4$, where $\bar{\gamma}$ is the energy of the α_{1g} vibration of the isotopically pure ^{35}Cl complex. Exactly this pattern
has been observed by Patterson and co-workers [134] in the low-
temperature luminescence spectrum of the $PtCl_4^{2-}$ ion doped into
single crystals of Cs_2ZrCl_6, and by Tacon et al. [135] in the crystal spectrum of $Cs_2[MnCl_4] \cdot CsCl$. Similarly, although the structure
could not be resolved, the marked broadening of the higher vibrational members in the spectrum of $(Nmph)_2CuCl_4$ was interpreted [39]
in terms of an isotopic splitting effect.

For vibronically allowed d-d transitions, the band is built on
an origin of energy equal to the pure electronic origin, plus one
quantum of the u mode inducing intensity into the transition (see
Sec. III). Thus, if the peak due to the pure electronic transition
can be observed, either because of the intensity from a magnetic
dipole mechanism, or because of an intensity contribution due to a
small noncentrosymmetric, static contribution to the ligand field,
the difference between this peak and the first member of the
vibronically allowed band gives the energy in the excited electronic
state of one quantum of the u mode inducing the band intensity.
This has been used, for instance, to show that the vibronic intensity of the band due to the transition $^1T_{1g} \leftarrow {}^1A_{1g}$ in the crystal
spectrum of $[Co(NH_3)_6](ClO_4)_2Cl \cdot KCl$ is due to coupling with the
metal-ligand rocking vibrations of τ_{2u} and τ_{1u} symmetry [124]. In
this case it was observed that on cooling from room temperature to
$\sim$50 K, the total band area decreases, as expected from the vibronic
intensity mechanism (see Sec. IV.B.1). Below this temperature, the
band area actually *increases* somewhat, and in addition a weak sharp
peak appears, assigned as the transition to the pure electronic
origin E_{00} the intensity being derived from a low-symmetry

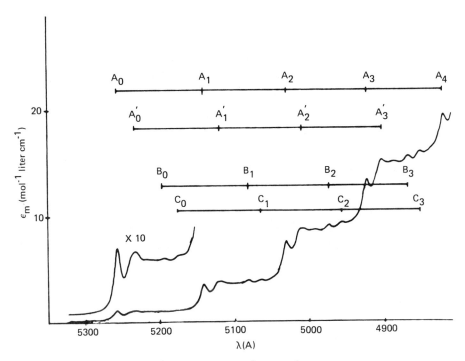

Figure 22   Polarized spectrum of the $^1T_{1g} \leftarrow {}^1A_{1g}$ of $[Co(NH_3)]$-$(ClO_4)_2Cl \cdot KCl$ measured at 8 K with the electric vector along the unique crystal axis of the uniaxial crystal.   The progression labeled A is built on the electronic origin, that labeled A' is built on the additional excitation of one quantum of a lattice mode of energy 89 cm^{-1}, while those designated B and C involve the excitation of one quantum each of metal-ligand vibrations of t_{2u} and t_{1u} symmetry having energies 216 cm^{-1} and 314 cm^{-1}, respectively.   In each case the progression is in the α_{1g} totally symmetric stretching mode.   (Data from Ref. 124.)

perturbation to the ligand field which becomes active at very low temperatures.   The spectrum at 8 K of the low-energy side of the band in one polarization is shown in Fig. 22.   It can be seen that the band is dominated by four progressions, each occurring in the same vibrational frequency, 429 cm^{-1}, this being a combination of the α_{1g} and ε_g modes associated with the change in geometry accompanying the electronic excitation (see Sec. IV.C) [124].   In addition to that built on E_{00} itself (A), a second progression

(A') occurs with the additional excitation of one quantum of energy 89 cm^{-1}, and this is assigned to a lattice mode of α_1 symmetry. The other two progressions (B and C) are built on origins 218 and 304 cm^{-1} higher in energy than E_{00}, and these are assigned to the (τ_{2u}) and (τ_{1u}) metal-ligand rocking vibrations, respectively, these being somewhat lower in energy than is observed in the ground electronic state, as expected. The assignments were confirmed by observing the energy shifts in the progressions upon deuteration of the complex [124]. A similar analysis has been carried out on the crystal spectrum of $Co(en)_3Cl_3$ [47], on the vibronic structure in the ^2E_g excited state of the $Cr(NH_3)_6^{3+}$ ion [125], and also on structure observed in the absorption and magnetocircular dichroism spectra of crystals containing the $Ni(H_2O)_6^{2+}$ ion [113,136].

For the vibronically allowed d-d transitions of centrosymmetric complexes, the observation of hot bands can, in principle, also provide information on the energy $\bar{\gamma}_u$ of the u mode inducing intensity, since this should be built on an origin $\sim2\bar{\gamma}_u$ lower in energy that that built upon the 0 → 1 vibration (see Sec. IV.B). In practice, it has not often been possible to observe individual hot-band components, although in the crystal spectrum of $[(CH_3)_4N]_2UCl_6$, the position and temperature dependence of such a transition were investigated [137] and found to be in good agreement with the predictions of simple theory.

The polarization properties of the vibrational structure observed in the d-d spectra of centrosymmetric complexes can also provide information on the energies of u active modes in the excited state, although again in practice this has generally been used largely to confirm the correctness of a particular vibronic mechanism. The way in which this is done can be illustrated by the $^2A_{1g}(d_{z^2}) \leftarrow {}^2B_{1g}(d_{x^2-y^2})$ transition of the planar $CuCl_4^{2-}$ ion present in $(methadonium)_2CuCl_4$, the xy and z spectra of which [74] are shown in Fig. 12, and in "stick" form in Fig. 23. In z polarization, the band is composed of a single progression in the α_{1g} mode,

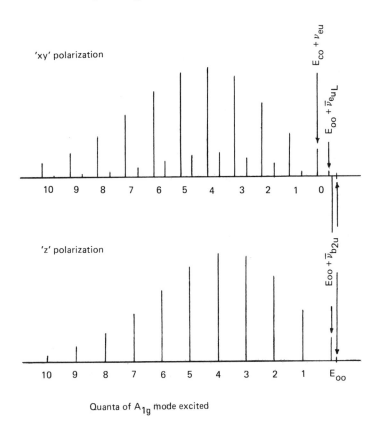

Figure 23 The relative positions and intensities of the progressional members of the $^2A_{1g}(d_{z^2}) \leftarrow {^2B_{1g}}(d_{x^2-y^2})$ transition of (methadonium)$_2$CuCl$_4$ in xy and z polarization.

with the first member occurring at 14,910 cm^{-1}. In this polarization, the transition is allowed by vibrations of β_{2u} symmetry. For a planar tetrachlorocomplex, the only vibration of this symmetry is the out-of-plane stretching mode (Table 5, Fig. 11), and the temperature dependence of the band suggests that this has an energy of ~ 50 cm^{-1} (Sec. IV.B.1). The vibronic intensity model suggests that at low temperature a band is built on an origin of energy $E_{00} + \overline{\gamma}_u$, where E_{00} is the energy of the pure electronic transition

and $\bar{\gamma}_u$ is the energy of the active ungerade vibration in the
excited electronic state. Assuming that the energy of this vibration is similar to that in the ground electronic state, this suggests a value of $E_{00} \simeq 14{,}860$ cm^{-1}. In xy polarization the
$^2A_{1g}(dz^2) \leftarrow {}^2B_{1g}(d_{x^2-y^2})$ transition is allowed by vibrational modes
of ε_u symmetry. The observed spectrum (Figs. 12 and 23) consist
of two progressions, the energies of the initial members being
14,930 and 15,050 cm^{-1}. The value $E_{00} \simeq 14{,}860$ cm^{-1} suggests that
the active u modes have energies of ~70 and ~190 cm^{-1}. Metal-
ligand vibrations of this symmetry have energies of 290 and ~188
cm^{-1} [74], implying that the more intense progression in xy polarization is due to coupling with the in-plane bending mode (energy
188 cm^{-1}), while the weaker progression presumably gains intensity
by coupling with a lattice mode of energy ~70 cm^{-1}. The observed
temperature dependence of the band is in good agreement with this
assignment (see Sec. IV.B.1, Fig. 17).

In addition to giving valuable information concerning vibronic
coupling mechanisms, vibrational fine structure has occasionally
provided a useful way of distinguishing intraligand and charge-
transfer excitations from d-d transitions when these occur in a
similar spectral region (see Sec. IV.F.3).

E. Metal-Ligand Bonding Parameters

1. Interpretation of Energy Levels in Metal Complexes

One of the most important applications of polarized crystal
spectroscopy as far as the coordination chemist is concerned is as
a means of accurately identifying the energy levels in low-symmetry metal complexes, so that these may be utilized to derive
metal-ligand bonding parameters. The polarization properties of
the electronic transitions can be especially useful in this respect, both as an aid to band assignment (see Sec. IV.A), and in
improving the precision with which energy levels may be located.
The various schemes that may be used to interpret these energy

levels have been summarized elsewhere in a number of recent books [6,7,138] and review articles [6,139,140]. It is, however, worthwhile to compare briefly the most important methods and to look at some representative examples of the interpretation of crystal spectra.

To interpret the transition energies obtained from crystal spectra, it is necessary to set up a mathematical model involving the various energy interactions in the complex, the relevant Hamiltonian operator normally being represented as

$$H = V_{ML} + \frac{e^2}{r_e} + \xi \ell s \qquad (27)$$

Here V_{ML}, e^2/r_e, and $\xi \ell s$ are the operators describing the metal-ligand, interelectron repulsion, and spin-orbit interactions, respectively. The matrix equation involving these operators acting within the d-orbital basis set is then solved, and the resulting eigenvalues are compared with the observed transition energies. For first-row transition metal ions, the effects of spin-orbit coupling on the energies of electronic transitions are comparatively small, causing splittings of $<\sim 1000$ cm^{-1}. The breadth of the spin-allowed bands due to d-d transitions are usually such that these cannot be resolved, even at low temperature, so that it is frequently possible to ignore spin-orbit interactions if the major aspect of interest is the metal-ligand interactions in a complex. This is often not the case, however, for spin-forbidden transitions, and when one of these lies close in energy to a spin-allowed transition, spin-orbit coupling between the two states may give rise to unusual effects. This occurs, for instance, for the $^3T_{1g}(F) \leftarrow ^3A_{2g}$ and $^1E_g \leftarrow ^3A_{2g}$ transitions of Ni(H$_2$O)$_6^{2+}$, and the spectra of crystals containing this ion have been the subject of several detailed investigations [113,136]. When spin-orbit splittings of orbitally degenerate excited states can be resolved, these are often observed to be smaller than expected, owing to quenching of the orbital angular momentum by a dynamic Jahn-Teller process. This effect,

first recognized by Ham [141], has been observed, for instance, for
the $^4T_{2g} \leftarrow {}^4A_{2g}$ transition of V^{3+} doped into Al_2O_3 [142], and also
for the analogous transition of $Cr(NH_3)_6^{3+}$ [125], and the analysis
of the electronic spectrum in each case allowed a quantitative description of the vibronic interactions in the excited electronic
state. It should also be noted that as spin-forbidden transitions
gain the bulk of their intensity via spin-orbit coupling, any
quantitative considerations of relative band intensities must include this interaction.

The effects of interelectron repulsion and the metal-ligand
interactions in a first-row transition metal complex are generally
comparable in size, being an order of magnitude greater than those
due to spin-orbit coupling. The second of these is generally of
most interest to the coordination chemist, since it is the d-
orbital energies which are most sensitive to the stereochemistry of
a complex and the bonding properties of the ligands. However, there
has also been considerable discussion over the best way in which the
interelectron repulsion interactions in a complex may be parametrized. Many workers have utilized the Racah parameters B and C,
using the observed spectra to determine the amount by which these
are reduced from the free ion values B' and C' via the relationships

$$B = \beta B' \qquad C = \beta C' \tag{28}$$

In this situation, the single parameter β that best produces the
observed energy levels in the complex is determined. Physically,
β is taken to represent the "nephelauxetic effect" of the ligands,
this being related to the covalency of the bonding and the effective charge of the metal in the complex [4,143]. When enough
experimental data are available, the parametrization of the Racah
parameters in octahedral complexes has sometimes been extended by
representing the reduction in interelectron repulsion using two
parameters, β_{33} and β_{55}, where the subscripts 3 and 5 indicate the
involvement of e_g and t_{2g} electrons, respectively, in the appropriate two-center integrals [144]. One would expect that β_{33} should

be smaller than β_{55}, as the e_g orbital should have a greater ligand contribution than the t_{2g} molecular orbital, and indeed this has generally been found to be the case [144].

The procedure above is essentially a "strong-field" approach in the sense that it attempts to describe the interelectron repulsion in terms of effects involving the d orbitals in a complex. This approach has been criticized by Ferguson and co-workers [6] because it is extremely cumbersome to reproduce the free-ion term energies accurately using Racah parameters, which are linear combinations of the two-electron repulsion integrals. Instead, it is suggested that it is better to use the "weak-field" or "free-atom" approximation, in which the experimentally observed free-ion term energies are taken as the starting point of the calculation of the energy levels in the complex. The energy separation between these is then varied in addition to the energy separations between the d orbitals until optimum agreement with experiment is obtained. The relative merits of the two approaches have also been discussed by Gerloch and Slade [138], who have concluded that each has certain merits, and that it is probably best to choose the method most suited to the particular problem in hand.

Probably the most valuable aspect of electronic spectroscopy as far as the coordination chemist is concerned is that it is the most direct method currently available for estimating the d orbital energies and hence the metal-ligand bonding interactions in a complex. It is well established that the measurement of the energy difference between the d orbitals in high-symmetry complexes having regular octahedral and tetrahedral coordination geometries allows ligands to be arranged into a spectrochemical series ranging from "strong" ligands such as CN^- to "weak" ligands such as I^-. The differences in splitting capacity have conventionally been interpreted in terms of the σ- and π-bonding capabilities of the various ligands, those high in the series being strong σ donors and/or π acceptors, while those low in the series are thought to be weak σ donors and/or π donors [145]. Although these ideas are certainly

in qualitative agreement with current views on the nature of metal-
ligand interactions, it is impossible to obtain quantitative estimates of the relative importance of σ- and π-bonding interactions
from the single energy difference which may be measured from the
electronic spectrum of a complex of O_h or T_d symmetry. In order to
quantify σ- and π-bonding interactions independently, complexes of
lower symmetry must be studied, and it is in accurately assigning
the energy levels in these that polarized crystal spectroscopy can
make a very significant contribution.

It is convenient to classify the various methods that have
been used to describe the bonding involving the d orbitals in a
low-symmetry metal complex into two classes: those that parametrize
the metal-ligand interaction in terms of the *overall* effect of the
ligands as expressed by a series of potentials conforming to the
symmetry of the complex, and those that parametrize the *individual*
interaction between each ligand and the metal and then sum these
over the complex as a whole. The best known example of the former
method is the crystal field model (CFM), while the latter is exem-
plified by the angular overlap model (AOM).

The CFM was the first quantitative approach used by chemists
to interpret the spectra of metal complexes [41,146]. In this
model, the energy levels in a complex are derived by considering
that the metal d orbitals are perturbed by an electrostatic potential V conforming to the symmetry of the complex. This field is
represented as a series of normalized spherical harmonics, and for
a complex of regular octahedral or tetrahedral symmetry, the d
orbitals are predicted to split into two sets, the energy separation conventionally being represented by the parameter 10Dq. This
is related to the metal-ligand bond distance a by the expression

$$Dq = \frac{ze^2\overline{r^4}}{6a^5} \tag{29}$$

where z is the charge on the ligand and $\overline{r^4}$ is the average value of
the fourth power of the radius of a d orbital. In an octahedral

complex the $(d_{x^2-y^2}, d_{z^2})$ set are higher in energy than the (d_{xy}, d_{yz}, d_{xz}) set, whereas in a tetrahedral complex the reverse is true, and the model predicts that if the bond distances are identical, the splitting in a tetrahedral complex should be -4/9 that in the corresponding octahedral complex. In agreement with this, the value of Dq in $NiCl_4^{2-}$ and $CoCl_4^{2-}$ is $\sim 50\%$ of that in analogous octahedral complexes [147].

In the CFM, lower-symmetry complexes are conventionally treated in terms of deviations from a regular octahedral or tetrahedral ligand potential. Angular distortions require the specification of an additional parameter Cp, defined as

$$Cp = \frac{2ze^2\overline{r^2}}{7a^3} \tag{30}$$

Values of Dq and Cp have been deduced from the spectral and magnetic properties for a range of complexes of different stereochemistries, and these results, and a detailed discussion of the physical meaning of the parameter Cp, are given in the book by Gerloch and Slade [138]. A particularly common type of distortion involves the lowering of the symmetry of a complex from O_h to D_{4h}, such as occurs in a mixed-ligand complex of the type trans-ML_4X_2. The ligand potential in such a system is conveniently described using the parameters Dq, Ds, and Dt, the latter being defined as

$$Ds = Cp(L) - Cp(X) \tag{31}$$

$$Dt = \frac{4}{7[Dq(L) - Dq(X)]} \tag{32}$$

The relationship between the d-orbital energies in a complex trans-ML_4X_2 to those of the parent complex ML_6, using these parameters, is illustrated in Fig. 24. It should be noted that the sign of the tetragonal perturbation is important, the present convention following that of Ballhausen [148]. The matrix elements have been published for all d configurations in crystal fields of tetragonal symmetry, including interelectron repulsion using the Racah formalism and spin-orbit coupling, and the variation of the energy levels

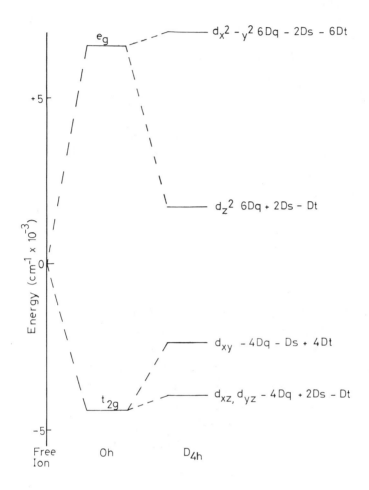

Figure 24   Energies of the d orbitals in a metal complex of
tetragonal symmetry expressed using the crystal field parameters
Dq, Ds, and Dt.   The values used are those estimated for trans-
Ni(pyridine)$_4$Br$_2$.

as a function of Dq, Ds, and Dt has been published as a series of
energy diagrams by Kremer and König [149].   The transition energies
obtained from the crystal spectra of many complexes have been
interpreted in terms of the parameters above, including several
six-coordinate nickel(II) histidine complexes [89], a range of

complexes of the type NiL_4X_2, where L is an aromatic amine and X a halide ion [55,82] or water molecule [82], the $PtCl_4^{2-}$ ion [78], $CoCl_2 \cdot 6H_2O$ [90], $CoCl_2 \cdot 2H_2O$ [92], and K_2CoF_4 [19]. The spectra of a range of cobalt(II) and nickel(II) complexes has also been analyzed in conjunction with magnetic susceptibility measurements by Gerloch and co-workers, and the chemical significance of these and many other results have been discussed in Ref. 138. Recently, a more generalized crystal field treatment, the normalized spherical harmonic (NSH) approach, has been described by Lever and co-workers [150]. It has been suggested [139] that it is advantageous to analyze spectra in terms of both the NSH crystal field parameters and the angular overlap parameters discussed below, since the former provide a group-theoretical appreciation of the symmetry of the ligand field in the complex, while the latter give an indication of the individual ligand σ- and π-bonding interactions. The crystal spectra of a range of nickel(II) [100,101,151] and cobalt(II) [99, 152] diamine complexes have been interpreted in this manner and the results summarized in a recent review article [139].

Although crystal field models are still used quite widely, particularly by physicists, an increasing number of chemists now interpret electronic spectra using the angular overlap model (AOM) of the bonding in metal complexes, developed originally by Jørgensen [153] and Schäffer [154-156]. Several recent reviews of this model have appeared [157-159]. It differs from the CFM in two important respects. First, each metal-ligand interaction is considered individually, the overall effect being obtained by summing over all the ligands using the angular overlap matrix appropriate to the geometry of the complex. Second, the d orbitals are considered to be perturbed in energy by a weak covalent interaction with the ligand orbitals. Both σ and π interactions are considered, and the energy e by which a d orbital is raised upon interaction with a ligand orbital of the appropriate symmetry is taken to be proportional to the square of the diatomic overlap integral S:

$$e_\sigma = K_\sigma S_\sigma^2 \qquad e_\pi = K_\pi S_\pi^2 \tag{33}$$

Here the proportionality constants K are related to the diagonal-matrix elements of the metal and ligand orbitals, H_M and H_L:

$$K \approx \frac{H_L^2}{H_M - H_L} \tag{34}$$

The energy of each d orbital is then obtained by summing over all the ligand orbitals (including off-diagonal matrix elements when necessary) using the appropriate angular overlap matrix. The latter matrix is readily derived for a complex of any geometry in terms of the angular relationships between the various ligands [154,159]. It is important to recognize that neither the CFM nor the AOM are ways of *calculating* the d orbital energies in a complex. Rather, both provide a way of *parametrizing* observed energy levels. Also, although the bonding in the CFM was originally envisaged to be electrostatic, and that in the AOM covalent, both models depend merely on symmetry arguments for their operation. Thus it is not invalid to interpret the "crystal field" parameters, Dq, Ds, and Dt in terms of covalent interactions, while the angular overlap parameters e_σ and e_π could well include an electrostatic contribution [155,160]. The relationship between the two bonding models has been discussed by Gerloch and co-workers [138,140,161]. Several workers have described crystal field approaches that sum the electrostatic effects of individual ligands in a manner analogous to that in the AOM [162,163], while in a model developed by Smith [164] the metal-ligand bonding in a complex is described in terms of angular overlap parameters plus additional electrostatic perturbations due to point charges located at the positions of the ligand nuclei.

Although the CFM and AOM are equally "correct" in the sense that both can simply be viewed as ways of representing the d orbital energy differences in a metal complex, in the opinion of the present author the latter approach is much to be preferred if the purpose of the spectral interpretation is to extract chemical information about the metal-ligand bonding. This is because the AOM utilizes parameters that are readily interpretable within the framework of the qualitative simple molecular orbital schemes currently used by coordination chemists to describe the bonding in metal complexes. In fact, in principle at least, the model provides a powerful means of quantifying the σ- and π-bonding interactions which are so often invoked to explain the chemical behavior of metal complexes.

The AOM can be used at various levels of sophistication. At the simplest level, the energy differences obtained from spectra may simply be translated into values of e_σ and e_π for every independent ligand in the complex, where each e parameter simply represents the σ- and π-antibonding energy produced by one ligand on a real d orbital of the appropriate symmetry. In general, the d-orbital energies are obtained by solving a determinant. This determinant has a particularly simple form when all the ligands in the complex are located on the cartesian axes. A schematic diagram of a general molecule of this kind is shown in Fig. 25. Here, x_i, y_i, and z_i represent ligand-based coordinate systems, while x, y, and z define the metal-based coordinate system of the complex as a whole. Each metal-ligand interaction is described in terms of a σ interaction along z_i and two π interactions, which may be labeled $e_{\pi x}$ and $e_{\pi y}$. The d-orbital-energy determinant appropriate to the complex is given in Table 8. It may be noted that the d_{xz}, d_{yz}, d_{xy} set of orbitals experience only π interactions, and the $d_{x^2-y^2}$ and d_{z^2}, only σ interactions. Moreover, only the latter two d orbitals are coupled by an off-diagonal element, this being proportional to the difference in the total ligand interaction along the x and y molecular axes. An important feature of the AOM is that it incorporates the concept that the energy levels in a complex are decided by what has been termed [165] the "holohedrized" ligand symmetry. This means that the energy levels are given by the total ligand interaction along each cartesian axis, irrespective of how the ligands are situated along these. Whether or not a complex has an inversion center is therefore assumed to have no direct effect on the energy

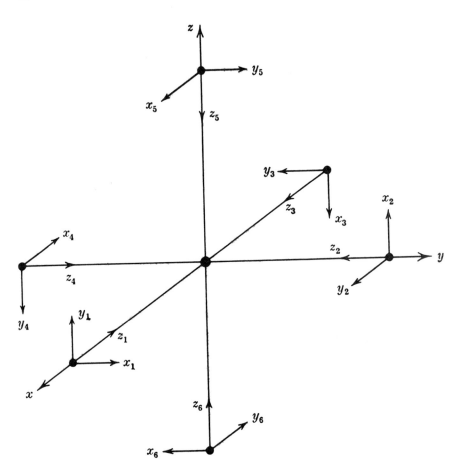

Figure 25   Schematic diagram of the metal- and ligand-based
coordinate systems of a typical ortho-axial complex.

levels, although of course it can have a significant impact on the
transition intensities. The fact that the d-orbital energies are
obtained simply by adding the individual ligand contributions means
that the matrix in Table 8 can be used for complexes having a wide
range of stereochemistries (linear, square planar, rhombic, and if
any angular distortions are neglected, square-based pyramidal).
Moreover, the simple additivity of ligand effects means that the d-
orbital energies of mixed-ligand complexes can be handled in a very

Table 8   Angular Overlap Matrix for All Orthoaxial Metal Complexes Derived from the General Structure Illustrated in Fig. 25

	$d_{x^2-y^2}$	d_{z^2}	d_{xy}	d_{xz}	d_{yz}
$d_{x^2-y^2}$	$0.75[e_\sigma(1) + e_\sigma(2) + e_\sigma(3) + e_\sigma(4)]$	$0.25\{3^{1/2}[e_\sigma(1) + e_\sigma(3) - e_\sigma(2) - e_\sigma(4)]\}$	0	0	0
d_{z^2}	$0.25\{3^{1/2}[e_\sigma(1) + e_\sigma(3) - e_\sigma(2) - e_\sigma(4)]\}$	$e_\sigma(5) + e_\sigma(6) + 0.25[e_\sigma(1) + e_\sigma(2) + e_\sigma(3) + e_\sigma(4)]$	0	0	0
d_{xy}	0	0	$e_{\pi x}(1) + e_{\pi x}(3) + e_{\pi y}(2) + e_{\pi y}(4)$	0	0
d_{xz}	0	0	0	$e_{\pi y}(1) + e_{\pi y}(3) + e_{\pi x}(5) + e_{\pi x}(6)$	0
d_{yz}	0	0	0	0	$e_{\pi y}(2) + e_{\pi y}(4) + e_{\pi y}(5) + e_{\pi y}(6)$

straightforward manner. For instance, the d-orbital energies predicted for a series of octahedral complexes of formula ML_6, ML_5X, trans-ML_4X_2, and cis-ML_4X_2 are shown to scale in Fig. 26. The diagram has been drawn for L = NH_3 and X = halide ion, which allows the simplifying assumption to be made that $e_{\pi x} = e_{\pi y} \approx 0$ for NH_3 and $e_{\pi x} = e_{\pi y}$ for X. Also, it is assumed that the same products of K and S occur in each case. Note that the model predicts that the parent e_g and t_{2g} levels of the regular octahedral complex are each split by an equal amount in ML_5X and cis-ML_4X_2, this being half that in trans-ML_4X_2, in agreement with general observations [166].

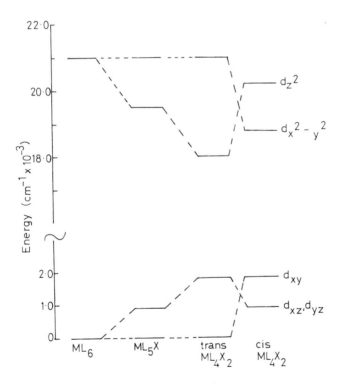

Figure 26 Energies of the d orbitals predicted by the angular overlap model for various complexes. Note that for cis-ML_4X_2 the x and y axes coincide with the M-X bonds. The ligand field parameters are assumed constant for the range of complexes, and the values used are those estimated for trans-$[Cr(NH_3)_4Br_2]^+$.

Note also that the *holohedral* symmetry of cis-ML_4X_2 retains the four-fold rotational axis, so that x and y may be defined to lie along the L-M-X bond directions. Although the d orbital energy matrix is more complicated when the ligands do not lie along the cartesian axes, it may still be derived in a quite straightforward manner using the angular relationships between the various ligand coordinate systems. The procedure whereby this may be done for a complex of any stereochemistry has been described in detail elsewhere [156,158,159].

A major problem in the derivation of metal-ligand bonding parameters from optical spectra lies in the fact that it is impossible to measure more than four differences in energy between the five d orbitals. This means that if no further experimental data are available and no simplifying assumptions are made, only complexes containing one kind of independent ligand may be treated using the foregoing approach. As an example, we may consider the planar complex $Cu(acac)_2$ discussed in Sec. II.C. The four ligand-oxygen atoms make an almost perfect square-planar arrangement about the copper(II) ion [35], and as far as the energy levels in the complex go, the molecule may be treated in the point group D_{4h} (note that this is not the case as far as the band intensities are concerned, since these depend strongly on the electronic structure of the ligands (see Sec. IV.A.2). The d-orbital energies are readily given in terms of the AOM bonding parameters of the four equivalent ligands (Table 8):

$$E(d_{x^2-y^2}) = 3e_\sigma \tag{35a}$$

$$E(d_{z^2}) = e_\sigma \tag{35b}$$

$$E(d_{xy}) = 4e_{\pi x} \tag{35c}$$

$$E(d_{xz}, d_{yz}) = 2e_{\pi y} + 2e_{\pi x} \tag{35d}$$

where x lies in the plane of the chelating ligand. The crystal spectrum of the complex [35] shows three bands, centered at 14,500, 16,300, and 18,000 cm^{-1}, and the most likely assignment of these

suggests that they represent excitations from the d_{z^2}, d_{xy} and
d_{xz}, d_{yz} orbitals to $d_{x^2-y^2}$ [9,32,45]. Assuming an uncertainty of
250 cm^{-1} in each band maximum, the Eqs. (35a) to (35d) yield the
values e_σ = 7250 ± 250 cm^{-1}, $e_{\pi x}$ = 1350 ± 250 cm^{-1}, and $e_{\pi y}$ =
1880 ± 500 cm^{-1} for the metal-ligand bonding parameters. These
results seem chemically sensible, suggesting that the ligand functions as a σ and π donor, with the π interaction ∿20% as strong as
the σ interaction. It should be noted that the π-bonding parameters
are relatively poorly defined, since their determination depends on
rather small energy differences. It is also noteworthy that as a
planar complex, $Cu(acac)_2$ is unusual in producing chemically reasonable bonding parameters from a simple analysis of this kind. It has
been observed that in truly four-coordinate, planar complexes the
d_{z^2} orbital is generally substantially shifted in energy from the
position predicted by simple bonding theories [161] (this feature
is discussed more fully in Sec. IV.E.2).

When complexes involving either the same ligand at more than
one bond distance, or two or more different ligands, are studied,
the electronic spectrum alone normally cannot provide sufficient
information to allow separate e_σ and e_π parameters to be derived
for each independent ligand. One way out of this dilemma is to ex-
tend the experimental data to include ground-state properties of
the complex, such as its magnetic susceptibility and molecular g
values. This procedure has been followed by Gerloch, McMeeking,
and co-workers, who have developed a powerful computer program [167]
which calculates the electronic transition energies and principal
magnetic susceptibility and g-value magnitudes and directions for a
single crystal of a complex of any transition ion as a function of
the molecular geometry and crystal structure, using as input the
angular overlap parameters of the ligands. These may then be varied
until optimum agreement with all the experimentally measured parameters is obtained. The magnetic behavior may be calculated at
various temperatures, which provides an additional powerful

constraint on the possible range of ligand bonding parameters consistent with the experimental observations. The single-crystal spectral and magnetic properties of a number of distorted tetrahedral cobalt(II) and nickel(II) complexes have been analyzed in this way [168]. A similar approach has been applied to a number of high-spin cobalt(II) complexes by a group of Italian workers, who have summarized the way in which the electronic and EPR spectra and magnetic properties are expected to vary as a function of the metal-ligand AOM bonding parameters for a wide range of stereochemistries [169]. A summary of typical ligand bonding parameters obtained by Gerloch and co-workers is given in Table 9.

Another way of reducing the number of bonding parameters to be derived from the energy levels of mixed-ligand complexes to a manageable level is to determine *differences* between these, rather than their absolute values. In particular, following initial suggestions by Yamatera [170] and McClure [171], the band splittings observed in the electronic spectra of a number of trans-disubstituted halide complexes of cobalt (III) [94], chromium(III) [95-97], and nickel(II) [172] amines have been interpreted in terms of $\delta\sigma$ and $\delta\pi$, the difference in σ- and π- antibonding energies produced by the axial and in-plane ligands, and Δ, the ligand field splitting appropriate to a regular octahedral arrangement of the in-plane ligands. An interesting application of this approach has been obtained from analysis of the spectra of the series trans-$[Cr(en)_2X_2]^+$, for X = Br^-, Cl^-, and F^-, which yielded the values $\delta\sigma$ = -1780, -1240, and +600 cm^{-1}, $\delta\pi$ = +750, +1040, and +2000 cm^{-1} [96,97], respectively, where $\delta\sigma$ = e_σ(halide) - e_σ(amine) and $\delta\pi$ = e_π(halide - e_π(amine). This suggests that while the chloride and bromide ions are weaker σ donors than ethylenediamine, the fluoride ion actually produces a slightly *stronger* σ perturbation than the amine in the complex above. The high fluoride σ interaction is accompanied by a concomitantly large π interaction, and it is the latter that is thought to provide much of the driving force for the "hard acid" behavior of the Cr^{3+} ion [173].

Table 9 Angular Overlap Metal-Ligand Bonding Parameters Obtained by Analyzing the Magnetic Susceptibilities and Electronic Spectra of Some Nickel(II) and Cobalt(II) Complexes of Known Crystal Structure[a]

Complex[b]	Phosphorus ligand			Halide ligand			Amine ligand		
	e_σ (cm^{-1})	e_π (cm^{-1})	M-L Distance (Å)	e_σ (cm^{-1})	e_π (cm^{-1})	M-L Distance (Å)	e_σ (cm^{-1})	e_π (cm^{-1})	M-L Distance (Å)
Ni(C$_6$H$_5$)$_3$PBr$_3$$^-$	5000	-1500	2.32	3000	700	2.37			
Ni(C$_6$H$_5$)$_3$PI$_3$$^-$	6000	-1500	2.28	2000	600	2.55			
Ni(POP)Cl$_2$	5000	-1500	2.32	3600	1500	2.22			
Ni(dabco)Cl$_3$				3250	1000	2.24	6100	0	2.04
Ni(dabco)Br$_3$				3000	850	2.38	5900	0	2.04
Co(dabco)Cl$_3$				3500	1100	2.26	4250	0	2.09
Co(dabco)Br$_3$				3500	1000	2.38	4000	0	2.13
Ni(quin)Br$_3$				3600	500	2.37	3600	-600	2.03
Ni(biquin)Br$_2$				3500	850	2.34	4200	-1000	1.99

[a]Data from Ref. 168.

[b]POP, (C$_6$H$_5$)$_2$PCH$_2$CH$_2$-O-CH$_2$CH$_2$P(C$_5$H$_5$)$_2$; dabco, N-ethyl-1,4-diazabicyclo[2.2.2]octonium$^+$; quin, quinoline; biquin, biquinoline.

For complexes involving saturated amines, the number of parameters to be determined from the spectra may be reduced if it is assumed that the π-bonding interaction from the amine ligands is zero. Within the framework of the model this should be true to a good approximation as far as covalent interactions are concerned. An experimental test of this hypothesis is provided by the energy levels of low-symmetry complexes involving only saturated amines. The crystal spectrum of a planar nickel(II) complex of this type suggested [77] a ratio e_π/e_σ in the range 0.08-0.17 for the amine, and similar values have been inferred for a number of tetragonally distorted copper(II) amine complexes [174,175]. The contribution to the π bonding, which although small is not insignificant, could be due to an ionic contribution to the bonding, or a breakdown of the AOM in this simple form (see Sec. IV.E.2). Since the model should work best for molecules that are close to octahedral or tetrahedral symmetry, the assumption that $e_\pi \approx 0$ for saturated amines should work quite well for mixed-ligand complexes of these stereochemistries, and this has been confirmed for several nickel-(II) complexes by Gerloch and co-workers [168]. The crystal spectra of a range of cobalt(II) and nickel(II) haloacetate, nitrate, and nitrite complexes formed by various substituted diamines have been interpreted using this assumption by Lever and co-workers [176]. It was also assumed in this work that the π interaction of the oxyanion in the plane of the ligand is zero, and some of the results are summarized in Table 10. The e_π parameters estimated for several members of this set of compounds are anomalous, being negative (corresponding to π acceptance, rather than π donation, by the ligands); the reason for this is not clear. Another assumption which has sometimes been made [177] is that the metal-ligand π interaction involving aromatic amines is zero in the plane of the ligand, and this has been confirmed experimentally in several cases by Gerloch and co-workers [168] (see Table 9). The AOM bonding parameters for the $Cren_2X_2^+$ complexes, estimated by setting e_π for the amines to zero, are also included in Table 10.

Table 10   Angular Overlap Metal-Ligand Bonding Parameters Estimated from the Polarized Crystal Spectra of Various trans-Nickel(II) and trans-Chromium(III) Amine Complexes

Compound	Bonding parameter (cm^{-1})				
	$e_\sigma(N)$	$e_\pi(N)$	$e_\sigma(anion)$	$e_\pi(anion)$	Ref.
$[Ni(2meim)_4Br]Br$	5820	1310^a	2710^b	430^b	55
$Ni(pyridine)_4Br_2$	4500	500^a	2450^b	340^b	55
$Ni(pyrazole)_4Br_2$	5400	1350^a	1980^b	240^b	55
$Ni(pyridine)_4Cl_2$	4670	570^a	2980^b	540^b	55
$Ni(pyrazole)_4Cl_2$	5480	1370^a	2540^b	380^b	55
$Ni(NN'dieen)_2Br_2$	3923	0^c	1178	-644	139
$Ni(NN'dieen)_2Cl_2$	3972	0^c	1712	-276	139
$Ni(NN'dimen)_2(CCl_3CO_2)_2$	4100	0^c	2425	-215^d	139
$Ni(NNdimen)_2(CCl_3CO_2)_2$	4700^e, 3675^e	0^c	2800	460^d	139
$Ni(en)_2(NCS)_2$	4010	0^c	2133	-409	85
$[Cr(en)_2F_2]^+$	7230	0^c	7830	2000	97
$[Cr(en)_2Cl_2]^+$	7500	0^c	6260	1040	96
$[Cr(en)_2Br_2]^+$	7500	0^c	5720	750	96
$[Cr(en)_2(H_2O)_2]^{3+}$	7830	0^c	7570	1410	96

[a] Estimated assuming an isotropic π interaction.

[b] Estimated assuming that the ratio $e_\sigma : e_\pi$ is equal to the ratio of the square of the overlap between the nickel(II) 3d and halide p atomic orbitals.

[c] The π interaction from the amines was assumed to be zero.

[d] Represents the out-of-plane π interaction; the in-plane π interaction was set equal to zero.

[e] Values of primary and tertiary amine groups.

Another way in which the AOM has been used to reduce the number of independent metal-ligand bonding parameters makes use of the fact that for a spherical ligand such as a halide ion, the ratio of the e_σ and e_π values should equal the ratio of the squares of the appropriate diatomic overlap integrals S_σ and S_π [Eq. (30)]. This procedure was used by the present author to interpret the crystal spectrum of the five-coordinate complex [Ni(2meim)$_4$Br]Br, and a number of other tetragonal nickel(II) bromide and chloride complexes involving a range of nickel-halide bond distances and various heterocyclic amines [55]. The values of e_σ and e_π obtained in this way are shown in Table 10. Clearly, a major uncertainty in the process concerns the reliability of the overlap integrals, and to investigate the sensitivity of the method to these, the analysis was carried out using values derived with wave functions estimated for a charge distribution ranging from Ni^0 halide through to Ni^{2+} halide$^-$. Although this was found to have a substantial effect on the overlap integrals, it had little effect on the estimated values of e_σ and e_π, since these depend on the *ratio* of the overlap integrals rather than their absolute values. In the procedure described above, it was assumed that the ligand bonding occurred solely via the p orbitals, and it has been pointed out [158] that the neglect of the ligand s orbitals, which would contribute to σ but not π interactions, is a source of error in the procedure. Although this is certainly true, the ligand s orbitals are thought to be considerably lower in energy than the corresponding p orbitals, and simple calculations [178] as well as EPR superhyperfine measurements [179] suggest that they should produce a comparatively minor perturbation on the metal d orbitals. Except for the π-bonding parameters estimated in the studies by Lever and co-workers, which are subject to rather large uncertainties, the general self-consistency of the bonding parameters (Table 10) tends to suggest that the model is not too unrealistic. Thus the parameters estimated for each amine are quite similar when one complex is compared with another, while the halide parameters change in a manner consistent with the observed

differences in bond distance. The parameters are also approximately
equal to those estimated for analogous ligands by Gerloch and co-
workers (Table 9).

The fact that similar e_σ and e_π values are observed for a
range of compounds raises the question of whether the AOM ligand
bonding parameters can be transferred quantitatively from one complex to another. That is, how well can the energy levels in a
range of complexes involving a particular ligand be parametrized
using just one value of the constant K (or, where appropriate, K_σ,
$K_{\pi x}$, and $K_{\pi y}$) in Eq. (33)? This has been investigated by Smith,
who attempted to fit the energy levels obtained from the crystal
spectra of a wide range of copper(II) complexes involving oxygen
[180,181], nitrogen [178], and halide [182] ligands in this manner.
The model used was an extension of the AOM in which a small additional electrostatic component to the bonding was included. The
results suggested that in each case the energy levels could be explained quite well using a single value for $K_\parallel$ and $K_\perp$. Moreover,
agreement was rather better than would be the case using a purely
electrostatic crystal field approach, particularly as far as estimating the effect of distant ligands was concerned [183]. Subsequent work has led Smith to conclude that the inclusion of the minor
electrostatic contribution to the metal-ligand bonding is probably
an unnecessary complication to the model [184], but this is unlikely
to affect the general conclusions. A similar study has been carried
out by the present author for the chloride ion coordinated to
copper(II) [185]. Here it was found that the transition energies
derived from the crystal spectra of chlorocuprates having a wide
range of stereochemistries could be fitted reasonably well using
just two parameters, K_σ and K_π, to define the σ and π interaction
between the chloride ion and copper (II) (Table 11). The one ex-
ception in this process is the transition to the A_{1g} (d_{z^2}) state in
the planar $CuCl_4^{2-}$ ion, which is observed to be ~ 5000 cm^{-1} higher
in energy than is predicted by the model. It was suggested that the
discrepancy is due to configuration interaction between the metal

$a_{1g}(d_{z^2})$ and $a_{1g}(4s)$ orbitals, so that this represents a breakdown of the AOM in its simple form (see Sec. IV.E.2). It is noteworthy that when this transition is excluded from the fitting procedure, the values of K_σ and K_π giving optimum agreement between the calculated and observed transition energies were found to be equal, within experimental error, as predicted for a spherically symmetric ligand such as a halide ion. With the foregoing proviso, therefore, it would appear that at least for rather similar complexes, AOM parameters can be transferred from one molecule to another. However, more experimental studies are required before it becomes clear to what general extent this is possible. It must also be noted that whereas the parameters e_σ and e_π are obtained directly from the transition energies, the parameters K_σ and K_π are strongly dependent on calculated overlap integrals. Before values of the latter derived by different workers can be compared, it is therefore essential to ascertain that the overlap integrals were estimated using identical wave functions. If future work confirms that the metal-ligand bonding parameters are generally transferable in the manner described above, the AOM will provide a powerful method of predicting the energy levels of a complex of any geometry. This should prove particularly useful in interpreting the spectra of biologically important molecules which are not readily amenable to structural investigation by x-ray methods.

Since a major advantage of the AOM, as far as the coordination chemist is concerned, is that it used parameters which are easily interpreted in terms of the qualitative bonding schemes currently used to describe the properties of metal complexes, it is worthwhile briefly considering how the data accumulated up to the present time fit into this picture. A representative sample of these data are presented in Tables 9 and 10, and as already mentioned, it is apparent that these are reasonably self-consistent with the exception of the negative π-bonding parameters reported by Lever and co-workers [176]. They also seem generally chemically sensible. Thus the halide ions are fairly weak σ and π donors, the ligand

field strength decreasing along the series $F^- > Cl^- > Br^- > I^-$.
The π interaction is $\sim20\%$ the σ interaction, as expected from the
ratio of the square of the overlap integrals. Saturated amine
ligands are stronger σ donors than the halides [with the exception
of F^- toward chromium(III), as discussed above] and the π perturbation produced by these amines is, as expected, small. Triphenyl-
phosphine, at least toward nickel(II), is a moderate σ donor and a
moderate π acceptor. The role of the phosphorus d orbitals in complex formation has long been invoked at a qualitative level [186],
and it is pleasing to see that the AOM parameters apparently confirm this viewpoint. The bonding parameters of aromatic amines are
the least consistent of the classes of ligands studies so far.
Several investigations suggest that pyridine is a moderate σ donor
and weak π donor toward divalent metal ions [55,166,172,187], although it should be noted that Schäffer and co-workers have found
it to be a moderate σ donor and weak π acceptor in a study of the
solution spectra of a range of chromium(III) complexes [177]. The
present author has inferred that 2-methylimidazole and pyrazole both
act as quite strong σ donors and moderate π donors in several
nickel(II) complexes (Table 10) [55]. However, in this study the
approximation was made that the halide $e_\sigma : e_\pi$ ratios equaled the
ratios of the square of the overlap integrals involving the metal d
and ligand p orbitals. Gerloch and co-workers, on the other hand,
have found that quinoline and biquinoline behave as moderate σ
donors and π acceptors in some tetrahedral nickel(II) complexes
[168]. It is not yet clear whether these differences represent
real variations in bonding characteristics, or are merely artifacts
of the derivation process. In a paper specifically addressed to the
chemical significance of AOM parameters, Gerloch and co-workers have
argued [168] that the σ- and π-bonding parameters of a ligand are
expected to vary from one complex to another, even if the metal-
ligand bond distance remains constant and that this, in fact, provides much useful information about the bonding—for instance, on
features such as synergic effects. Should future experimental work

bear this out, it would certainly increase the value of the AOM, although, of course, it would also mean that ligand bonding parameters could not confidently be transferred from one complex to another.

It is generally to be expected that as the metal-ligand bond distance increases, the bonding interaction should decrease, and the data clearly support this. This is particularly striking for amine ligands bound to nickel(II), which range from $e_\sigma \approx 3700$ cm^{-1} for sterically hindered tertiary groups (Ni-N ≈ 2.2 Å) through to $e_\sigma \approx 10,000$ cm^{-1} in a planar, diamagnetic Ni amine complex (Ni-N ≈ 1.94 Å) [77]. It is also noteworthy that the bonding parameters for the trivalent Co^{3+} and Cr^{3+} ions are substantially higher than those of the divalent metal ions. It is often stated that for any particular ligand, the d-orbital splitting approximately doubles on going from the +2 to the +3 oxidation state [188]. However, it is noteworthy that the examples cited normally involve metals such as cobalt, where there is a substantial change in metal-ligand bond distance [Co(II)-N = 2.114 Å, Co(III)-N = 1.97 Å in the hexamine complexes] [189], and this may well be associated more with the change in occupancy of the e_g^* antibonding orbitals than with the change in oxidation state as such [190,191]. In fact, at a constant metal-ligand bond length, an electrostatic model would predict a substantial *decrease* in ligand field splitting when the oxidation state of the metal increases, owing to the contraction of the d orbitals [Eq. (29)]. The situation as far as the AOM is concerned is more complicated. Although the contraction of the d orbitals would cause a decrease in the metal-ligand overlap, the parameter K in Eq. (34) should increase in magnitude on oxidation of the metal as the ligand and metal orbitals become closer in energy. The two factors could well approximately balance, so that at a constant bond distance, the d orbital splitting would be roughly independent of metal oxidation state. This is borne out by the fact that the d-orbital energy separation increases as much (by ∿130%) on going from octahedral Ni(en)$_3^{2+}$ to planar Ni(diamine)$_2^{2+}$ as it does on going from Co(NH$_3$)$_6^{3+}$ to Co(NH$_3$)$_6^{3+}$ [192]. In each case, the increase accompanies a decrease in metal-ligand bond length of ∿0.16 Å [49,77,189], suggesting that this is the dominant cause of the changes in the d-antibonding energies.

Another potentially useful feature of the AOM which has, as yet, been little exploited concerns the way in which metal-ligand bonding parameters vary among different metal ions. On traversing each transition series, the effective nuclear charge increases as the atomic number rises. This means that the parameter K of Eq. (31) for any particular ligand is expected to increase as the d orbitals approach the ligand orbitals in energy. In agreement with this, the present author has found that K for acetylacetonato-type ligands increases by ∿20% on going from nickel(II) to copper(II) [193]. However, if the metal-ligand bond length remains similar, the over-lap integral S will decrease, owing to the contraction of the d orbit-als. The two effects could well be comparable, so that the bonding parameters e_σ and e_π are expected to be roughly independent of the metal ion. Although few investigations of this aspect have yet been made, the fact that the AOM includes the two factors metal-ligand orbital overlap and metal-ligand orbital energy difference in its description of the bonding in a complex makes it considerably more powerful than the simple crystal field approach.

2. Apparent Breakdowns in Simple Models of the Bonding in Metal Complexes

It is important to recognize that the models above are so sim-plistic that they cannot be expected to do more than provide a useful way of parametrizing the ligand interactions with the metal d orbit-als in a complex. However, if they are to be of value, they must be reasonably self-consistent and a number of potential flaws in models of this kind have been suggested. At a quite fundamental level, it is normally assumed that the electronic spectrum of a complex of a metal ion with a d^1 or d^9 electron configuration may be interpreted simply in terms of the energy differences between the d orbitals, that is, that interelectron-repulsion effects within the d shell may in these cases be neglected. This idea has been challenged by Smith

[194], who suggested that as the electrons occupying σ-type orbitals are more delocalized than those in orbitals of π symmetry, interelectron repulsion effects could be significant even in systems having a single d electron. Calculations were presented suggesting that as a result of these effects the energy levels in the distorted octahedral $CuCl_6^{4-}$ chromaphore should be substantially different from those predicted by a simple model based just on a direct ligand d orbital interaction [194]. The crystal spectra of compounds containing the complex above, however, are in good agreement with the predictions of simple bonding schemes [185,195], so that it would seem that in practice it is unnecessary to include the interelectron repulsion corrections suggested by Smith. The reason this is the case is not clear.

In the simple form in which the AOM is most generally used, ligand-ligand interactions are neglected. The effects of this on the energy levels of a model planar copper(II) complex formed by four nitrogen donor ligands has also been estimated by Smith [196] and the results are predicted to be fairly small. Similarly, it is often assumed that interactions with ligand s orbitals are negligible compared with those involving the corresponding p orbitals, and again simple calculations [178] suggest that this is likely to be a fairly good approximation. As discussed in the preceding section, it has also sometimes been assumed that the π bonding capability of saturated amine ligands is negligible. One way in which these assumptions can be tested is to study the electronic transitions of a planar copper-(II) tetramine complex, since the AOM in its simple form predicts that in such a complex the transitions $^2B_{2g}(d_{xy}) \leftarrow {}^2B_{1g}(d_{x^2-y^2})$ and $^2E_g(d_{xz},d_{yz}) \leftarrow {}^2B_{1g}(d_{x^2-y^2})$ should occur at an identical energy. The polarized spectra of several complexes of general formula $Cu(NH_3)_4X_2$ suggested that the transitions above are in fact split by $\sim$2000 cm^{-1} [197]. This was interpreted by Smith [198] in terms of an electrostatic contribution to the bonding (which would raise the energy of the d_{xy} orbital relative to d_{xz}, d_{yz}) and led to the

formulation [164] of a model in which a crystal field contribution
was added to the AOM covalent interaction. However, the polarized
spectrum of the complex $Na_4Cu(NH_3)_4[Cu(S_2O_3)_2]\cdot NH_3$, which contains
essentially four-coordinate, planar $Cu(NH_3)_4^{2+}$ ions, suggests [199]
that the $^2B_{2g}(d_{xy})$ and $^2E(d_{xz},d_{yz})$ excited states are probably
quite close in energy, as predicted by the AOM model, thus obviat-
ing the need to use the foregoing combined crystal field/AOM
approach [158]. A study of the crystal spectrum of the planar complex $[Ni(DACO)_2](ClO_4)_2\cdot 2H_2O$ (where DACO is 1,5-diazacyclooctane)
has suggested a π interaction 12 ± 4% of the σ interaction [77],
while in several tetrahedral nickel complexes involving saturated
amines, the π interaction was found to be probably essentially zero
[200]. All in all, therefore, it would seem that as far as the
factors above go, the simple AOM works remarkably well.

The spectrum of the foregoing planar nickel(II) complex did,
however, show one feature that cannot be explained by the AOM in the
simple form given above. The transition from the d_{z^2} orbital to the
empty $d_{x^2-y^2}$ orbital occurs quite close in energy to those from the
effectively nonbinding d_{xy}, d_{xz}, and d_{yz} orbitals, despite the fact
that the AOM (or a simple electrostatic model) predicts that the d_{z^2}
orbital should be raised in energy to one-third that of the $d_{x^2-y^2}$
orbital by a σ interaction with the ligands. Studies on the crystal
spectra of various other square-planar compounds of copper(II) [39,
76,116], iron(II) [75,201], and platinum (II) [202] have shown a
similar effect, and it is clear that this lowering of the d_{z^2} orbital by between 5000 and 10,000 cm^{-1} from the value predicted by a
simple bonding model is a general phenomenon for complexes of this
stereochemistry. It has been suggested [203,204] that the depression is due to configuration interaction between the metal $a_{1g}(s)$
and $a_{1g}(d_{z^2})$ orbitals, and the magnitude of the effect implies a

mixing coefficient of the s orbital of 0.2, in good agreement with
EPR studies on analogous cobalt(II) complexes [205]. It is
interesting to note that the effect apparently becomes important
only in truly square-planar complexes. For instance, the d_{z^2}
orbital is depressed in energy by $\sim$5000 cm^{-1} in the truly four-
coordinate planar $CuCl_4^{2-}$ ion present in complexes with certain
large organic cations [39,74,116], while in similar complexes containing planar $CuCl_4^{2-}$ units bridged by long (Cu-Cl $\sim$ 3.0 Å) axial
bonds, the depression is $\sim$1400 cm^{-1} [185] (see Table 11). The reason for this is probably the very diffuse nature of the metal s
orbital. The extent of the mixing depends on the difference in the
ligand interaction with the metal d_{z^2} and s orbitals along the z and
xy axes [204], and the extended nature of the s orbital may well
mean that the axial ligands must be completely absent in order for
this difference to be large. The energy of the d_{z^2} orbital in planar
complexes of the type bisacetylacetonato copper(II) is of some
interest in this context. Although this has been the subject of
some controversy [9,32,45,103-106,193], the bulk of the experimental
evidence would seem to suggest that in all these compounds the energy
of the d_{z^2} orbital can be interpreted quite satisfactorily using the
simple AOM [45,193] (see Sec. IV.E.1), and the question naturally
arises as to why configuration interaction with the 4s orbital
apparently does not occur. Crystal structure determinations have
been carried out on several complexes of this type, and it has
invariably been observed that the central carbon atom of the actylace-
tonate ring of a neighboring molecule is situated $\sim$3.1 Å above and
below the copper(II) ion [206]. This has led to the suggestion [206]
that a weak bonding interaction may occur between the metal and the
ligand π system, and possibly this "semicoordination" may be sufficient to suppress the admixture of the metal 4s orbital into the
$a_{1g}(d_{z^2})$ orbital.

Table 11 Spectral Transition Energies Calculated by a Least-Squares Procedure for Various Chlorocuprate Complexes Using the Angular Overlap Model[a]

Compound	Type[b]	Bond lengths (Å)	Transition	Energies (cm^{-1} × 10^{-3}) Calculated	Calculated[c]	Observed
$[Cr(NH_3)_6][CuCl_5]$	TB	2.30	$d_{z^2}, d_{xy} \rightarrow d_{z^2}$	8.25	7.94	8.70
		2.39	$d_{xz}, d_{yz} \rightarrow d_{z^2}$	10.23	10.31	10.80
Cs_2CuCl_4	T	2.24[d]	$d_{xz} \rightarrow d_{x^2-y^2}$	5.97	5.70	4.80
		2.22[e]	$d_{yz} \rightarrow d_{x^2-y^2}$	6.59	6.33	5.55
			$d_{xy} \rightarrow d_{x^2-y^2}$	7.83	8.19	7.90
			$d_{z^2} \rightarrow d_{x^2-y^2}$	9.70	9.41	9.05
$[C_6H_5N(CH_3)_3]_2CuCl_4$	T	2.256[f]	$d_{xz}, d_{yz} \rightarrow d_{x^2-y^2}$	6.97	6.68	5.92
			$d_{z^2} \rightarrow d_{x^2-y^2}$	9.72	9.35	8.85
$CsCuCl_3$	TO	2.32	$d_{xz}, d_{yz} \rightarrow d_{x^2-y^2}$	13.38	12.98	12.93
		2.78	$d_{xy} \rightarrow d_{x^2-y^2}$	10.68	10.90	10.00
			$d_{z^2} \rightarrow d_{x^2-y^2}$	8.07	7.48	8.30

Compound	Stereochem.[b]	Bond length	Transition			
		3.04	$d_{xy} \rightarrow d_{x^2-y^2}$	11.10	11.46	12.39
			$d_{z^2} \rightarrow d_{x^2-y^2}$	10.53	9.76	11.13
$(n\text{-PrNH}_3)_2\text{CuCl}_4$	TO	2.281	$d_{xz}, d_{yz} \rightarrow d_{x^2-y^2}$	14.43	13.97	13.50
		2.975	$d_{xy} \rightarrow d_{x^2-y^2}$	11.01	11.33	12.30
			$d_{z^2} \rightarrow d_{x^2-y^2}$	10.72	9.93	11.30
$(C_6H_5CH_2CH_2NH_2CH_3)_2\text{CuCl}_4$	P	2.248	$d_{xz} \rightarrow d_{x^2-y^2}$	15.17	14.72	14.15
		2.281	$d_{yz} \rightarrow d_{x^2-y^2}$	15.65	15.09	14.40
			$d_{xy} \rightarrow d_{x^2-y^2}$	11.45	11.86	12.50
			$d_{z^2} \rightarrow d_{x^2-y^2}$	12.91	11.87	16.90

[a] See the text for the "best-fit" ligand field parameters.

[b] Complex stereochemistry: TB, trigonal bipyramid; T, distorted tetrahedral; TO, elongated tetragonal octahedral; P, square planar.

[c] In this calculation the fitting procedure was carried out without including the $^2B_1(d_{x^2-y^2}) \rightarrow {}^2A_1(d_{z^2})$ transition of $(C_6H_5CH_2CH_2NH_2CH_3)_2\text{CuCl}_4$.

[d] ClCuCl = 131.2°.

[e] ClCuCl = 127.1°.

[f] ClCuCl = 132.5°.

Source: Ref. 185.

F. Deviations from the Oriented Gas Model of Crystal Spectra

1. *Cooperative Interactions*

The interpretation of crystal electronic spectra in terms of simple static and vibronic selection rules depends on the assumption that the crystal lattice simply acts as a matrix to hold the complex in a fixed orientation in space, with the energy levels and vibrational perturbations remaining essentially those of isolated molecules. Although this will often be a good approximation, there are certain circumstances where it may be expected to break down, and it is worthwhile considering these briefly. One factor that may complicate the interpretation of spectra is the presence of magnetic interactions between the metal ions in a crystal. The effects of this may range from a minor enhancement of spin-forbidden transitions when the magnetic coupling is weak, to such dramatic changes that the spectrum of the solid may bear little resemblance to that of an isolated chromaphore. Of course, an analysis of the spectra provides a powerful means of investigating magnetic exchange phenomena, but the means by which this is done is outside the scope of the present chapter. A summary of some of the important work in the area is given in a recent article by Ferguson [6].

Another factor that may cause the optical spectrum of a crystal to differ from that expected for the sum of its component molecules is the presence of a Davydov effect [207-209]. In essence, this effect is due to significant perturbations to the excited electronic state of a molecule from its neighbors in the crystal lattice. These interactions cause splittings in the excited states relative to those of an isolated molecule, together with changes in the band intensities and polarization properties. Under these circumstances, the oriented gas model breaks down and the spectra must be interpreted in terms of the unit cell of the crystal as a whole. It was suggested by Difkgraaf [36] that a Davydov interaction might be responsible for the anomalous polarization properties observed in the electronic crystal spectrum of $Cu(acac)_2$ (see Sec. IV.A.2). However, Belford and co-workers subsequently showed that

no such effect is present in this complex [37], and the likely
circumstances under which this kind of interaction might be observed
in a complex of this type were discussed in an analysis of the crystal spectra of various forms of $Cu(acac_2en)$ [46]. The effect is
expected to increase in importance as the separation between the
metal ions in the lattice decreases, and the intensity of the d-d
transitions becomes greater. It was concluded that no significant
Davydov effect is expected or observed in the crystal spectra of the
various forms of $Cu(acac_2en)$. In general, such effects are unlikely
to be important when band intensities are less than ∿500 liters
mol^{-1} cm^{-1} and intermetal separations are greater than ∿3.5 Å. One
class of complex for which Davydov effects do significantly modify
what are formally d-d transitions are those planar complexes of
Ni(II), Pd(II), and Pt(II) which crystallize to give chain structures producing quite short metal-metal distances. Perhaps the best
example of this effect is provided by the study by Day and co-workers [210] of a series of complexes of general formula $[Pt(RNH_2)_4]$-
$[PtCl_4]$ in which the metal-metal separation varies according to the
size of the substituent R. When R = C_2H_5, the Pt-Pt distance is
3.40 Å and the spectrum in the visible and near-UV region is not too
different from a superposition of the spectra of isolated $Pt(NH_3)_4^{2+}$
and $PtCl_4^{2-}$ ions. However, when R = H, the intermetal separation
falls to 3.24 Å and the ligand-field transitions are red-shifted by
∿4000 cm^{-1}, and also increase substantially in intensity in the
polarization along the metal-metal direction. The reason for this
is thought to be a substantial Davydov splitting of an intense transition in the UV region, which interacts via vibronic coupling with
the d-d transitions [210]. A rather similar effect apparently
causes the shifts in the d-d transitions of bis(dimethylglyoxime)-
nickel(II) which give rise to the unusual red color of this solid
[211]; a large Davydov splitting of the ligand field bands has also
been reported in the crystal spectrum of $PtenCl_2$ [212]. It may be
noted that significant interactions of the type described above are
always accompanied by a substantial difference between the

electronic spectrum in the solid state and in solution. For a
summary of the effects of cooperative interactions up d-d spectra,
the reader is referred to several recent review articles by Day
[211,213,214].

2. Lattice Interactions

In an idealized oriented gas model it is assumed that only
metal-ligand vibrational modes couple with the electronic states of
a molecule. However, recent studies have shown that interactions
with the crystal lattice may also sometimes be important. Thus
some of the vibrational fine structure observed in the electronic
spectrum of $PdCl_4^{2-}$ doped into crystals of Cs_2ZrCl_6 has been interpreted in terms of coupling with lattice modes [79]. Similarly,
one band in the crystal spectrum of $(Nmph)_2CuCl_4$ shows several
progressions which are apparently built on transitions involving
the excitation of what are formally lattice modes [39]. Moreover,
it has been suggested that although these only contribute a minor
portion (10%) of the total band intensity at 10 K, because of their
low energy, the contribution at room temperature is likely to be
quite significant ($\sim$50%) [39]. As yet, comparatively few complexes
have revealed sufficiently detailed vibrational structure in their
electronic spectra for the nature of the vibrations to be assigned
unambiguously, so that it is hard to tell to what extent lattice
interactions affect d-d spectra in general. Although it is reasonable to assume that for the kinds of complex considered in the
present chapter the transition energies and probably also the overall band polarizations will be dominated by the nearest-neighbor
metal-ligand interactions, any detailed interpretation of the spectrum involving the temperature dependence of vibrational fine
structure should include the possibility of coupling with lattice
modes.

Although not strictly a lattice effect, it is noteworthy that
occasionally coupling between d-d transitions and internal ligand
vibrations has been observed. Thus weak sharp peaks assigned to
the excitation of a quantum of the OH stretching mode in addition

to the electronic transition have been observed in the crystal spectra of several hydrate complexes [91,92,112]; a similar coupling of the d-d transitions to the NH symmetric stretching mode has been observed [215] for the $Ni(NH_3)_6^{2+}$ ion. In this context it should be noted that overtones and combination bands due to vibrational transitions often give rise to quite intense absorptions in the near-infrared region. Those due to OH and NH vibrations are particularly pronounced, and care should be taken both that these are not confused with d-d transitions, and that they do not obscure bands due to electronic excitations. The vibrational transitions are usually much sharper than spin-allowed d-d transitions, and may be identified by comparing the frequencies with those of the fundamental absorptions and, if necessary, by deuteration of the complex. The latter procedure may sometimes reveal a band due to a d-d transition. This was the case for the $Cu(H_2O)_6^{2+}$ ion present in various Tutton's salts [216], where the study of crystals of deuterated samples revealed the presence of an electronic transition at $\sim$6800 cm^{-1} which had not been detected in a previous study [217] because of the masking effects of infrared overtones of the water molecules.

3. Low-Energy Intraligand and Charge Transfer Transitions

Occasionally, charge transfer or internal ligand transitions may occur at comparatively low energy and intensity, so that they may be incorrectly assigned as d-d transitions. This occurred for a weak band at $\sim$26,000 cm^{-1} in the spectrum of $Cu(acac)_2$ assigned originally as a d-d excitation [33,34], but subsequently shown to probably be a weak charge transfer or intraligand transition [218]. Similarly, a band at $\sim$27,000 cm^{-1} in the spectrum of dimeric $Cu_2(CH_3CO_2)_4 \cdot 2H_2O$ was for many years the subject of considerable controversy, being variously assigned as a transition within the molecular orbitals of a strongly coupled dimer [219,220], a double-electron excitation [221], or a charge transfer transition [222]. A detailed study of polarization properties and the behavior of the band over a temperature range using a single crystal has since shown that the peak is probably due to a weakly allowed ligand → metal charge transfer transition [222]. The single-crystal electronic

spectra of compounds containing the dimeric $Cu_2Cl_6{}^{2-}$ ion show a
rather similar peak, and in this case the band has also been
assigned as a weak ligand-metal charge transfer transition [223,
224]. The crystal spectra of a number of nickel(II) complexes
containing chelating nitrite ions have been found to exhibit a band
centered at $\sim$23,000 cm^{-1}, which shows considerable vibrational fine
structure at low temperature [13,225], and this has been attributed
by Lever and co-workers [13] to a spin-forbidden internal nitrite
transition, which probably gains intensity via the high spin-orbit
coupling constant of the metal ion. Early studies of the electronic
spectra of single crystals of nickel(II) nitrocomplexes assigned the
band centered at $\sim$20,000 cm^{-1} to the second spin-allowed d-d transition [84,85]. The vibrational fine structure observed at low
temperature in more recent investigations however, strongly suggests that the bulk of the intensity is not d-d in origin, but
probably arises from a weak metal $\rightarrow$ ligand charge transfer transition [86,225,226]. Similarly, the electronic spectra of a number
of polymeric nickel(II)nitrite complexes are anomalous in that they
show two bands in the visible region, centered at $\sim$17,000 and
$\sim$20,000 cm^{-1}. As these compounds contain metal ions in two types
of ligand environment, the spectra were originally assigned in
terms of the superimposition of the d-d spectra of these two kinds
of nickel(II) [227]. More recent measurements of the low-temperature crystal spectra, however, have revealed vibrational structure
of the band at $\sim$20,000 cm^{-1} in certain of the complexes (Fig. 27)
[228]. The energy of the progression, $\sim$625 cm^{-1}, is too high for
assignment to any metal-ligand vibration, being consistent with the
δ_{NO_2} nitrite wagging mode of an excited electronic state in which
an electron has been promoted into the nitrite π^* orbital. It has
therefore been suggested [228,229] that while the band at $\sim$17,000
cm^{-1} is due to a d-d transition, that at $\sim$20,000 cm^{-1} is probably
a weak metal $\rightarrow$ ligand electron transfer transition associated with
the nitrogen bound

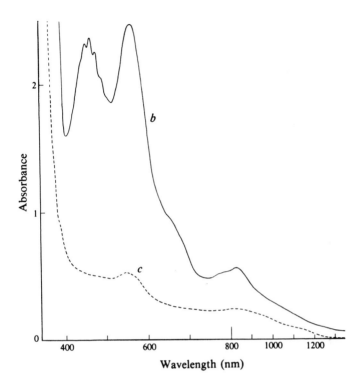

Figure 27 Polarized spectrum of the (100) crystal face of [Ni(4-methylpyridine)$_2$(NO$_2$)$_2$]$_2$·2C$_6$H$_6$ measured at 8 K with the electric vector along the b and c crystal axes. (From Ref. 228.)

linkages present in these complexes. Similar, comparatively low energy metal → ligand π* transitions have also been observed in the crystal spectra of iron(II) and ruthenium(II) dipyridyl complexes [230,231].

Finally, it should be noted that small amounts of intensely colored impurities may sometimes give rise to anomalous peaks in crystal absorption spectra. Thus compounds such as Cs$_2$MnCl$_4$ may contain small amounts of the corresponding CoCl$_4^{2-}$ species, which

gives rise to a band at 15,000 cm^{-1} comparable in intensity to the
spin-forbidden transitions due to the Mn^{2+} ion [232]. Similarly,
the crystal spectra of $Cs_3Ti_2Cl_9$ [233] and $Cs_2[Cr(H_2O)_4Cl_2]Cl$ [234]
both show anomalous bands in the region 330-370 nm, and it has been
suggested that these may be due to charge transfer transitions
associated with trace amounts of iron(III) impurities. These examples clearly show that before seeking any more sophisticated explanation of anomalous bands in the electronic spectrum of a complex,
it is advisable to consider the possibility of the presence of a
small amount of highly absorbing impurity.

V. GENERAL CONCLUSIONS AND SUGGESTIONS FOR FUTURE WORK

Hopefully, this chapter has shown that the measurement of electronic
spectra using single crystals and polarized light can provide the
transition metal chemist with useful information not readily available by other means. This information is basically of two kinds:
direct evidence on the nature of the electronic wave functions in
the ground and excited states and of the way in which these are
coupled to the vibrational modes of a complex, and indirect evidence
on the bonding properties of the ligands and molecular geometry in
the excited electronic states obtained by interpreting band energies
and vibrational fine structure.

Data of the latter kind are potentially of great value in wide-
ranging areas of transition metal chemistry, providing as it does
quantitative information about the σ- and π-bonding properties of
ligands, and the geometries of complexes in excited states and how
these relate to the electronic structure of the metal ion. However, it is important to remember that reliable information of this
sort can only be obtained if a sufficiently large and reliable body
of knowledge of the first kind has been built up to form a firm
basis on which crystal spectra may be interpreted. For example,
the polarization properties of d-d transitions provide a powerful
means of assigning the excited electronic states in a complex, and
these are directly related to the σ- and π-bonding properties of

the ligands. However, the band polarizations can be properly
utilized only if it is known under what conditions the selection
rules used to interpret the spectra are likely to be obeyed.
Although the theoretical basis describing the factors that
influence the energies and intensities of d-d spectra has been
established for a considerable time, remarkably little experimental
work has been carried out to investigate how well these ideas are
obeyed in practice. This is particularly true as far as the
vibronic interactions in centrosymmetric complexes are concerned,
and in the author's view there is a real need for detailed studies
to be made of the polarized spectra of a number of simple complexes
of this kind, as well as noncentrosymmetric complexes in which the
inversion center is destroyed by relatively small ligand perturbations. The kind of questions that such investigations should help
to answer are:

1. How well is the oriented gas model obeyed, and, in particular, to what extent does coupling with lattice modes affect
   the intensities of d-d transitions?

2. What are the factors that influence the "activity" of the
   various u normal modes in inducing intensity in vibronically allowed transitions?

3. To what extent does the nature of the u excited electronic
   states influence the intensities of the d-d transitions,
   and how important is the electronic structure of the ligands in the intensity mechanism?

4. How well is the temperature dependence of the intensities
   of d-d transitions represented by the $coth^{-1}$ rule?

5. What are the factors that cause the shifts in d-d band
   maxima when the temperature is changed, and how may these
   be related to changes in molecular geometry?

Although important results have been reported in most of the
foregoing areas, for instance by Ferguson [19,90,92], Patterson
[42,43,128,129], Pedro-Smith [61,114], and Solomon [124,125,127,

136] and their co-workers on points 1 and 2, by Belford and
co-workers [9,32,45,46] on point 3, and by Dingle [47,49,93,102]
and Mason [107,113] and their collaborators on points 2 and 4, much
work remains to be done before an acceptable, integrated picture of
the factors controlling d-d transition energies and intensities is
established. Important criteria that should be considered in select-
ing complexes suitable for studying the factors above are that the
symmetry should be neither too high nor too low, so that relatively
simple polarization behavior of the electronic transitions is expected (a point group such as D_{4h}, D_{2h}, or C_{2v} is ideal in this
respect). Also, the complex should involve simple ligands, and the
vibrational spectrum should be fully characterized, preferably at
the factor group level. Ideally, the electronic spectrum should
exhibit vibrational fine structure, and should be recorded not only
at low temperature, but also over a temperature range, with the
intensities measured in absolute, rather than arbitrary, absorption
units.

The measurement of polarized crystal spectra provides the best
method of characterizing the excited electronic states of a complex, although care must be exercised in the interpretation of
spectra for the reasons given earlier. The excited-state energies
may then be used to provide valuable quantitative data on the
metal-ligand interactions in a complex, and in the author's view
the most promising method by which this may currently be done is by
the use of the angular overlap model. This parametrizes the metal-
ligand interactions in terms of σ- and π-bonding effects, and it is
clearly of interest to see whether the values obtained are self-
consistent and "chemically reasonable," that is, agree with the
presently accepted general view point of the bonding in transition
metal complexes. The evaluation of the model may best be achieved
by studying related series of complexes in which just the parameters of interest are varied. Some useful studies might involve:

1. The construction of a "two-dimensional" spectrochemical
   series in which the σ- and π-bonding properties of ligands

toward a specific metal ion are compared. The bonding
properties of ligands such as CN⁻ which are high in the
conventional one-dimensional spectrochemical series would
be of particular interest in this context.

2. The investigation of the transferability of bonding parameters among complexes having the same metal and ligands,
   but differing stereochemistries.

3. The investigation of the effect on the bonding parameters
   of:

   a. The metal-ligand bond length.

   b. The oxidation state of the metal.

   c. The nature of the metal ion.

The compilation of data along the foregoing lines has begun,
particularly due to the work of Lever [139,166], Gatteschi [50,51,
54,169], Schäffer [177], and Gerloch [140,161,168], and their co-
workers, but much remains to be done before it is clear to what extent a coherent, self-consistent description of the bonding in metal
complexes can be built with the model. Should this prove possible,
it will be of benefit in several ways, perhaps the most important being that the qualitative simple molecular orbital schemes currently
used to describe the bonding in metal complexes can be put on a
more quantitative basis. Hopefully, this may be of value in areas
such as reaction kinetics, in which the σ- and π-bonding behavior
of ligands is often invoked to rationalize experimental observations. It should also make the deduction of the nature and stereochemistry of metal complexes from spectral measurements far more
reliable, which should be particularly valuable in biochemical
applications.

A second area of considerable interest is in the deduction of
the geometry and vibrational properties of complexes in excited
electronic states from an analysis of band contours and structure.
This is clearly of importance in helping to understand the photoreactivity of metal complexes, but it also provides a unique
opportunity to study the way in which the geometry and vibrational

force constants depend on the electronic configuration of a
molecule. Although a start has been made in this area, particularly
due to the research of Patterson [43,79,129], Solomon [124,125], and
their co-workers, in the author's view this aspect of the spectra of
metal complexes should be exploited more fully in the future.

One of the most attractive features of transition metal complexes is the beautiful range of colors exhibited by their crystals,
and it is to be hoped that the present chapter has shown that these
are not only aesthetically satisfying, but can provide, via the
study of their polarized electronic spectra, useful insight into
various aspects of the chemical behavior of this important class of
compounds.

ACKNOWLEDGMENTS

The author is grateful to Professor B. N. Figgis, of the University
of Western Australia, for useful suggestions and for the patience
that he has exercised during the preparation of this chapter, and
to R. G. McDonald, M. L. Riley and R. J. Deeth of the University
of Tasmania for providing some of the data used in the text. The
financial assistance of the Australian Research Grants Commission
is gratefully acknowledged.

LIGAND AND CATION ABBREVIATIONS

Nmesal: $\underline{N}$-methylsalicylaldimine

MeOac :   Methoxyacetate, $CH_3OCO_2^-$

benzac: Benzoylacetonate, $C_6H_5COCHCOCH_3^-$

acac :   Acetylacetonate, $CH_3COCHCOCH_3^-$

$acac_2$en: $\underline{N},\underline{N}$'-ethylenebis(acetylacetonate)

en   :   1,2-diaminoethane, $CH_2NH_2CH_2NH_2$

methadone: 3-heptanone, 6-(dimethylamine)-4,4 diphenyl

$C_2H_5COC(C_6H_5)_2CH_2CHNH(CH_3)CH_3$

Nmph :   N-methylphenethylammonium, $C_6H_5C_2H_4NH_2CH_3^+$

DACO :   1,5-diazacyclooctane

$\underline{NN}$'dieen: $\underline{N},\underline{N}$'diethyl-1,2-diaminoethane, $CH_2NH(C_2H_5)CH_2NH(C_2H_5)$

$\underline{NN}$'dimen: $\underline{N},\underline{N}$'-dimethyl-1,2-diaminoethane, $CH_2NH(CH_3)CH_2NH(CH_3)$

$\underline{NN}$ dimen: $\underline{N},\underline{N}$-dimethyl-1,2-diaminoethane, $CH_2N(CH_3)_2CH_2NH_2$

2meim :   2-methylimidazole

bzpipzn: $\underline{N}$-benzylpiperazinium

NOTES AND REFERENCES

1. H. A. Bethe, *Ann. Phys.*, 3:133 (1929); J. H. Van Vleck, *J. Chem. Phys.*, 3:803, 807 (1935).

2. R. J. M. Hobbs and N. S. Hush, *Prog. Inorg. Chem.*, 10:259 (1968).

3. Royal Society of Chemistry Specialist Reports, *Electronic Structure and Magnetism of Inorganic Compounds* (P. Day, ed.), Royal Society of Chemistry, London.

4. An excellent introduction to the electronic spectra of metal complexes is given by C. K. Jørgensen, *Absorption Spectra and Chemical Bonding in Complexes*, Pergamon, Oxford, 1962.

5. A. B. P. Lever, *Inorganic Electronic Spectroscopy*, Elsevier, Amsterdam, 1968.

6. J. Ferguson, *Prog. Inorg. Chem.*, 12:159 (1970).

7. C. J. Ballhausen, Measurement and interpretation of transition ion crystal spectra, in *Spectroscopy in Inorganic Chemistry*, (C. N. R. Rao and J. R. Ferraro, eds.), Academic Press, New York, 1970.

8. J. Ferguson, Introduction to linearly polarized electronic spectra of inorganic crystals, in *Electronic States of Inorganic Compounds: New Experimental Techniques*, D. Reidel, Dordrecht, The Netherlands, 1974.

9. R. L. Belford and J. W. Carmichael, Jr., *J. Chem. Phys.*, 46: 4515 (1967).

10. P. Day, *Inorg. Chim. Acta Rev.*, 3:81 (1969).

11. P. Day, *J. Mol. Struct.*, 59:109 (1980).

12. Al Holden and P. Singer, *Crystals and Crystal Growing*, Bell Telephone Laboratories, Murray Hill, N. J., 1962; K. Nassau, *Growing Synthetic Crystals*, Bell Telephone Laboratories, Murray Hill, N. J., 1964.

13. I. M. Walker, A. B. P. Lever, and P. J. McCarthy, *Can. J. Chem.*, 58:823 (1980); P. J. McCarthy, private communication.

14. E. E. Wahlstrom, *Optical Crystallography*, Wiley, New York, 1969.

15. In the Cary 17 spectrophotometer used by the author, a Hamamatsu R636 photomultiplier has been found to work very well in the region 300-850 nm.

16. A good discussion of the interaction of electromagnetic radiation with a transition metal ion is given by J. S. Griffith, *The Theory of Transition-Metal Ions*, Cambridge University Press, Cambridge, 1964, Chaps. 3 and 11.

17. P. W. Atkins, *Quanta, A Handbook of Concepts*, Oxford University Press, London, 1974, p. 162.

18. J. Ferguson, H. J. Guggenheim, and D. J. Wood, *J. Chem. Phys.*, 40:822 (1964); J. Ferguson and H. J. Guggenheim, *J. Chem. Phys.*, 44:1095 (1966).

19. J. Ferguson, T. E. Wood, and H. J. Guggenheim, *Inorg. Chem.*, 14:177 (1975).

20. The absorption ellipsoid of the electronic spectrum is analogous to the molecular magnetic susceptibility tensor and the tensor g^2, the derivation of which from crystal measurements has been the subject of considerable interest; see, for example; K. Dawson, M. A. Hitchman, C. K. Prout, and F. J. C. Rossotti, *J. Chem. Soc., Dalton Trans.*, 1509 (1972); and P. Ganguli, V. R. Marathe, and S. Mitra, *Inorg. Chem.*, 5:970 (1975).

21. M. A. Hitchman, *J. Chem. Soc., Faraday Trans. II*, 72:54 (1976).

22. See, for example, S. G. Lipson and H. Lipson, *Optical Physics*, Cambridge University Press, Cambridge, 1969, pp. 308-311. Note that this condition may not always be satisfied, particularly when aromatic ligands are involved; see Ref. 21 for a discussion of the way in which the problem may be approached under these circumstances.

23. D. E. Billing, R. Dudley, B. J. Hathaway, P. Nicholls, and I. M. Procter, *J. Chem. Soc. A*, 265 (1969).

24. B. J. Hathaway, M. J. Bew, and D. E. Billing, *J. Chem. Soc. A*, 1090 (1970).

25. M. J. Bew, D. E. Billing, R. J. Dudley, and B. J. Hathaway, *J. Chem. Soc. A*, 2640 (1970).

26. K. Dawson, M. A. Hitchman, C. K. Prout, and F. J. C. Rossotti, *J. Chem. Soc., Dalton Trans.*, 1509 (1972).

27. M. A. Hitchman, C. D. Olsen, and R. L. Belford, *J. Chem. Phys.*, 50:1195 (1969); R. L. Belford, B. Harrowfield, and J. R. Pilbrow, *J. Magn. Res.*, 28:433 (1977).

28. B. J. Hathaway and D. E. Billing, *Coord. Chem. Rev.*, 5:143 (1970).

29. J. Ferguson, *J. Chem. Phys.*, 34:611 (1961).

30. J. Ferguson, *J. Chem. Phys.*, 35:1612 (1961).

31. B. W. Moores and R. L. Belford, in *Electron Spin Resonance of Metal Complexes* (T. F. Yen, ed.), Plenum, New York, 1969, p. 17.

32. A more detailed description is given in M. A. Hitchman and R. L. Belford, *Inorg. Chem.*, 10:904 (1971).

33. J. Ferguson, *J. Chem. Phys.*, 34:1609 (1961).

34. D. P. Graddon, *J. Inorg. Nucl. Chem.*, 14:161 (1960).

35. T. S. Piper and R. L. Belford, *Mol. Phys.*, 5:169 (1962).

36. C. Dijkgraaf, *Theor. Chim. Acta (Berlin)*, 3:38 (1965).

37. R. L. Belford and G. G. Belford, *Theor. Chim. Acta (Berlin)*, 3:465 (1965).

38. H. Koyama, Y. Saito, and H. Kuroya, *J. Inst. Polytech. Osaka City Univ.*, C4:43 (1953).

39. M. A. Hitchman and P. J. Cassidy, *Inorg. Chem.*, 18:1745 (1979).

40. B. P. Straughan and S. Walker, eds., *Spectroscopy*, Vol. 3, Chapman & Hall, London, 1976.

41. C. J. Ballhausen, *Molecular Electronic Structures of Transition Metal Complexes*, McGraw-Hill, New York, 1979.

42. H. H. Patterson, T. G. Harrison, and R. J. Belair, *Inorg. Chem.*, 15:1461 (1976).

43. H. H. Patterson, J. J. Godfrey, and S. M. Khan, *Inorg. Chem.*, 11:2872 (1972).

44. F. A. Cotton, *Chemical Applications of Group Theory*, 2nd ed., Wiley-Interscience, New York, 1971.

44a. L. Antolini, L. Menahue, G. C. Pellacini, M. Saladini, G. Marcotrigiano, and W. Porzio, *J. Chem. Soc., Dalton Trans.*, 1753 (1981).

45. M. A. Hitchman, *Inorg. Chem.*, 13:2218 (1974).

46. C. D. Olson, G. Basu, and R. L. Belford, *J. Coord. Chem.*, 1:17 (1971).

47. R. Dingle and C. J. Ballhausen, *Mat. Fys., Medd., Dan., Vid., Selsk.*, 35:1 (1967).

48. P. J. McCarthy and M. T. Vala, *Mol. Phys.*, 25:17 (1973).

49. R. Dingle and R. A. Palmer, *Theor. Chim. Acta (Berlin)*, 6:249 (1966).

50. I. Bertini, P. Dapporto, D. Gatteschi, and A. Scozzafava, *Inorg. Chem.*, 14:1639 (1975).

51. I. Bertini, M. Ciampolini, P. Dapporto, and D. Gatteschi, *Inorg. Chem.*, 11:2254 (1972).

52. N. Nemiroff and S. L. Holt, *Inorg. Chem.*, 12:2032 (1973).

53. D. Gatteschi and A. Scozzafava, *Inorg. Chim. Acta*, 21:223 (1977).

54. I. Bertini and D. Gatteschi, *J. Coord. Chem.*, 1:285 (1971).

55. M. A. Hitchman, *Inorg. Chem.*, 11:2387 (1972).

56. B. J. Hathaway, *Struct. Bond. (Berlin)*, 14:49 (1973).

57. J. P. Jesson, *J. Chem. Phys.*, 48:161 (1968).

58. J. Ferguson, *J. Chem. Phys.*, 39:116 (1963).

59. M. Hawada and I. Tsujika, *J. Phys. Soc. Jap.*, 41:1264 (1976).

60. V. J. Koester and T. M. Dunn, *Inorg. Chem.*, 14:1811 (1975).

61. T. W. Couch and G. Pedro-Smith, *J. Chem. Phys.*, 53:1336 (1970).

62. D. H. Brown, A. Hunter, and W. E. Smith, *Spectrochim. Acta*, 38A:703 (1982).

63. A. Mooney, R. H. Nuttall, and W. E. Smith, *J. Chem. Soc.*, *Dalton Trans.*, 1096 (1972); *J. Chem. Soc.*, *Dalton Trans.*, 1920 (1973).

64. J. Ferguson, *J. Chem. Phys.*, 40:3406 (1964).

65. P. Ros and C. A. Schuit, *Theor. Chim. Acta (Berlin)*, 4:1 (1966).

66. N. J. Trappeniers, G. de Brouchiére, and C. A. Ten Seldam, *Chem. Phys. Lett.*, 8:327 (1971).

67. J. Demuynek, A. Veillard, and U. Wahlgren, *J. Am. Chem. Soc.*, 95:5563 (1973).

68. Ref. 17, p. 78.

69. P. J. Stephens, Vibrational-electronic interactions, in *Electronic States of Inorganic Compounds* (P. Day, ed.), D. Reidel, Dordrecht, The Netherlands, 1975.

70. C. D. Flint, *Coord. Chem. Rev.*, 14:47 (1974).

71. M. Cieślak-Golonka, A. Bartechi, and S. P. Sinka, *Coord. Chem. Rev.*, 31:251 (1980).

72. See, for example, E. B. Wilson, J. C. Decius, and P. C. Cross, *Molecular Vibrations*, McGraw-Hill, New York, 1955.

73. D. W. Smith, *J. Chem. Soc.*, *Dalton Trans.*, 1853 (1973).

74. M. A. Hitchman and R. G. McDonald, to be published.

75. R. G. Burns, M. G. Clark, and A. J. Stone, *Inorg. Chem.*, 5:1268 (1966).

76. R. J. Ford and M. A. Hitchman, *Inorg. Chim. Acta*, 33:L167-L170 (1979).

77. M. A. Hitchman and J. B. Bremner, *Inorg. Chim. Acta*, 27:L61-L63 (1978).

78. D. S. Martin, Jr., M. A. Tucker, and A. J. Kassman, *Inorg. Chem.*, 4:1682 (1965).

79. T. G. Harrison, H. H. Patterson, and J. J. Godfrey, *Inorg. Chem.*, 15:1291 (1976).

80. R. M. Rush, D. S. Martin, Jr., and R. G. Legrand, *Inorg. Chem.*, 14:2543 (1975).

81. L. G. Vanquickenborne and A. Ceulemans, *Inorg. Chem.*, 20:796
     (1981).

82. J. S. Merriam and R. Perumareddi, *J. Phys. Chem.*, 79:142
     (1975).

83. C. W. Reimann, *J. Phys. Chem.*, 74:561 (1970).

84. C. R. Hare and C. J. Ballhausen, *J. Chem. Phys.*, 40:792 (1964).

85. I. Bertini, D. Gatteschi, and A. Scozzafava, *Inorg. Chem.*, 15:
     203 (1976).

86. M. A. Hitchman and G. L. Rowbottom, *Inorg. Chem.*, 21:823
     (1982).

87. A. J. Finney, M. A. Hitchman, C. L. Raston, G. L. Rowbottom,
     and A. H. White, *Aust. J. Chem.*, 34:2047 (1981).

88. M. Gerloch, J. Lewis, and W. R. Snail, *J. Chem. Soc. A*, 2686
     (1963).

89. P. L. Meredith and R. A. Palmer, *Inorg. Chem.*, 10:1049 (1971).

90. B. J. Hathaway and A. A. G. Tomlinson, *Coord. Chem. Rev.*, 5:1
     (1970).

91. J. Ferguson and T. E. Wood, *Inorg. Chem.*, 14:184 (1975).

92. J. Ferguson and T. E. Wood, *Inorg. Chem.*, 14:190 (1975).

93. R. Dingle, *J. Chem. Phys.*, 46:1 (1967).

94. R. A. D. Wentworth, *Inorg. Chem.*, 5:496 (1966).

95. S. Yamada, *Coord. Chem. Rev.*, 2:83 (1967).

96. L. Dubicki and P. Day, *Inorg. Chem.*, 10:2043 (1971).

97. L. Dubicki, M. A. Hitchman, and P. Day, *Inorg. Chem.*, 9:188
     (1970).

98. L. Dubicki and R. L. Martin, *Aust. J. Chem.*, 22:839 (1969), and
     references therein.

99. A. B. P. Lever, I. M. Walker, and P. J. McCarthy, *Inorg. Chim.
     Acta*, 39:81 (1980).

100. A. B. P. Lever, I. M. Walker, and P. J. McCarthy, *Spectrosc.
     Lett.*, 12:739 (1979).

101. A. B. P. Lever, I. M. Walker, and P. J. McCarthy, *Inorg. Chim.
     Acta*, 44:L143 (1980).

102. R. Dingle, *Inorg. Chem.*, 10:1141 (1971).

103. B. J. Hathaway, D. E. Billing, and R. J. Dudley, *J. Chem. Soc.
     A*, 1420 (1970).

104. F. A. Cotton and J. J. Wise, *Inorg. Chem.*, 6:917 (1967).

105. F. A. Cotton, C. B. Harris, and J. J. Wise, *Inorg. Chem.*, 6:
     909 (1967).

106. J. J. Wise, Ph.D. dissertation, Massachusetts Institute of Technology, 1965.

107. R. Gale, R. E. Godfrey, and S. F. Mason, *Chem. Phys. Lett.*, 38:441 (1976).

108. A. D. Liehr and C. J. Ballhausen, *Phys. Rev.*, 106:1161 (1957); *Ann. Phys.* (N. Y.) 3:304 (1958).

109. R. Englman, *Mol. Phys.*, 3, 23:49 (1960).

110. L. L. Lohr, Jr., *J. Chem. Phys.*, 50:4596 (1969).

111. M. A. Hitchman and M. J. Riley, unpublished work.

112. O. G. Holmes and D. S. McClure, *J. Chem. Phys.*, 26:1686 (1957).

113. M. J. Harding, S. F. Mason, D. J. Robbins, and A. J. Thomson, *J. Chem. Soc. A*, 3047 (1971).

114. J. Brynstead, H. L. Yakel, and G. Pedro-Smith, *J. Chem. Phys.*, 45:4652 (1966).

115. M. A. Hitchman and R. J. Deeth, unpublished work.

116. M. A. Hitchman, *J. Chem. Soc., Chem. Commun.*, 973 (1979).

117. D. Reinen and C. Friebel, *Struct. Bond. (Berlin)*, 37:1 (1979).

118. P. Day and E. A. Grant, *J. Chem. Soc., Chem. Commun.*, 123 (1969).

119. B. D. Bird, P. Day, and E. A. Grant, *J. Chem. Soc. A*, 100 (1970).

120. J. R. Henderson, M. Muramoto, and R. A. Willett, *J. Chem. Phys.*, 41:580 (1965).

121. J. R. Henderson, R. A. Willett, M. Muramoto, and D. C. Richardson, *A Table of Harmonic Franck-Condon Overlap Integrals Including Displacement of Normal Coordinates*, Douglas Report SM-45807, Jan. 1964.

122. H. Yersin, H. Otto, J. I. Zink, and G. Gliemann, *J. Am. Chem. Soc.*, 102:951 (1980).

123. A numerical error in this constant occurs in Ref. 122; J. I. Zink, private communication.

124. R. B. Wilson and E. I. Solomon, *J. Am. Chem. Soc.*, 102:4085 (1980).

125. R. B. Wilson and E. I. Solomon, *Inorg. Chem.*, 17:1729 (1978).

126. A. Pfeil, *Theor. Chim. Acta (Berlin)*, 20:159 (1971).

127. E. I. Solomon and D. S. McClure, *Phys. Rev. B*, 9:4690 (1974).

128. H. H. Patterson, W. J. Deberry, J. E. Byrne, M. T. Hsu, and J. A. Lomenzo, *Inorg. Chem.*, 16:1698 (1977).

129. M. P. Laurent, H. H. Patterson, W. Pike, and H. Engstrom, *Inorg. Chem.*, 20:372 (1981).

130. M. A. Hitchman, *Inorg. Chem.*, 21:821 (1982).

131. M. A. Hitchman and R. J. Deeth, unpublished work.

132. J. H. Fertel and H. Perry, *J. Phys. Chem. Solids*, 26:1773 (1965).

133. R. M. Badger, *J. Chem. Phys.*, 2:128 (1934); 3:710 (1935).

134. H. H. Patterson, T. G. Harrison, and R. J. Belair, *Inorg. Chem.*, 15:1461 (1976).

135. R. J. Tacon, P. Day, and R. G. Denning, *J. Chem. Phys.*, 61: 751 (1974).

136. E. I. Solomon and C. J. Ballhausen, *Mol. Phys.*, 29:279 (1975).

137. R. A. Satten and E. Y. Wong, *J. Chem. Phys.*, 43:3025 (1965).

138. M. Gerloch and R. C. Slade, *Ligand Field Parameters*, Cambridge University Press, Cambridge, 1973.

139. A. B. P. Lever, *Coord. Chem. Rev.*, 43:63 (1982).

140. M. Gerloch, J. H. Harding, and R. G. Woolley, *Struct. Bond. (Berlin)*, 46:1 (1981).

141. F. S. Ham, *Phys. Rev. A*, 138:1727 (1965).

142. W. C. Scott and M. D. Sturge, *Phys. Rev.*, 146:262 (1966).

143. E. König, *Struct. Bond. (Berlin)*, 9:175 (1971).

144. See Ref. 5, pp. 207-216.

145. See, for example, F. A. Cotton and G. Wilkinson, *Advanced Inorganic Chemistry*, Wiley, New York, 1980, pp. 630-636.

146. For a discussion of the crystal field model, see J. S. Griffith, *The Theory of Transition-Metal Ions*, Cambridge University Press, Cambridge, 1964; B. N. Figgis, *Introduction to Ligand Fields*, Wiley, New York, 1966; R. M. Golding, *Applied Wave Mechanics*, D. Van Nostrand, London, 1969.

147. D. W. Smith, *J. Inorg. Nucl. Chem.*, 34:3930 (1972).

148. C. J. Ballhausen, *Introduction to Ligand Field Theory*, McGraw-Hill, New York, 1962, Chap. 5. Note that an opposite sign convention has occasionally been used; J. R. Perumareddi, *J. Chem. Phys.*, 71:3144 (1967).

149. S. Kremer and E. König, *Ligand Field Energy Diagrams*, Plenum, New York, 1977.

150. J. C. Donini, B. R. Hollebone, and A. B. P. Lever, *Prog. Inorg. Chem.*, 22:225 (1976).

151. A. B. P. Lever, G. London, and P. J. McCarthy, *Can. J. Chem.*, 55:3172 (1977).

152. A. B. P. Lever, I. M. Walker, and P. J. McCarthy, *Inorg. Chim. Acta*, 39:81 (1980).

153. C. K. Jørgensen, *Modern Aspects of Ligand Field Theory*, North-Holland, Amsterdam, 1970, Chap. 13, and references therein.

154. C. E. Schäffer and C. K. Jørgensen, *Mol. Phys.*, 9:401 (1965).

155. C. E. Schäffer, *Struct. Bond. (Berlin)*, 5:68 (1968); 14:69 (1973).

156. C. E. Schäffer, *Theor. Chim. Acta (Berlin)*, 34:237 (1974).

157. J. K. Burdett, *Struct. Bond. (Berlin)*, 31:67 (1976).

158. D. W. Smith, *Struct. Bond. (Berlin)*, 35:87 (1978).

159. E. Larson and G. N. LaMar, *J. Chem. Educ.*, 51:633 (1974).

160. M. R. Kibler, *J. Chem. Phys.*, 55:1989 (1971); *Chem. Phys. Lett.*, 8:142 (1971).

161. M. Gerloch and R. G. Woolley, *Prog. Inorg. Chem.*, 31:371 (1983).

162. R. Krishnamurthy and W. B. Schaap, *J. Chem. Educ.*, 46:79 (1969); 47:433 (1970).

163. C. D. Garner and F. E. Mabbs, *J. Chem. Soc. A*, 1711 (1970).

164. D. W. Smith, *Struct. Bond. (Berlin)*, 12:49 (1972).

165. C. E. Schäffer and C. K. Jørgensen, *Math.-Fys. Medd. Selsk.*, 34, No. 13 (1965).

166. A. B. P. Lever, *Coord. Chem. Rev.*, 3:119 (1968).

167. CAMMAG Fortran program by D. Cruse, J. E. Davis, J. H. Harding, M. Gerloch, D. Mackey, and R. F. McMeeking, Inorganic Chemistry Laboratory, Lensfield Road, Cambridge, England; M. Gerloch and R. F. McMeeking, *J. Chem. Soc., Dalton Trans.*, 2443 (1975).

168. M. Gerloch and R. G. Woolley, *J. Chem. Soc., Dalton Trans.*, 1714 (1981).

169. L. Banci, A. Bencini, C. Benelli, D. Gatteschi, and C. Zanchini, *Struct. Bond. (Berlin)*, 52:37 (1982).

170. H. Yamatera, *Naturwissenschaften*, 44:375 (1957); *Bull. Chem. Soc. Jap.*, 31:95 (1958).

171. D. S. McClure, *Advances in the Chemistry of Coordination Compounds* (S. Kirschner, ed.), Macmillan, New York, 1961, p. 498.

172. A. F. Schreiner and D. J. Hamm, *Inorg. Chem.*, 12:2037 (1973).

173. J. Glerup and C. E. Schäffer, in *Progress in Coordination Chemistry* (M. Cais, ed.), Elsevier, Amsterdam, 1968, p. 500.

174. D. W. Smith, *Inorg. Chem.*, 5:2236 (1966).

175. Ref. 158, pp. 99, 100.

176. Many of these results are summarized in Ref. 139.

177. J. Glerup, O. Monsted, and C. E. Schäffer, *Inorg. Chem.*, 15: 13-9 (1976); 19:2855 (1980).

178. D. W. Smith, *J. Chem. Soc. A*, 1708 (1969), and references therein.

179. See, for example, G. F. Koksyka, C. W. Reimann, and H. C. Allen, Jr., *J. Chem. Phys.*, 71:121 (1967); C. Chow, K. Chang, and R. D. Willett, *J. Chem. Phys.*, 59:2629 (1973); A. Bencini, D. Gatteschi, and C. Zanchini, *J. Am. Chem. Soc.*, 102:5234 (1980).

180. D. W. Smith, *J. Chem. Soc. A*, 176 (1970).

181. D. W. Smith, *J. Chem. Soc. A*, 1209 (1971).

182. D. W. Smith, *J. Chem. Soc. A*, 2529 (1969).

183. D. W. Smith, *J. Chem. Soc. A*, 1024 (1971).

184. Ref. 164, p. 100.

185. M. A. Hitchman and P. J. Cassidy, *Inorg. Chem.*, 17:1682 (1978).

186. Ref. 145, p. 88.

187. M. Gerloch, R. F. McMeeking, and M. White, *J. Chem. Soc., Dalton Trans.*, 2453 (1975); 655 (1976).

188. Ref. 164, p. 662.

189. T. Barnet, B. M. Craven, H. C. Freeman, N. E. Kline, and J. A. Ibers, *J. Chem. Soc., Chem. Commun.*, 307 (1966). The value for Co(III) is an average: K. H. Schmidt and A. Müller, *Coord. Chem. Rev.*, 19:87 (1976).

190. N. J. Hair and J. K. Beattie, *Inorg. Chem.*, 16:245 (1977).

191. M. A. Hitchman, *Inorg. Chem.*, 21:821 (1982).

192. Ref. 4, p. 110.

193. M. A. Hitchman, *J. Chem. Soc., Faraday Trans. II*, 68:846 (1972).

194. D. W. Smith, *J. Chem. Soc., Dalton Trans.*, 1853 (1973).

195. R. Laiko, M. Natarajan, and M. Kaira, *Phys. Status Solidii A*, 15:311 (1973).

196. Ref. 164, p. 90.

197. A. A. G. Tomlinson, B. J. Hathaway, D. E. Billing, and P. Nichols, *J. Chem. Soc. A*, 65 (1969).

198. D. W. Smith, *J. Chem. Soc. A*, 1509 (1969).

199. B. J. Hathaway and F. Stephens, *J. Chem. Soc. A*, 884 (1970).

200. M. Gerloch, L. R. Hanton, and M. R. Manning, *Inorg. Chim Acta*, 48:205 (1981), and references therein.

201. D. J. Mackey, R. F. McMeeking, and M. A. Hitchman, *J. Chem. Soc., Dalton Trans.*, 299 (1979).

202. L. G. Vanquickenborne and A. Ceulemons, *Inorg. Chem.*, 20:796 (1981).

203. H. Basch and H. B. Gray, *Inorg. Chem.*, 6:365 (1967).

204. D. W. Smith, *Inorg. Chim. Acta*, 22:107 (1977).

205. B. R. McGarvey, *Can. J. Chem.*, 53:2498 (1975); A. Rockenbauer, E. Budó-Zákonyi, and L. J. Sináudi, *J. Chem. Soc. Dalton Trans.*, 1729 (1975).

206. See R. L. Belford, N. D. Chasteen, M. A. Hitchman, P. K. Hon, C. E. Pfluger, and I. C. Paul, *Inorg. Chem.*, 8:1312 (1969) for a discussion of this feature.

207. A. S. Davydov, *Theory of Molecular Excitons* (M. Kaska and M. Oppenheimer, Jr., trans.), McGraw-Hill, New York, 1962.

208. R. M. Hochstrasser, *Molecular Aspects of Symmetry*, W. A. Benjamin, New York, 1966, Chap. 10.

209. D. P. Craig and S. H. Walmsley, *Excitons in Molecular Crystals*, W. A. Benjamin, New York, 1968.

210. P. Day, A. F. Orchard, A. J. Thomson, and R. J. P. Williams, *J. Chem. Phys.*, 42:1973 (1965); 43:3763 (1966).

211. P. Day, *Inorg. Chim. Acta Rev.*, 3:81 (1969).

212. D. S. Martin, Jr., L. D. Hunter, R. Kroening, and R. F. Coley, *J. Am. Chem. Soc.*, 93:5433 (1971).

213. P. Day, *Local and Collective States in Single and Mixed Valency Chain Compounds*, ACS Symp. Ser. No. 5, Vol. 17, American Chemical Society, Washington, D. C., p. 234.

214. P. Day, Collective States in Single and Mixed Valence Metal Chain Compounds, in *Chemistry and Physics of One-Dimensional Metals* (H. J. Kellar, ed.), Plenum, New York, 1977, p. 197.

215. D. J. Hamm and A. F. Schreiner, *Inorg. Chem.*, 14:519 (1975).

216. M. A. Hitchman and T. D. Waite, *Inorg. Chem.*, 15:2150 (1976).

217. R. C. Marshall and D. W. James, *J. Inorg. Nucl. Chem.*, 32:2543; *J. Phys. Chem.*, 78:1235 (1974).

218. J. W. Carmichael, L. K. Steinrauf, and R. L. Belford, *J. Chem. Phys.*, 43:3959 (1965).

219. E. A. Boudreaux, *Inorg. Chem.*, 3:506 (1964).

220. L. S. Forster and C. J. Ballhausen, *Acta Chem. Scand.*, 16:1385 (1962).

221. A. E. Hansen and C. J. Ballhausen, *Trans. Faraday Soc.*, 61:631 (1965).

222. L. Dubicki, *Aust. J. Chem.*, $\underline{25}$:1141 (1972).

223. R. D. Willett and O. L. Liles, *Inorg. Chem.*, $\underline{6}$:1666 (1967).

224. P. J. Hay, J. C. Bribeault, and R. Hoffmann, *J. Am. Chem. Soc.*, $\underline{97}$:4884 (1975).

225. A. J. Finney, M. A. Hitchman, C. L. Raston, G. L. Rowbottom, and A. H. White, *Aust. J. Chem.*, $\underline{34}$:2069 (1981).

226. A. J. Finney, M. A. Hitchman, C. L. Raston, G. L. Rowbottom, and A. H. White, *Aust. J. Chem.*, $\underline{34}$:2085 (1981).

227. D. M. L. Goodgame, M. A. Hitchman, and D. F. Marsham, *J. Chem. Soc. A*, 259 (1971).

228. A. J. Finney, M. A. Hitchman, C. L. Raston, G. L. Rowbottom, and A. H. White, *Aust. J. Chem.*, $\underline{34}$:2125 (1981).

229. A. J. Finney, M. A. Hitchman, C. L. Raston, G. L. Rowbottom, and A. H. White, *Aust. J. Chem.*, $\underline{34}$:2113 (1981).

230. F. Felix, J. Ferguson, H. U. Güdel, and A. Ludi, *J. Am. Chem. Soc.*, $\underline{102}$:4102 (1980).

231. D. P. Rillema and K. B. Mack, *Inorg. Chem.*, $\underline{21}$:3849 (1982).

232. M. A. Hitchman, unpublished work.

233. B. Briat, O. Kahn, I. Morganstern-Badarau, and J. C. Rivoal, *Inorg. Chem.*, $\underline{20}$:4193 (1981).

234. P. J. McCarthy, J. C. Lauffenburger, P. M. Skoneyry, and D. C. Rohrer, *Inorg. Chem.*, $\underline{20}$:1566 (1981).

235. T. G. Harrison, H. H. Patterson, and M. T. Hsu, *Inorg. Chem.*, $\underline{15}$:3018 (1976).

236. Estimated using data from Ref. 39.

237. Estimated using data from Ref. 61.

2

UV Photoelectron Spectroscopy of Transition Metal Complexes

H. van DAM* and A. OSKAM

University of Amsterdam
Amsterdam, The Netherlands

*Present affiliation: Research and Development, Océ Nederland BV, Venlo, The Netherlands

I. INTRODUCTION

In the last 10 years ultraviolet (UV) photoelectron spectroscopy of
transition metal complexes has become more and more popular in
inorganic chemistry. The unique feature of this technique is its
ability to eject electrons, using sufficiently high energy, from any
of the occupied energy levels in a molecule, and thereby provide a
representation of a molecular orbital diagram. Also, by interpreting
fine structure in the photoelectron (PE) bands, intensity changes upon variation of the light wavelength, angular dependence, and so on,
detailed information can be gained concerning vibrational frequencies and geometries in the cation states, localization and bonding
properties of the molecular orbitals, and so on. It is therefore
probably the most direct method available for studying the electronic
structure of molecules. It is clear that photoelectron spectroscopy

and quantum chemistry are complementary techniques, with PE results as a severe experimental test for the calculations.

Especially for transition metal compounds, with their wide variety of valences, charge distributions, and bonding mechanisms, this technique has proven to be very fruitful.

A. Fundamental Process of Photoelectron Spectroscopy

UV photoelectron spectroscopy (UPS) involves measurements of electrons ejected, usually from gaseous molecules, after irradiating with monochromatic light of sufficiently high energy. The monochromatic light sources in UPS are normally produced by inert-gas discharges with, as typical examples, He(I) 21.21 eV, He(II) 40.81 eV, and Ne(I) 16.67/Ne(II) 16.85 eV. The kinetic energy of the ejected electrons is measured, and applying the well-known energy conservation relationship

$$h\nu = IE + E_{kin}$$

the ionization energy (IE)* values can be calculated. (In this equation the kinetic energy of the remaining cation is neglected.) These IE values correspond to the energy differences between the ground state of the molecule and the various cation states. These IE values can also be related to one-electron orbital energies from molecular orbital (MO) calculations via Koopmans' theorem, which states that the molecular IE values are equal to the negatives of the MO eigenvalues. This approximation is widely employed by PE spectroscopists and deserves detailed consideration, so that its limitations and virtues are defined (see below).

Advantages of the use of UPS for molecules in the gas phase are the high resolution (20-30 meV), the fact that it is possible to measure "isolated" molecules, and the absence of surface effects such as

---

*IE can be written as $IE = E_j + E_{vib}^+ + E_{rot}^+$, where E_j is the adiabatic IE for ejection of an electron from level j and E_{vib}^+ and E_{rot}^+ are the vibrational and rotational energies of the positive ion.

surface charging and surface damage, often annoying in solid-state
PE spectra. The disadvantage of UPS, especially for the study of
transition metal complexes, is the demand that the molecules be
stable in the gas phase and sufficiently volatile. This is the main
limitation of the technique.

B. Transition Metal Compounds

Transition metal compounds continue to be of interest because of
both their theoretical importance and practical applications. A
wide variety of bonding mechanisms in this type of complex have been
elucidated in the last few years, in which UPS has played an important role: complexes with σ-bonded ligands, σ-π synergism en-
countered in bonding in special ligands such as ethylene and
cyclopentadienyl, metal-metal bonds, bonding in complexes with large ,
crystal field splittings, spin-orbit couplings, and so on. UPS
gives a well-defined description of the whole valence shell of these
compounds, including d orbitals and both delocalized and localized
orbitals on the metals and ligands. In many cases it gives an out-
standing source of information and a check for corresponding MO
calculations.

   This chapter covers recent literature on UPS and related topics
of transition metal complexes from 1976 to September 1983. Some
aspects of earlier work are also discussed if relevant for more recent work. In the field of UPS of transition metal complexes, several reviews have appeared [1-2,3] covering earlier work. Special
emphasis is given to the He(I)/He(II) intensity variations, particularly as a diagnostic tool for the assignment of spectral bands (see
below).

1. Koopmans' Theorem

   For the interpretation of PE spectra generally, extensive use
is made of molecular orbital calculations. The most rigorous
approach within the Hartree-Fock method would be the direct method
by which separate calculations are performed on the ground state of

the neutral molecule and the various states of the molecular ion using correlated wave functions. This method, however, is very costly in terms of both personnel and computer time. Computer limitations are, of course, also of importance. Therefore, most of the PE investigations until now have employed calculations on only the ground state of the neutral molecule. The calculations are then used by applying Koopmans' theorem, which states that the molecular IE values are equal to the negatives of the MO eigenvalues. Applications of Koopmans' theorem have been discussed by Rabalais [4].

When applying Koopmans' theorem to general molecular photoionization phenomena, two well-known approximations are necessary:

1. The "frozen orbital" approximation: that is, upon photoionization the orbitals are taken to be the same in molecule and ion. In other words, the remaining electrons do not interact with the hole created, and no relaxation takes place.

2. Correlation energy changes are neglected. In a single determinantal Hartree-Fock calculation the probability of finding two electrons in the same space is given the same weight as that of finding them separated [5], while in reality they will tend to keep apart--in other words, they are correlated. The largest contributions to this energy originate from two electrons of different spin occupying the same spatial orbital, and since the ion has one electron fewer than the neutral molecule, the correlation energy will be different and will generally be less in the ion than in the molecule.

A third and less well known approximation is the relativistic energy approximation, in which it is assumed that since the normal Hartree-Fock theory does not consider relativistic effects, the relativistic energy is the same in both the molecule and the ion. This is a good approximation for valence electrons, but the magnitude of the relativistic effects becomes larger with the larger

kinetic energy of the electrons and will thus be more important in
heavy atoms.

.Assessing these approximations, it appears remarkable that
Koopmans' theorem is so popular, but there is a very good reason for
this. The relaxation and correlation energy terms tend to cancel
each other, at least in organic molecules. A pictorial representation of this effect is given in the following scheme:

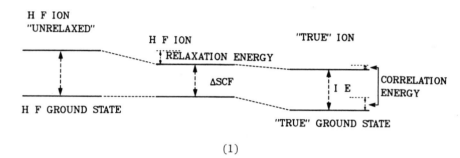

(1)

Starting on the left we have a normal ground-state calculation which
gives us the one-electron energy eigenvalue and thus (Koopmans'
theorem) gives us the energy difference between the Hartree-Fock
ground state and the unrelaxed ion state. The relaxation energy
correction, which can be calculated by performing a SCF (self-consistent field) calculation on the ion state and subtracting the
total energies of the calculations (the ΔSCF method), stabilizes the
ion and we get an energy difference which is generally smaller than
ε. Then, applying correlation energy corrections and assuming that
the correlation energy is less in the ion than in the neutral molecule, we arrive at the "true" energies of the ground and ion states.

Now it can be seen that the relaxation and correlation contributions cancel under favorable conditions. This cancellation generally
occurs in organic systems, with the important consequence, of course,
that the ordering and spacings of the experimental IE values are
generally reasonably well reproduced by the calculations.

However, things become entirely different for molecules
containing transition metals and in general molecules that contain
very localized MOs. In these systems different relaxations occur
for different types of MOs. When this differential relaxation
occurs, Koopmans' theorem can no longer be applied and one has to
improve the calculations and rely on other assignment criteria.
Examples of this breakdown of Koopmans' theorem will be given.

2. Assignment Criteria in PE Spectroscopy

UPS has evolved as one of the best methods for obtaining information about the geometries and vibrational frequencies of the ion
states, and in general about the nature of the electronic states of
molecular ions. For this it is crucial to have unambiguous assignments, and thus to have reliable assignment criteria. It is therefore one of the most important tasks in PE spectroscopy to develop
and evaluate assignment criteria. A reasonably large number can be
applied in PE studies. Apart from MO calculations and qualitative
MO considerations, several empirical criteria are used. Band shapes
and fine structure are interpreted, yielding information about
vibrational frequencies, spin-orbit coupling, Jahn-Teller and Renner
effects, and so on. The interpretation of fine structure is very
important in making assignments. Correlations within series of related compounds, substituent effects (perfluoro effect, etc.), and
electronegativity considerations are also of considerable use. The
use of different excitation sources such as Ne(I), He(I), He(II),
or x-rays can produce large changes in spectral intensities which
can help in making the assignments. We will discuss only the last
criterion in more detail, since it is used extensively in this chapter. Detailed discussions about most of the other criteria can be
found in any textbook on UPS and the reader is referred to them.

Some general remarks can be made, however:

1. The more independent the assignment criteria used which are
   consistent with a given interpretation, the more firmly

established is the assignment. This means that assignments
based only on, for instance, MO calculations or only on
trends in a few He(I) spectra should be viewed with caution.
This seems trivial but several astonishing--to say the least
--assignments have been made this way.

2. We feel that at this moment it is unjustified not to use
   He(II) spectra in the assignment of transition metal complexes except in very clear-cut cases. The technique of
   cross-section variation (see below) is so powerful that
   questionable assignments can be prevented, many of which at
   the moment unfortunately fill the literature.

3. Intensities in Photoelectron Spectra

In the past, much attention was paid to the interpretation of
IE values in PE spectra, while less information was obtained from
the corresponding intensities. Only in the last few years have
empirical rules come into use which have proved reasonably reliable
for the assignment of the ion states [6]:

1. The photoionization cross sections of metal d orbitals increase in He(I) on going from 3d to 4d to 5d (the heavy-
   atom effect).

2. The cross sections of metal d orbitals increase on going
   from He(I) to He(II) radiation.

3. The cross sections for 4p orbitals of, for instance, P, S,
   and Cl decrease on going from He(I) to He(II) radiation.

4. Orbitals of lone-pair oxygen 2p character have larger
   cross sections in He(II) than in He(I).

5. Orbitals of C and N 2p atomic orbital (AO) character hardly
   change in cross section. In general, it can be said that
   there is a crude relationship between the spectral intensity
   and orbital degeneracy of these types of orbitals. This
   assumption should be viewed with caution, however, since the
   generalization is accurate only for the ionization of electrons with similar localization properties.

4. *Some Comments on the Use of MO Methods in Transition Metal Chemistry*

The MO methods suitable for transition metal complexes are unfortunately rather approximate in nature. One should, of course, for complete agreement with the experiments, use a true ab initio method, using very extended bases, in which correlated wave functions are used for both the ground and ionic states of the molecule so as to yield "beyond-Hartree-Fock" reliability. This is impossible at the moment, owing to the limited capacities of current computers. A more "down-to-earth" ab initio method is currently practicable for relatively large transition metal complexes (using limited bases) which uses single determinantal wave functions for the description of the ground states. This all-electron method generally yields reasonably good agreements with experiment. Currently, ab initio schemes using limited configuration interaction in large transition metal complexes are rapidly becoming more popular. Generally, improvements have been found this way in the theoretical descriptions. However, this procedure involves considerable expenditure of computer time.

A second method with quantitative ambitions is the Slater $X\alpha$ method. On the basis of the $X\alpha$ model a number of calculational schemes have been developed during the past decade:

1. The multiple-scattered-wave $X\alpha$ method introduced by Johnson [7]. First, it was used in the muffin-tin approximation form. The advantage was that large and heavy molecules, such as $PtCl_4^{2-}$, could also be calculated. Large planar molecules, however, showed large errors. Also, large errors in the dissociation energy, the total energy, and hence in the optimized geometry and bond lengths, were found [8]. It has also been found empirically by Rösch et al. [9] that the $X\alpha$ method with overlapping spheres gives better agreement with experiment.

2. The discrete variational linear combination of atomic orbitals (LCAO)-$X\alpha$ method developed by Baerends, Ellis and

Ros [10]. This method is a numerical method whose accuracy depends on the number of sampling points. Sometimes a very large number of sampling points is required.

3. Other Xα methods as proposed by Sambe and Felton [11] or by Tylicki et al. [12].

Only the first two types of Hartree-Fock-Slater (HFS)-Xα methods have proven to give valuable results for transition metal complexes. The computation times of these methods are considerably shorter than for ab initio calculations, especially when a larger basis set is required. Both these more quantitatively oriented types of MO calculations will extensively be used in the discussions of this review.

Although the popularity of extended Hückel (EH) 'methods has decreased with the coming of large computer systems, this simple method produces surveyable schematic MO diagrams. In a series of molecules, trends in IE and charges calculated using the EH method also proved to be reliable in organometallic chemistry [13]. The lucid bonding schemes as calculated by Hoffmann for numerous classes of organometallic complexes are of great help in the interpretation of bonding interactions. The advantage of the EH method is, of course, the minimal computer time needed.

Also, semiempirical calculations based on the zero-differential-overlap (ZDO) approximation are much less expensive. For organic molecules and free ligands, CNDO/2 and CNDO/S (Complete Neglect of Differential Overlap) [14] are methods which are reasonably reliable for the interpretation of PE spectra, especially in series of molecules. No such scheme is currently practicable for transition metal complexes. Several different schemes of extended CNDO calculations that have been used in literature, with more or less success, will be outlined here. Several deficiencies of these schemes are now known and they can therefore be used in PE spectroscopy only with extreme care. Some schemes, however, proved quite successful in predicting trends in closely related series and in predicting shifts in IE of organic ligands upon complexation to a transition metal [15].

Semiempirical schemes can be used only for molecules for which results from more sophisticated MO schemes are already known as a reference, since physically unrealistic results may be calculated, and then reparametization of the semiempirical scheme may be needed.

II. METAL CARBONYLS

These molecules have been studied extensively, especially in the earlier days of PE spectroscopy [16-20]. The assignments of the He(I) spectra are reasonably straightforward. (For substituted metal carbonyls and polynuclear metal carbonyls, see Secs. III and XI.) Only two aspects of the studies will be discussed here: first, the detailed descriptions of metal-carbonyl bonding, and second, the use of cross-section variations in the study of the nature of the various doublet states.

A general description of bonding of CO to a transition metal consists of two components: first, σ donation from the carbon "lone pair" to the metal, and second, π back-donation from metal d electrons into vacant π^* ligand orbitals. This general description is also used for the description of complexation of other unsaturated molecules, such as olefins, acetylenes, isocyanides, and nitrosyls, to transition metals.

Using PE spectral data and results from ab initio calculations [20-22], a reasonably consistent picture emerged of M-CO bonding. π Back-bonding was suggested to play an important role in this bond, next to considerable σ bonding. However, the conclusions based on various MO schemes which were later used on some simple carbonyls [e.g., $Ni(CO)_4$ and $Cr(CO)_6$], contradicted each other on this vital description of the bonding. Discrete Variational (DV)-Xα [23], approximate HFS [24], and Hartree-Fock calculations [22] agreed on the importance of π back-bonding. From scattered-wave (SW)-Xα [25] calculations, on the other hand, it was concluded that π back-bonding is *not* important and that σ donation is the only bonding interaction. This was puzzling since there are experimentally based arguments in favor of π back-bonding [26] and this leaves us with doubts concerning the validity of the SW-X$_\alpha$ descriptions. Recently, these doubts were confirmed by the publication of two papers, one by Sherwood and Hall [27] in which, on the basis of vibrational data, it was argued that π back-bonding exists in $Cr(CO)_6$, and the other by Bursten et al. [28], in which it is shown that the absence of π back-bonding in the SW-X$_\alpha$ results [25] originated from interpretation errors. They used a projected X$_\alpha$ method in which the wave function was projected on a normal AO basis. Then it could be visually demonstrated that π back-bonding also plays an important role in the SW-Xα results.

There are still some discrepancies concerning the relative amounts of π back-bonding and σ donation. The values obtained for the metal charge range from -1.0e [29] to +1.8e [24]. A direct study of the charge density distribution in crystalline $Cr(CO)_6$ by the method of precise x-ray and neutron diffraction (called the X-N method) by Rees and Mitschler [30] showed that the atomic charges are very small: Cr, +0.15 ± 0.12; C, 0.09 ± 0.05; and O, -0.12 ± 0.05. This is in contrast with most of the MO results. Of course, one must keep in mind that the definition of atomic charge is not the same. The method of space partitioning used by Rees and Mitschler for the determination of atomic charges suffers from some arbitrariness, but it is probably sounder than the Mulliken definition used generally in theoretical work, which divides the overlap population equally between bonded atoms.

It can be seen from the various MO schemes that the same general picture of bonding results, chromium being slightly positive, and a near balance of σ and π contributions. Two deviations should be noted: first, the DV-Xα method, with a very high positive charge on the metal (this is generally seen with this scheme), and second, the SW-Xα method with σ bonding still, be it slightly, dominating over π back-bonding, yielding a net negative charge on the metal.

A second aspect of the metal-carbonyl studies that will be discussed is the use of cross-section variations in the study of the nature of the various doublet states. The discussion will be limited

Table 1   Relative Band Intensities in the He(I) and He(II) Spectra for $MO(CO)_6$

Band[a]:	A (metal d)	B_1	B_2-B_7	C_1	C_2
$Cr(CO)_6$					
He(I)	1.2	3	14		
He(II)	2.1	3	14	5.3	3.1
$Mo(CO)_6$					
He(I)	1.9	3	15		
He(II)	2.3	3	14	5.0	1.8
$W(CO)_6$					
He(I)	2.5	3	15		
He(II)	2.5	3	14	4.8	1.5

[a]See Figs. 1 and 2.
Source: Ref. 20.

to chromium hexacarbonyl. This molecule is representative for a whole class of transition metal carbonyls.

Combined He(I)/He(II) investigations have appeared for $Cr(CO)_6$ [17]. Comparing the intensity data (Table 1), it is apparent that there is an increase in intensity of the metal d orbitals (band A, Fig. 1).

The remaining bands originate from the CO ligands and are more difficult to assign. Upon coordination of CO to chromium, the symmetry-adapted combinations of the 5σ and 1π orbitals of the CO molecules come into the same energy region (13-16 eV). All of the theoretical calculations on $Cr(CO)_6$ confirm this. Therefore, it is difficult, if not impossible, to resolve these energy levels in a PE spectrum, independent of the resolution. Attempts to assign the B and C bands in more detail have been made using combined UPS/x-ray PS (XPS) studies [20], but it could only be concluded that band C has more s character than band D, which is in contrast with the results from ab initio calculations. It seems that x-ray PE

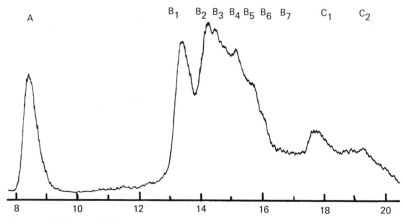

Figure 1(a)   He(I) spectrum of Co(CO)$_6$.   (From Ref. 20.)

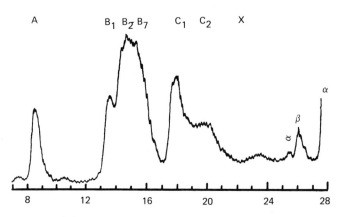

Figure 1(b)   He(II) spectrum of Co(CO)$_6$.   (From Ref. 20.)

intensity correlations in the valence electron region may be quite
complicated [20].

The group VIB hexacarbonyls are also very nice molecules to
demonstrate another cross-section effect. On proceeding down this
group (Cr → Mo → W) the intensity of the metal d band increases in
He(I) with respect to the σ, π CO band structure [for the He(I)

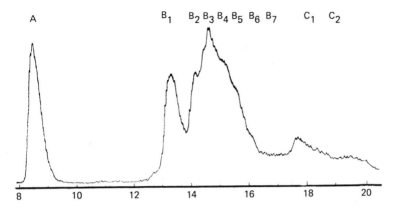

Figure 2(a)   He(I) spectrum of $Mo(CO)_6$.   (From Ref. 20.)

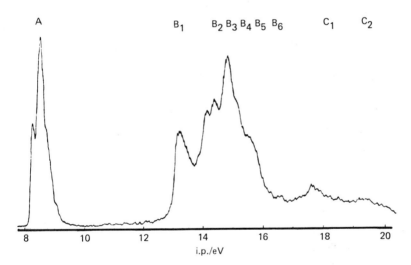

i.p./eV

Figure 2(b)   He(I) spectrum of $W(CO)_6$.   (From Ref. 20.)

spectra of $Mo(CO)_6$ and $W(CO)_6$, see Fig. 2], while the He(I) to the He(II) cross-section increase of this band diminishes.   This is a very good example of the "heavy-metal" effect (see Sec. I).

III. SUBSTITUTED METAL CARBONYLS

Substituted metal carbonyls were investigated extensively in the
period 1970-1976. More recently, only a few publications on this
subject have appeared. For a detailed review of work on $Mn(CO)_5R$
(R = H,CH_3,Cl, etc.) and the analogous rhenium complexes [31-35],
group VIB pentacarbonyl L-type complexes (L = amine, phosphine, sul-
fine, pyridine, carbenes, etc.) [8,36-38], the reader is referred
to the Cowley review [2]. Only three groups of complexes will be
discussed here: $M(CO)_5CX$-type complexes, with special emphasis on
bonding interactions; He(I)/He(II) studies of group VIB pentacarbonyl (N and P donor ligand)-type molecules, and the $Fe(CO)_4$ carbenes, with special emphasis on the correlation with results from
MO calculations.

A. $M(CO)_5CX$-Type Complexes

Lichtenberger and Fenske [39] have published the He(I) PE spectra
of $Cr(CO)_5CS$ and $W(CO)_5CS$. They found that the ionizations which
are associated predominantly with the highest-occupied σ and π
levels of the thiocarbonyl ligand are clearly separated from the
other ionizations in these complexes and display quite different
ionization band envelopes. The remaining ionization bands of these
complexes are comparable to the bands observed in the PE spectra of
the corresponding carbonyl complexes. This general picture was also
seen in the $Cr(CO)_5CSe$, He(I) spectrum published by English et al.
[40]. On going from CO to CS to CSe, a decrease in IE is found in
the first band (see Table 2). In the spectrum of $Cr(CO)_6$ the first
ionization band originates from the metal t_{2g} orbitals. The other
molecules, however, belong to the C_{4v} point group, and the highest
occupied orbitals, which are also predominantly d in character,
transform according to the e and b_2 representations.

There is no evidence in the PE spectra for loss of degeneracy
in the metal d ionization. The observation of a shift to lower IE
values upon going from the carbonyl to the thio- and selenocarbonyl

Table 2 Ionization Potentials of $Cr(CO)_6$, $W(CO)_5CS$, $Cr(CO)_5(CS)$, and $Cr(CO)_5(CSe)$

$Cr(CO)_6$ [20]	$W(CO)_5CS^a$ [39]	$Cr(CO)_5(CS)^a$ [39]	$Cr(CO)_5(CSe)$ [40]
8.40 ($2t_{2g}$; 3d, π^*)	8.08 (3d)	8.16 ($2b_2$ + 7e; 3d, π^*)	8.03 (b_2 + e; 3d, π^*)
	8.25-8.35		
	10.92 (7σ, CS)		10.26 (9σ, CSe)
	11.90 (2π, CS)	11.88 (2π, CS)	11.42 (3π, CSe)
	12.03	12.08	
	12.16	12.17	
13.38 ($8t_{1u}$)(5σ, CO)			13.46 (5σ, CO)
14.21 ($1t_{1g}$)			14.12 (CO core)
14.40 ($1t_{2u}$)			15.04
15.12 ($7t_{1u}$)			

[a]A set of broad, overlapping peaks was observed for this complex above 13 eV, but the peak maxima were not reported.

complexes seems to be inconsistent with the expected better π acceptor ability of these ligands arising from the lower-lying π^* acceptor orbitals. A rationalization of this effect has been given by Lichtenberger and Fenske [39], and more recently Hubbard and Lichtenberger [41] have published a short communication in which the consequences of ligand-metal π interactions were described in more detail. They suggest that although more π back-donation occurs, which should stabilize the metal e orbital, there is also a destabilizing effect on the metal d orbitals originating from an increase in filled ligand π versus filled metal d interaction. These orbitals form bonding and antibonding MOs with the bonding combination largely ligand π in character but with metal d admixture. The antibonding combination is largely metal d in character, with some delocalization into the ligand π orbital. Because both orbitals are totally occupied, there is no net change in metal d-electron density in this interaction.

The antibonding combination has a much more favorable energy for back-donation than the unperturbed metal orbital, but it is partially delocalized onto the ligand and has less available metal electron density. The removal of accessible metal π back-bonding density is enhanced by the low-lying and effective π^* acceptor orbitals.

Fenske-Hall calculations show [39] that the combined result of these interactions is a decreased stability of the MO which is mostly metal in character, together with a decrease in d-electron density.

Differences in relaxation energy of the various systems are probably not responsible for the trend in the IE values. Hubbard and Lichtenberger [41] argued that the relaxation energy should decrease in the more delocalized CS complex and thus that the trend should, if Koopmans' defects were large, be opposite to that observed. Another explanation could be that the increased σ-donor ability of the CX ligands upon going from CO to CS to CSe is causing the observed destabilization. Unfortunately, in Ref. 39 no detailed results are given concerning the donor ability of the CS ligand.

The increase in σ bonding could be the cause of the observed destabilization. It has been suggested [42] that relatively small changes in π back-bonding are invisible on the metal atom, owing to compensating changes in π back-bonding of the carbonyl ligands and also that the metal is more sensitive to σ-bonding effects, which are not as effectively compensated as the π effects.

B. $M(CO)_5L$ Complexes (M = Cr, Mo, W and L = N- and P-Donor Ligand)

Daamen et al. have investigated large series of the above-mentioned complexes using extensive He(I)/He(II) intensity differences, mutual comparisons, substituent effects, and so on [43-47].

In Ref. 43 the photoelectron spectra [He(I) and He(II)] of some free N-donor ligands, that is, a series of substituted pyridines, are presented. With the aid of assignments in literature based on MO calculations and the perfluoro effect, empirical rules concerning the intensity behavior on going from He(I) to He(II) excitation could be deduced. The determination of the experimental intensities from the spectra is described and applied to the bands belonging to the nitrogen lone pair, $\pi(a_2)$ and $\pi(b_1)$. In some cases the differences in the ionization potentials proved to be too small to make use of the results of the MO calculations or of the perfluoro effect for a proper assignment. In those cases the He(I) and He(II) intensity changes could be practiced as general rules and used as an elegant assignment criterion (see Table 3).

In Ref. 44 the PE spectra of some chromium and tungsten amine and pyridine complexes are discussed. The assignment of the spectra was based on comparison with the PE spectra of the metal hexacarbonyls and the free ligands (see Tables 4 and 5). It was shown by the stabilization of ligand orbitals that electron density was transferred from the ligand to the $M(CO)_5$ moiety. So σ donation is much more important than π back-bonding when L is a N-donor ligand. This view was supported by the splitting $\Delta\pi$ of the d orbitals and the increase of the spin-orbit coupling ζ compared with the metal

Table 3 Ionization Potentials (eV) and Assignment of the PE Spectra of Some Substituted Pyridines

Pyridine	9.67-lpN(a_1)	9.79-π(a_2)	10.51-π(b_1)	
Pentafluoropyridine	10.27-π(a_2)	11.37-π(b_1)	12.08-lp(a_1)	
2-Fluoropyridine	9.85-π_3	10.45-lpN	10.85-π_2	
α-Picoline	9.25-π_3	9.39-lpN	10.29-π_2	
2-Cyanopyridine	10.12-π_3	10.42-lpN	11.10-π_2	
2-Aminopyridine	8.34-π_4	9.57-lpN	10.15-π_3	11.16-π_2
Pyrazine	9.63-lpN(A_g)	10.18-π(b_{2g})	11.35-lpN(b_{2u})	11.77-π(b_{1u})

Source: Ref. 43.

Table 4   Vertical Ionization Potentials of $M(CO)_5$amine   (M = Cr, W) and the Corresponding Free Ligand (eV)

	Metal d-orbitals			M-L bonding (lone pair N)
$Cr(CO)_5N(CH_3)_3$		7.45	7.76	10.57
$W(CO)_5N(CH_3)_3$	7.41	7.62	7.96	10.75
$N(CH_3)_3$				8.45
$Cr(CO)_5NH(CH_2)_5{}^a$		7.39	7.69	10.50
$W(CO)_5NH(CH_2)_5{}^a$	7.35	7.55	7.87	10.59
$NH(CH_2)_5{}^b$				8.67
$W(CO)_5NH(CH_3)_2$	7.41	7.62	7.95	11.14
$NH(CH_3)_2$				8.95
$Cr(CO)_5NH_3$		7.56	7.85	-
$W(CO)_5NH_3$	7.54	7.75	8.06	-
NH_3				10.85

[a]$NH(CH_2)_5$ is piperidine.
Source: Ref. 44.

hexacarbonyls. It was concluded that π back-bonding was significant-ly reduced in the N-donor complexes with respect to those of carbon monoxide ζ and $\Delta\pi$ did not vary within the series of N-donor ligands and seemed to be only very crude parameters for the description of the metal-ligand bond. The ionization potential of the metal $d(b_2)$ varied according to the basicity of the ligand (pK_a). An anomaly in the relation was observed, however, on going from a pyridine like ligand to an amine. Despite the strong basicity as well as the higher stabilization of the amine lone pair, the ionization poten-tial of the metal $d(b_2)$ was higher than for pyridine complexes. It was tentatively assumed that interaction between the ligand $\pi(b_1)$ and metal orbitals with proper symmetry occurred. Also the different hybridization of the nitrogen lone pair may play an important role in this case.

Table 5 Vertical Ionization of M(CO)$_5$imine (M = Cr, W) and the Corresponding Free Ligand (eV)

	Metal d orbitals			$a_2(\pi)$	$b_1(\pi)$	M-N bonding (lone pair N)	Other lone pair
Cr(CO)$_5$ pyridine	7.29		7.61	10.39	11.46	11.46	
W(CO)$_5$ pyridine	7.20	7.42	7.77	10.42	11.41	11.41	
Pyridine				9.79	10.51	9.67	
Cr(CO)$_5$ 4-picoline	7.29		7.60	10.21	10.72	11.32	
W(CO)$_5$ 4-picoline	7.17	7.43	7.79	10.22	10.79	11.39	
4-Picoline				9.58	9.94	9.46	
Cr(CO)$_5$ 2-picoline	7.28		7.60	9.88	10.91	11.25	
2-Picoline				9.25	10.29	9.39	
Cr(CO)$_5$ 4-tert-butylpyridine	7.18		7.51	10.02	10.45	11.26	
4-Tert-butylpyridine				9.48	9.80	9.39	

Cr(CO)$_5$ 2,4-lutidine	7.23		7.49	9.81	10.55	11.09	12.23
2,4-Lutidine				8.98	9.80	9.15	12.24
Cr(CO)$_5$ 4-Cl-pyridine	7.34		7.65	10.52	10.52	11.66	11.75
W(CO)$_5$ 4-Cl-pyridine	7.33	7.55	7.89	10.59	10.59	11.68	11.43
4-Cl-Pyridine				10.11	10.11	10.11	11.47
Cr(CO)$_5$ 4-Br-pyridine	7.34		7.67	10.38	10.38	11.37	11.00
W(CO)$_5$ 4-Br-pyridine	7.31	7.51	7.86	10.42	10.42	11.38	10.41
4-Br-Pyridine				9.82	9.82	9.82	11.35
Cr(CO)$_5$ pyrazine	7.62		7.93	10.72	–	–	
Pyrazine				10.18[a]	11.77[b]	9.63	10.28
Cr(CO)$_5$ pyridazine	7.22		7.51	11.15	–	–	
Pyridazine				10.61[c]	11.3[c]	9.31	11.3

[a] b_{2g} symmetry.

[b] b_{1g} symmetry.

[c] The main axis of rotation is in the plane of the ring perpendicular to the N-N bond.

Source: Ref. 44.

Recently, this anomaly has been studied using extended CNDO/2 MO calculations [48]. It was concluded that π back-bonding is relatively unimportant in $Cr(CO)_5$pyridine and thus that the Cr-N bonding in $Cr(CO)_5$piperidine and $Cr(CO)_5$pyridine is of a similar nature.

In Ref. 45 the study is extended to azole ligands and compared with pyridine and pyrazine (see Tables 6 and 7). Apart from the different ring size, groups within the ring were also varied. Despite the stronger variations the azole complexes closely resembled the pyridine complex. A weaker σ donation was deduced from the lower stabilization of the nitrogen lone pair and the higher metal $d(b_2)$ ionization potential. This is in agreement with the azole basicity and lone-pair ionization potential compared with pyridine. From the destabilization of the lowest unoccupied π^* ligand orbital it was concluded that the back-bonding of azole was weaker than for pyridine and pyrazine. The difference between the metal $d(b_2)$ ionization potential in the azole and pyrazine complexes confirmed this conclusion. The ^{13}C-nuclear magnetic resonance (NMR) carbonyl resonances of the azole complexes did not significantly differ from the pyridine complexes. The down-field shift of the ligand ^{13}C chemical shift on complexation was correlated qualitatively to a reduced diamagnetic shielding.

The PE spectra of complexes with phosphorous-donor ligands have been studied [46,47]. In comparison with Refs. 44 and 45, some significant differences between N- and P-donor ligands were revealed.

Reference 46 was restricted to phosphorus trihalides. From the ionization potential of metal d orbitals and the stabilization of the phosphorus lone pair it was concluded that σ donation increases in the order $PF_3 < PCl_3 \sim PBR_3$. The splitting of the d orbitals, $\Delta\pi$, and the spin-orbit coupling ζ are much smaller than in nitrogen-donor complexes, proving that π interaction in PX_3 is much more important (see Tables 8 and 9).

σ Donation was much weaker, however. PF_3 was even a better electron-withdrawing ligand than CO. The intensity changes in the PE spectra on going from He(I) to He(II) were measured for the bands

Table 6   Vertical Ionization Potentials and Their Assignment of the Free Azoles (eV)

	π_3	π_2	σ_N	σ_S
Pyrazole	9.15	9.88	10.7	
Isoxazole	10.20	11.38	11.38	
Thiazole	9.50	10.24	10.48	12.77
Isothiazole	9.62	10.26	10.80	12.42

Source: Ref. 45.

Table 7   Vertical Ionization Potentials and Their Assignment of the $Cr(CO)_5$(Azole) Complexes (eV)

	Metal d orbitals		π_3	π_2	$\sigma(MN)$
Pyrazole	7.40	7.71	10.32	10.80	
Isoxazole	7.42	7.65	10.92	11.85	
Thiazole	7.36	7.63	10.3	11.2	12.0
Isothiazole	7.32	7.63	10.3	10.8	

Source: Ref. 45.

belonging to the ligand orbitals both in the complexes and in the free ligands [43]. It was noted that the intensity behavior of bands belonging to the free and complexed ligand was very similar. This was used as an important assignment criterion. The intensity of the Cl and Br lone-pair bands dropped, whereas the d band was strongly enhanced. The latter observation was also made for N-donor complexes. From this intensity behavior it was also concluded that the phosphorus lone pair interacted only weakly with the empty d_{z^2} orbital. The ionization potential of the carbonyl 4σ orbital reflected the charge on CO.

The PE spectra results for both phosphine and phosphite complexes have also been reported [47] (Tables 10 and 11). The σ-donor properties increased in the expected order:

Table 8 Vertical Ionization Potentials (eV), Relative Intensities (I), and Assignment of the Free PX_3 (X = F, Cl, Br)

	PF_3				PCl_3				PBr_3		
IP	$I_{He\ I}$	$I_{He\ II}$		IP	$I_{He\ I}$	$I_{He\ II}$		IP	$I_{He\ I}$	$I_{He\ II}$	
12.28	1.0	1.0	a_1	10.54	1.0	1.0	a_1	9.99	1.0	1.0	a_1
15.89	4.8	7.3	e	11.71	1.4	0.6	a_2	10.59	2.6	2.1	e
16.29			a_2	12.01	3.5	1.5	e	10.80			a_2
17.35	5.0	3.0	e	12.96	3.5	1.5	e	11.11	1.7	1.5	e
18.51	2.6	1.1	a_1	14.25	1.4	0.8	a_1	11.78	3.1	2.5	e
19.31	8.2	3.6	e	15.22	2.2	1.4	e	13.07	1.0	0.8	a_1
22.4		1.4	a_1	18.86		0.5	a_1	14.04	1.7	1.6	e
											a_1

Source: Ref. 46.

Table 9 Vertical Ionization Potentials (eV) and Assignment of $M(CO)_5PX_3$ (M = Cr, Mo, W and X = F, Cl, Br)

	Metal d orbitals	σ M-P	5σ, 1πCO		e + a₂ l.p.	4σCO c l.p.	l.p. + eσ	a₁ σ
$Cr(CO)_5PF_3$	8.56	12.48	13.64	14.26	15.7	17.8	19.4	22.43
$Mo(CO)_5PF_3$	8.55							
$W(CO)_5PF_3$	8.68	12.48	13.65	14.90	15.7	17.7	19.3	22.35

	Metal d orbitals	σ M-P	a₂ l.p. e l.p.	e l.p.	5σ, 1πCO			4σCO	l.p. + eσ	a₁ σ
$Cr(CO)_5PCl_3$	8.32	11.08	11.76	12.83	13.40	14.24	15.23	17.8	19.2	23.4
$Mo(CO)_5PCl_3$	8.36	10.96	11.66	12.75	13.15	14.40	15.07	17.6	19.4	23.5
$W(CO)_5PCl_3$	8.39	10.99	11.61	12.70	13.11	14.69		17.6	19.9	23.3

	Metal d orbitals	σ M-P e l.p.	a₂ l.p.	e l.p.	a₁ l.p.	5σ, 1πCO	4σCO	l.p. + eσ	a₁ σ
$Cr(CO)_5PBr_3$	8.32	10.51	10.97	11.72	13.29	14.04	17.6	19.7	22.8
$Mo(CO)_5PBr_3$	8.33								

l.p. = lone pair.
Source: Ref. 46.

Table 10   Vertical Ionization Potentials (eV) of the Metal d
Orbitals

$Cr(CO)_5P(C_6H_{11})_3$		7.24	7.41
$Mo(CO)_5P(C_6H_{11})_3$		7.44	7.62
$W(CO)_5P(C_6H_{11})_3$	7.29	7.47	7.70
$Cr(CO)_5P(C_6H_5)_3$		7.30	7.50
$W(CO)_5P(C_6H_5)_3$	7.36	7.55	7.71
$Cr(CO)_5P(O-i-C_3H_7)_3$		7.61	
$W(CO)_5P(O-i-C_3H_7)_3$		7.82	
$Cr(CO)_5P(OC_6H_5)_3$		7.67	
$W(CO)_5P(OC_6H_5)_3$		7.90	
$W(CO)_5As(C_6H_5)_3$	7.37	7.60	7.78

Source: Ref. 47.

$P(OC_6H_5)_3 < P(O-i-C_3H_7)_3 < P(C_6H_5)_3 < P(C_6H_{11})$, whereas the π-acceptor
properties diminished. Steric effects did not seem to dominate with-
in the series. The differences in the PE spectra of the $P(C_6H_{11})_3$
and $P(C_6H_5)_3$ complexes on one side and the $P(CH_3)_3$ complex on the
other side has to be attributed to steric effects, however. The
splitting of the d orbitals showed that π interaction was stronger
in all the P-donor complexes with respect to an N-donor complex.
This stronger back-bonding was ascribed to better overlap rather than
to the low energy of the empty phosphorus d orbital. A d_{xz}, d_{yz}
orbital is much more directed along the metal-ligand z axis than a
p_x, p_y orbital. From the lower stabilization of the P-donor lone
pair with respect to the N-donor lone pair upon complexation, one
tends to conclude that P-donor ligands form a weaker σ bond. Owing
to the different π back-bonding properties of N- and P-donor ligands,
inductive effects become important as well. So unambiguous conclusions about the relative strength of the σ bond cannot be drawn.

Comparison between $Cr(CO)_5L$ and $Fe(CO)_4L$ showed that the Fe-L σ
interaction was stronger. Furthermore, the splitting between the
iron e' and e" orbital did not parallel the splitting of the chromium

Table 11 Vertical Ionization Potentials (eV) of Bands Belonging to the Ligand Orbitals

Compound									
$P(C_6H_{11})_3$	7.75	9.38	10.3				17.9	19.4	22.9
$Cr(CO)_5P(C_6H_{11})_3$	9.16	9.66	10.5		12.5 ———— 17.0[a]		18.3	19.7	23.1
$Mo(CO)_5P(C_6H_{11})_3$	9.15	9.75							
$W(CO)_5P(C_6H_{11})_3$	9.37	9.80	10.5		12.4 ———— 16.8[a]		18.4	19.7	23.2
$P(C_6H_5)_3$	7.97	9.25	10.88		11.76		18.7		22.3
$Cr(CO)_5P(C_6H_5)_3$	8.77	9.41	10.41	11.2	12.5 — 16.8[a]		19.0		22.5
$W(CO)_5P(C_6H_5)_3$	8.80	9.42	10.50	11.3	12.3 — 16.8[a]		18.8		22.7
$P(O\text{-}i\text{-}C_3H_7)_3$	8.76	9.90	10.68	11.3	12.8		18.2	19.4	22.2
$Cr(CO)_5P(O\text{-}i\text{-}C_3H_7)_3$		9.70	10.5	11.2	12.7 — 17.3[a]		18.3	19.5	22.3
$W(CO)_5P(O\text{-}i\text{-}C_3H_7)_3$		9.80	10.4	11.2	12.7 — 17.3[a]		18.5	19.6	22.5
$P(OC_6H_5)_3$	8.80	9.47	10.9					19.3	22.8
$Cr(CO)_5P(OC_6H_5)_3$	8.96	9.45	10.7	11.1 ———— 17.2[a]				19.4	23.4
$W(CO)_5P(OC_6H_5)_3$	9.07	9.45	10.7	11.1 ———— 17.4[a]				19.6	23.3
$As(C_6H_5)_3$	8.11	9.15	10.49	11.8			18.6		22.2
$W(CO)_5As(C_6H_5)_3$	8.98	9.36	10.45	11.0	12.4 — 17.9[a]			19.3	22.3

[a]Vertical IP of band assigned to carbonyl 4σ-level.
Source: Ref. 47.

e and b_2 orbital. It was concluded that the energy difference
between e' and e" is not a good parameter for describing the π-bond-
ing properties of L in $Fe(CO)_4L$. The authors ascribed this to the
fact that the σ- and π-electronic system may mix in the equatorial
plane of penta-coordinated iron carbonyl complexes, whereas in the
octahedral group VIB metal pentacarbonyl complexes, strict σ-π
separation is present.

The ^{13}C chemical shifts from nonaromatic PR_3 ligands are shifted
down field on coordination similarly to the pyridine and azole ligands. The carbonyl ^{13}C resonances of the chromium complexes [44,45]
and [46,47] roughly parallelled the ionization potential of the metal
b_2 orbital or the net effect of σ donation and π back-bonding. For
the tungsten complexes, however, the energy difference between metal
e and b_2 or the π back-bonding alone seemed to be the ruling factor
for $\delta(^{13}CO)$.

C. Transition Metal Carbene Complexes

Of special interest in these complexes are the π-acceptor capability
of the carbene moiety and the related questions of chemical bonding
in transition metal complexes. Several carbene complexes of the
general formula $Cr(CO)_5C(X)Y$ have been examined using He(I) PE
spectroscopy and results from MO calculations by Block and Fenske
[38]. These workers have made consistent assignments of the low-
energy regions (7-11 eV) of the spectra where the Cr-3d MOs and the
Cr-carbene σ bond are found. When comparing the metal d IE values
of the carbene complexes with the t_{2g} Cr-3d IE value of $Cr(CO)_6$,
lower IE values are always found for the former complexes. This
suggests, assuming the relative validity of Koopmans' theorem, that
the carbenes are all worse π back-bonding ligands than CO.

Böhm et al. have published the He(I) PE spectra of some iron
tetracarbonyl carbene complexes [48]:

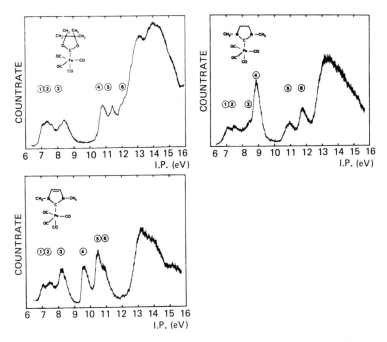

R = CH₃

of which the structures are known through x-ray determinations. Using various theoretical schemes based on the Intermediate Neglect of Differential Overlap (INDO) method and using mutual comparisons, the PE spectra of 1-3 were interpreted (Fig. 3).

Koopmans' theorem defects prevented interpretation of the PE spectra in terms of the ground-state INDO calculation. Two different theoretical approaches were therefore used: first, calculating the different cation states separately (ΔSCF method), and second, using

Figure 3 He(I) spectrum of some Fe(CO)₄ carbene complexes. (From Ref. 48.)

the transition operator model (TOM). This method has been developed
on the basis of Slater's transition state approximation by Goscinski
et al. [48a].

For a detailed description of the PE spectra a qualitative
bonding scheme is necessary. Letting the well-known frontier orbitals of $Fe(CO)_4$ (Fig. 4) in a "molecules-in-molecules" approach
interact with the carbenes, a reasonable first-order description of
the electronic structure can be made.

In C_{3v} symmetry the metal d orbitals split into two e orbitals
and one a_1 orbital. The occupied 1e combinations have primarily d_{xz}
and d_{yz} character. The other occupied e level is mainly $3d_{x^2-y^2}$ and
$3d_{xy}$ in character. The stabilization of the 1e level originates
mainly from π back-bonding with the CO ligands. The unoccupied a_1
orbital is mainly $3d_{z^2}$ in character, with some $4p_z$ admixture. This
acceptor orbital can interact with the occupied carbene donor orbital. According to the calculations this is the most important bonding interaction, while π back-bonding is, just as with the $Cr(CO)_5$
carbene complexes (see above), of negligible importance. This can
also be seen in the PE spectra when the metal d IE values of the
carbene complexes are compared with those of $Fe(CO)_5$. The assignments of the metal bands could be done satisfactorily only using the

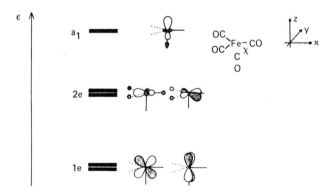

Figure 4.   Frontier orbitals of $Fe(CO)_4$.   (From Ref. 48.)

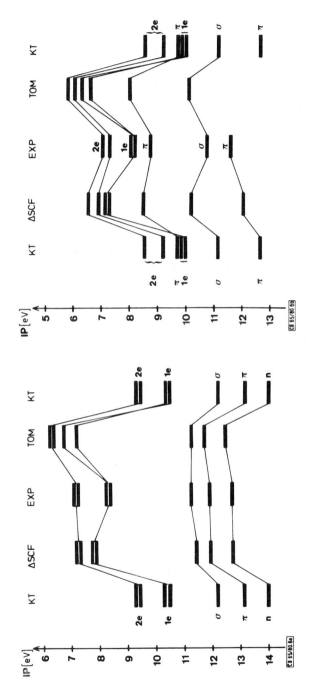

Figure 5 Comparison of experimental IP values and those calculated with Koopmans' theorem (KT), the ΔSCF method, and the TO method for compounds 1 (left) and 2 (right). (From Ref. 48.)

ΔSCF or TO method (Fig. 5). As can be seen from Fig. 5, good
agreements with the PE spectra are reached. As could be expected,
2- to 3-eV relaxation energies are calculated for the metal d orbitals, while these energies are somewhat lower for the ligand-based
orbitals. However, the latter energies are also considerable, owing
to the strong localization of these MOs. Assignments and IE values
are listed in Table 12.

IV. METALLOCENES

This class of complexes has received much attention from theoreti-
cians and spectroscopists. Numerous papers have appeared concerning
molecular orbital calculations, ranging from semiempirical schemes
to extended-basis ab initio calculations. A good starting point for
the discussion concerning bonding in these complexes is the work of
Lauher and Hoffmann [49]. Their discussion is based on the staggered
(D_{5d}) structure, although there is evidence that in the gas phase the
eclipsed structure (D_{5h}) is favored [50]. However, the irreducible
representations pertaining to the D_{5d} and D_{5h} point groups are quite
similar. In the D_{5d} symmetry the π orbitals of the two parallel
$C_5H_5^-$ ligands yield three sets of approximately degenerate orbitals:

Table 12   Vertical IP Values of Tetracarbonyl(carbene) Fe[0]
Complexes 1, 2, and 3[a] (eV)

	Band	1	2	3
d	1	7.3	7.1	7.0
d	2		7.3	7.5
d	3	8.3	8.3	8.2
	4	10.8 M-C	8.7 π	9.6 π
	5	11.5 π	10.8 M-C	10.5 M-C
	6	12.3 n	11.6 π	10.9 π

[a]The numbers refer to the species shown in Fig. 3 (page 155).
Source: Ref. 48.

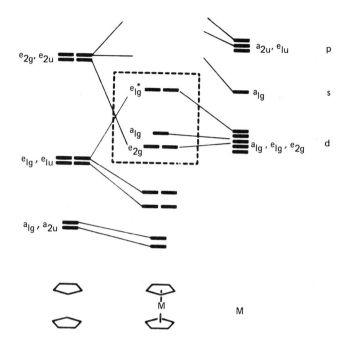

Figure 6 MO diagram for Cp_2M. The frontier orbitals are in the box. (From Ref. 49.)

a low-lying filled pair of a_{1g} and a_{2u} symmetry, a set of filled orbitals e_{1g} and e_{1u}, and a high-lying empty set of antibonding orbitals of symmetry e_{2g} and e_{2u}. These interact with the orbitals of the metal as shown in Fig. 6, which is a schematic interaction diagram for Cp_2M. There is a strong interaction with the metal s and p orbitals and also a strong bonding interaction with the e_{1g} (d_{xz}, d_{yz}) set. The remaining three d orbitals of the metal remain essentially nonbonding.

Although the measurement and interpretation of the PE spectra of metallocenes have been the subject of a considerable number of publications, the paper of Cauletti et al. [51] reexamined the problems on a much firmer basis using He(I) and He(II) intensity differences and substituent effects. The following conclusions could be given without reservation.

The decamethyl metallocenes of Ni, Co, Fe, and V have the same ground states as the unsubstituted analogs. The PE spectrum of $[CrCp_2]$ is consistent with an $^3E_{2g}$ ground state and not with a $^3A_{2g}$ ground state.

The He(I)/He(II) intensity changes led to a firm assignment of the PE spectrum of $[CrCp_2]$ and also to a complete assignment for the low-spin compound $[MnCp_2]$. A ligand field treatment including limited configuration interaction gives a good account of the energies of the ion states of $(MnCp_2)^+$. The values for Δ_2, B, and C derived from this ligand field treatment predict the right ordering of the ion states for vanadium, chromium, and iron metallocenes. The PE spectrum of the cobalt and nickel metallocenes remained incompletely assigned due to overlapping bands originating from d electrons and from ligand electrons.

A. Assignment of the Spectra

The PE spectra of all the metallocenes can be subdivided into three more-or-less separate regions commonly labeled A, B, and C (see Fig. 7). Region C is assigned to more strongly bonded ligand σ MOs, from which the bands in the He(II) spectrum are not so heavily depleted, possibly due to the fact that these orbitals have greater s character.

The B region is assigned to ionizations from σ MOs of the sandwich ligand together with the $a_{1g}(\pi)$ and $a_{2u}(\pi)$ orbitals. These bands are dramatically reduced in He(II) compared to He(I). In the decamethyl metallocenes the B band is much more widely spread (10-16 eV) than in the corresponding metallocenes (11-13 eV), as can be seen in Fig. 8. Region A varies greatly through the series. These bands are associated with ionizations from MOs of metal d character showing a considerable enhancement in the He(II) spectra relative to other bands.

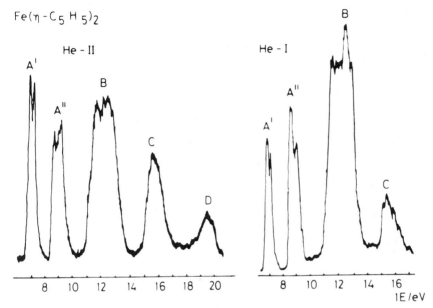

Figure 7   He(I) and He(II) spectra of Fe$(\eta$-C$_5$H$_5)_2$.   (From Ref. 51.)

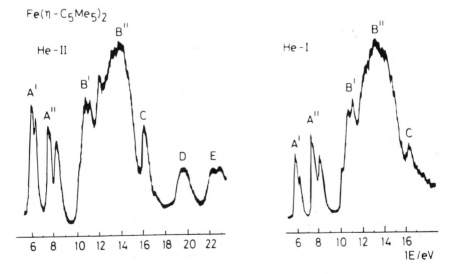

Figure 8   He(I) and He(II) spectra of Fe$(\eta$-C$_5$Me$_5)_2$.   (From Ref. 51.)

1. Ferrocene and Decamethyl Ferrocene (Fig. 9)

As ferrocene is a closed-shell molecule, ionizations from the first four MOs should give rise to four ion states: $^2E_{2g}$, $^2A_{1g}$, $^2E_{1u}$, and $^2E_{1g}$. In answer to earlier disputes about the assignment of the first two bands, the increase in intensity on going from He(I) to He(II) of the second band tells us that this band is associated with the $^2A_{1g}$ state having more d character than the $^2E_{2g}$ state. This intensity increase can be treated as diagnostic for electrons

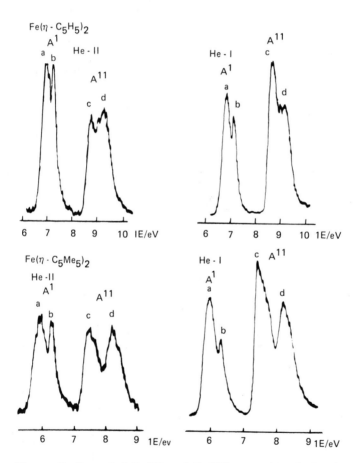

Figure 9   Expanded He(I) and He(II) spectra of the A region of ferrocene and the decamethyl derivative.   (From Ref. 51.)

originating from the a_{1g} orbital of neutral metallocenes since this feature is consistently predicted by most calculations and is in agreement with the findings for bis-arene metal complexes.

In the same way the third and fourth bands could be assigned to the associated ion states $^2E_{1u}$ and $^2E_{1g}$, respectively. The fourth band is relatively more intense in He(II), indicating that the MO from which this electron arises has more partial d character. This is confirmed by the electron-donating effect of the methyl groups on the spectra of $[Fe(CpMe_5)_2]$ and $[Fe(CpMe)_2]$.

The orbital that is most highly ligand localized, $e_{1g}(\pi)$, gives rise to the largest lowering of the IE upon methyl substitution (1.5 eV). The ionization from $e_{1g}(\pi)$, which has some metal d contribution, is lowered by 1.2 eV and the metal bands from e_{2g} and a_{1g} are lowered by 1.0 eV. Clearly, the more the orbital is localized on the ligand, the greater is the effect of methyl substitution.

Furthermore, it appears that the inductive effect of the methyl groups is additive since the lowering in $[Fe(CpMe_5)_2]$ (i.e., 1.0 eV) is five times as large as the lowering of the corresponding orbitals in $[Fe(CpMe)_2]$ (i.e., 0.2 eV).

2. *Manganocene, 1,1-Dimethyl Manganocene and Decamethyl Manganocene*

The photoelectron spectrum of decamethyl manganocene (Fig. 10c) differs substantially from that of manganocene (Fig. 10a). The assignment of the metal d orbital bands is straightforward, leading to the following ionization processes:

$$[MnCp_2] \ ^6A_{1g}(a_{1g}^1 e_{2g}^2 e_{1g}^2) \longrightarrow \ ^5E_{1g} \text{ (band a)}$$
$$^5A_{1g} \text{ (band c)}$$
$$^5A_{2g} \text{ (band d)}$$

$$[Mn(CpMe_5)_2] \ ^2E_{2g}(a_{1g}^2 e_{2g}^3) \longrightarrow \ ^3E_{2g} \text{ (band a')}$$
$$^1E_{1g} \text{ (band b')}$$
$$^3A_{2g} \text{ (band c')}$$
$$^1F_{1g} \text{ (band d')}$$
$$^1A_{1g} \text{ (band e')}$$

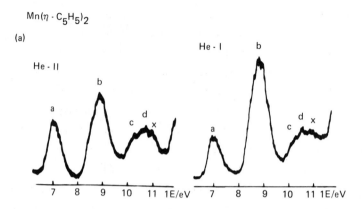

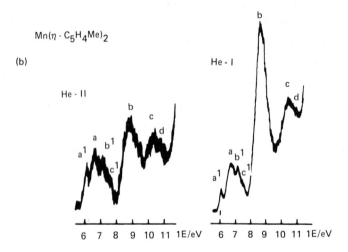

Figure 10 He(I) and He(II) spectra of manganocene and the decamethyl derivative. (From Ref. 51.)

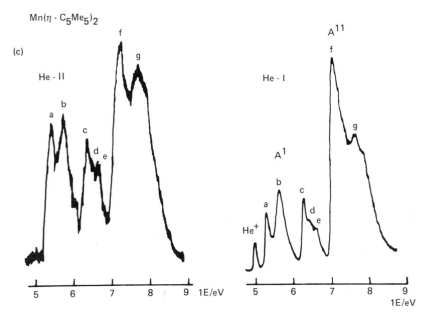

Figure 10 (Continued)

3. *Chromocene and Decamethyl Chromocene*

Both these spectra are similar (Fig. 11). The ground and ionization states are as expected from the He(I)/He(II) cross-section variation of the spectra.

$$[CrCp_2] \quad {}^3E_{2g}(e_{2g}^3 a_{1g}^1) \longrightarrow {}^2E_{2g} \quad \text{(band c)}$$

$$\phantom{[CrCp_2] \quad {}^3E_{2g}(e_{2g}^3 a_{1g}^1) \longrightarrow} {}^4A_{2g} \quad \text{(band a)}$$

$$\phantom{[CrCp_2] \quad {}^3E_{2g}(e_{2g}^3 a_{1g}^1) \longrightarrow} {}^2E_{1g} \quad \text{(band b)}$$

$$\phantom{[CrCp_2] \quad {}^3E_{2g}(e_{2g}^3 a_{1g}^1) \longrightarrow} {}^2A_{1g} \quad \text{(band d)}$$

$$\phantom{[CrCp_2] \quad {}^3E_{2g}(e_{2g}^3 a_{1g}^1) \longrightarrow} {}^2A_{2g} \quad \text{(band d)}$$

4. *Vanadocene and Decamethyl Vanadocene*

He(I) and He(II) PE spectra of both complexes, shown in Fig. 12, confirm the assignment of Evans et al. [52]. The ground state $^4A_{2g}$ produces two excited ionization states, $^3A_{2g}$ and $^3E_{2g}$, giving rise to only one more band in the spectra.

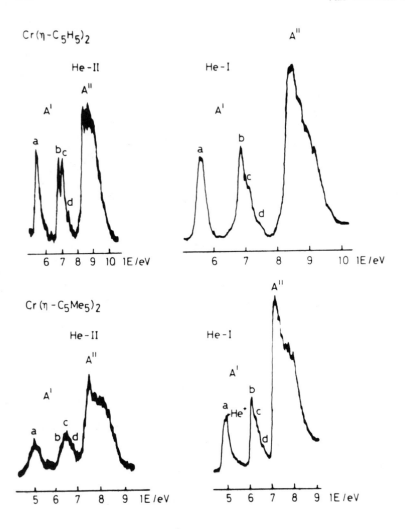

Figure 11   He(I) and He(II) spectra of chromocene and the decamethyl
derivative.   (From Ref. 51.)

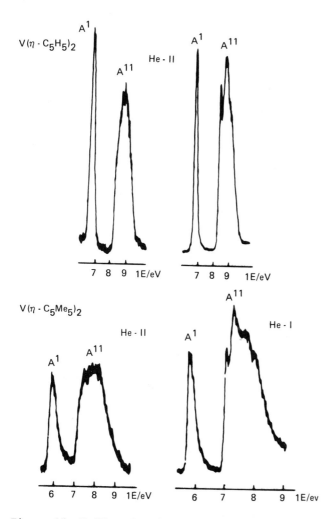

Figure 12 He(I) and He(II) spectra of vanadocene and the decamethyl derivative. (From Ref. 51.)

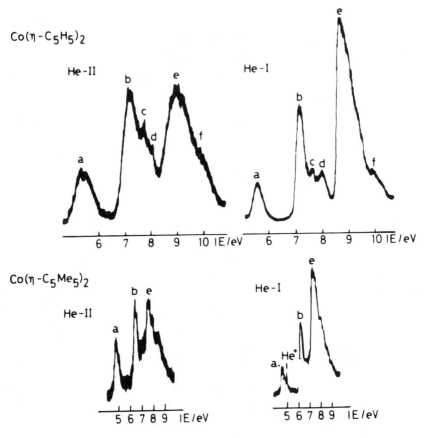

Figure 13 He(I) and He(II) spectra of cobaltocene and decamethyl
cobaltocene. (From Ref. 51.)

5. *Cobaltocene and Decamethyl Cobaltocene*

It is difficult to give a complete assignment of the PE spectra
(see Fig. 13). From the He(I) and He(II) intensities it is obvious
that all the bands (a, b, c, d, and f) are from d-orbital ionizations. The first band in the PE spectrum of $[CoCp_2]$ shows the
greatest intensity variation and is therefore assigned to the $^1A_{1g}$
ground state of the cation. The other d bands seem to overlap the
ligand π bands.

Table 13 Vertical Ionization Potentials[a] (eV)

$MnCp_2$ High spin $^6A_{1g} = (a_{1g}^1 e_{2g}^2 e_{1g}^2)$	$Mn(CpMe)_2$ High/low spin	$Mn(CpMe_5)_2$ Low spin $^2E_{2g} = (a_{1g}^2 e_{2g}^3)$
6.26 (a')	6.06 (a' = $^3E_{2g}$)	5.33 (a' = $^3E_{2g}$
7.01 (a = $^5E_{1g}$)	6.68 (a = $^5E_{1g}$)	
		5.72 (b' = $^3A_{2g}$)
	7.10 (b' = $^1E_{1g}$)	6.37 (c' = $^1E_{1g}$)
		6.50 (d' = $^1A_{1g}$)
	7.47 (c' = $^1E_{2g}$)	6.72 (e' = $^1E_{2g}$
8.85	8.55 (b = ligand)	7.26 (f = ligand)
		7.95 (g = ligand)
10.25 (c = $^5A_{1g}$)	9.88 (c = $^5A_{1g}$)	
10.57 (d = $^5A_{2g}$)	10.29 (d = $^5A_{2g}$)	

[a]Prime indicates low spin; without prime indicates high spin.
Source: Ref. 51.

The minor discrepancies in the assignment of Rabalais [53] and the one of Evans [52] could be decided on the basis of He(I)/He(II) intensity variations by Cauletti [51]. The assignment of Evans was justified as shown in Fig. 10.

The explanation for the large number of bands in the dimethyl manganocene complex is that the gas phase comprises a mixture of low- and high-spin molecules, compared to only low-spin molecules for decamethyl manganocene, and almost only high-spin molecules for manganocene itself.

The assignments, the correlation, and the trends for these three related complexes are given in Table 13.

6. Nickelocene and Decamethyl Nickelocene

The He(I) and He(II) spectra of nickelocene (see Fig. 14) suggest that a, b, and d are metal bands, whereas c is a ligand band. Relative shifts observed for the decamethyl nickelocene spectra also support these assignments. Band a, which may be assigned to the $^2E_{1g}$ state, shows a strong increase in intensity as the proton energy increases, as do the lowest IE bands of manganocene and cobaltocene. Band e, which is resolved only in the He(I) spectrum of $[NiCp_2]$, does not show an intensity increase in the He(II) spectrum and so is probably associated with ligand ionization.

7. Ruthenocene

The He(I) and He(II) spectra of ruthenocene (see Fig. 15) are in agreement with the assignment of Evans et al. [52]: namely, band a to $^2A_{1g}$ and $^2E_{2g}$, band b to $^2E_{1u}$, and band c to $^2E_{1g}$. The increase in intensity of the d orbitals relative to the π orbitals appears to be threefold on going from He(I) to He(II) for this metal.

From the PE spectra it was possible to test the validity of ligand field theory and to obtain ligand field parameters. In some cases a limited configuration interaction treatment was necessary. The results are shown in Table 14. These values for A_2, B and C predict the right ordering of the ion states for vanadium, chromium, and iron metallocenes. It is justified to conclude that characteristic intensity changes with photon energy for the various orbitals have led to a firm assignment of the PE spectra of metallocenes in general, and $[CrCp_2]$ and $[Mn(C_5Me_5)_2]$ in particular.

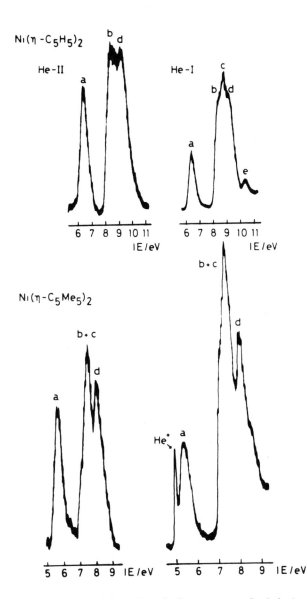

Figure 14 He(I) and He(II) spectra of nickelocene and decamethyl
nickelocene. (From Ref. 51.)

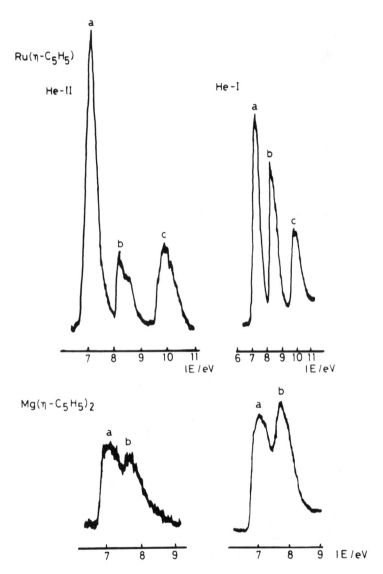

Figure 15   He(I) and He(II) spectra of ruthenocene and the magnesium analogon.   (From Ref. 51.)

Table 14   Energies of Excited States of the Decamethyl Metallocene Molecular Ions Calculated by Ligand Field Theory with Limited Configuration Interaction[a]

$\{V(\eta\text{-}C_5Me_5)_2\}^+$	$^3A_{2g}$	$^3E_{2g}$				
Calculated	0	0.02				
Experimental	0	0				

$\{Cr(\eta\text{-}C_5Me_5)_2\}^+$	$^4A_{2g}$	$^2E_{1g}$	$^2E_{2g}$	$^2A_{1g}$	$^2A_{2g}$	$[^2E_{2g}]$
Calculated	0	1.35	1.87	2.00	2.09	3.32
Experimental	0	1.25	1.41	1.76	1.76	

$\{Mn(\eta\text{-}C_5Me_5)_2\}^+$	$^3E_{2g}$	$^3A_{2g}$	$^1E_{1g}$	$^1A_{1g}$	$^1E_{2g}$	$[^1A_{1g}]$
Calculated	0	0.39	1.04	1.12	1.39	3.38
Experimental	0	0.39	1.04	1.17	1.39	

$\{Fe(\eta\text{-}C_5Me_5)_2\}^+$	$^2E_{2g}$	$^2A_{1g}$				
Calculated	0	0.72				
Experimental	0	0.40				

$\{Co(\eta\text{-}C_5Me_5)_2\}^+$	$^1A_{1g}$	$^3E_{1g}$	$^3E_{2g}$	$^1E_{1g}$	$^1E_{2g}$	$^3E_{1g}$	$^1E_{1g}$
Calculated[b]	0	1.68	1.99	2.51	2.64	2.65	4.42
Experimental[c]	0	1.68	— — — (2.3	— 4.3) —	— — — — —		

$\{Ni(\eta\text{-}C_5Me_5)_2\}^+$	$^2E_{1g}$	$^4A_{2g}$	$^4E_{2g}$	$^2A_{2g}$	$[^2E_{2g}]$	$^2E_{2g}$	$[^2A_{2g}]$	$[^2E_{2g}]$
Calculated[b]	0	1.65	1.67	2.60	2.90	3.31	3.41	5.22
Experimental[c]	0	1.65		2.58	— — —(1.2	— 3.2) — — — —		

[a]States in brackets are those with minor components accessible by a one-electron ionization of the ground state.   Values are calculated using B = 0.0925, C = 0.325, and Δ_2 = 1.13.

[b]Δ_1 = 2.67 (Co) and 2.95 (Ni).

[c]Complex band includes ionization from e_{1u} and e_{1g} orbitals.

Source: Ref. 51.

B. Recent Developments

Green et al. have published the He(I) and He(II) PE spectra of
$Fe(\eta^5-C_5H_5)(\eta^6-C_6Me_6)$, $Fe(\eta-C_5H_5)(\eta-C_6Et_6)$, $Fe(\eta-C_5H_5)[\eta-C_6H_3-$
$(CMe_3)_3]$, and $Fe(\eta-C_5Me_5)(\eta-C_6Me_6)$ [178]. The IE values are listed
in Table 15. $Fe(\eta-C_5Me_5)(\eta-C_6Me_6)$ has one of the lowest recorded
molecule ionization potentials (4.21 eV). The assignments have been
made using ligand field predictions as to the relative energies of
the ion states using relative intensities of the PE bands and correlations with results on analogous compounds. Ligand field parameters
were presented for $Fe(\eta-C_5H_5)(\eta-C_6Me_6)$ and $Fe(\eta-C_5Me_5)(\eta-C_6Me_6)$.

In the same paper the He(I) and He(II) spectra of some related
d^6 complexes--$Fe(\eta-C_5H_5)(\eta^5-C_6H_7)$, $Fe(\eta-C_5H_5)(\eta^5-C_6Me_6H)$, $Fe(\eta-C_5H_5)-$
$(\eta^5-C_6Me_5CH_2)$, and $Fe(\eta-C_5H_5)(\eta^5-C_6Me_5NH)$--were published together
with their assignments (see Table 16). These compounds have higher
IE values and are characteristic of d^6 species. The interpretation
of the PE spectra of these complexes suggests a high electron density
on the methylene carbon of $Fe(\eta-C_5H_5)(\eta^5-C_6H_6CH_2)$, which is consistent with its reactivity as a nucleophile.

Cabelli et al. [179] have reported the He(I) spectra of several
bis(arene)chromium complexes. The arenes used are listed in Table
17, together with the IE values.

The PE spectra have been interpreted using a qualitative perturbation molecular orbital model. It was found that the ionization
energies of the metal localized orbitals were influenced mainly by
ligand electronegativity, but there was also some evidence for the
importance of conjugative effects. The ionization energies of the
free and coordinated arenes are quite similar.

V. η^5-CYCLOPENTADIENYL METAL CARBONYL COMPLEXES

$[(\eta^5-C_5H_5)M(CO)_2X]$ (M = Mn, X = CO, CS; M = Re, X = CO; M = Cr,
X = NO, NX, and M = Fe, X = CH_3, Cl, Br, I) complexes have been
studied extensively using He(I) spectra and employing results from
Fenske-Hall calculations by Lichtenberger et al. [54-57]. For a

Table 15   Ionization Energies (eV) for $Fe(\eta-C_5H_5)(\eta-C_6Me_6)$ (I), $Fe(\eta-C_5H_5)(\eta-C_6Et_6)$ (II), $Fe(\eta-C_5H_5)(\eta-C_6H_3(CMe_3)_3)$ (III), and $Fe(\eta-C_5Me_5)(\eta-C_6Me_6)$ (IV)

I	III	Assignment	II	IV	Assignment
4.68	4.74	$^1A_1$	4.54	4.21	$^1A_1$
6.19	6.20	$^3E_1$	6.09	5.74	$^3E_1 + {}^3E_2$
6.92	6.87	$^3E_2 + {}^3E_1 + {}^1E_1$	6.92	6.32	$^1E_1 + {}^3E_1$
7.18	7.22	$^1E_2$		6.64	$^1E_2$
7.89	8.24	$e_1(Cp) + {}^1E_1$	7.77	(7.20)	$e_1(Cp)$
8.06	8.68	$+ e_1$ arene	8.02	7.71	
8.79			8.70	8.58	e_1 arene
10.6	10.2	Ring alkyl	10.3	10.2	Ring alkyl
12.7	13	Ring $a_1 + \sigma$	12.1	13	Ring $a_1 + \sigma$

Source: Ref. 178.

thorough understanding of bonding in this type of complex, the results for $[(\eta^5-C_5H_5)Mn(CO)_3]$ will be described in some detail.

[$CpMn(CO)_3$] has at most a single symmetry plane. This low symmetry indicates that no ionizations will be degenerate. The description is greatly simplified if advantage is taken of the fact that locally, the symmetry can be quite high. The cyclopentadienyl moiety transforms according to D_{5h} symmetry and the [$Mn(CO)_3$] portion to C_{3v} symmetry. These fragments will be allowed to interact using a molecules-in-molecules approach [58].

For a discussion of the interaction between the $[Mn(CO)_3]^+$ orbitals and the Cp^- ring orbitals, it is helpful to consider first the $[Mn(CO)_3]^+$ molecular orbital diagram (Fig. 16). Construction of the MO diagram from $(CO)_3$ and Mn^+ yields frontier orbitals which can interact with the Cp^- system. This interaction is shown in Fig. 17.

Table 16 Ionization Energies for $Fe(\eta\text{-}C_5H_5)(\eta^5\text{-}C_6H_7)$ (V), $Fe(\eta\text{-}C_5H_5)(\eta^5\text{-}C_6Me_6H)$ (VI), $Fe(\eta\text{-}C_5H_5)(\eta^5\text{-}C_6Me_5CH_2)$ (VII), and $Fe(\eta\text{-}C_5H_5)(\eta^5\text{-}C_6Me_5NH)$ (VIII)

V	Assignment	VI	Assignment	VII	Assignment	VIII	Assignment
6.65	d	6.27	d	6.22	d	6.65	d
6.98	d	6.64	d	6.95	$d + \pi_4$	7.71	d
7.15	d	7.29	d			7.79	4
7.97	π_3	8.27	π_3	8.79	$\pi_3 + \pi_2 + e_1(Cp)$	8.63	$\pi_3 + \pi_2 + e_1(Cp)$
9.07	$e_1(Cp)$	8.8	π_2	9.12		9.33	
9.30	π_2	10.05	$e_1(Cp)$	10.74	π_1 + ring Me	11.26	π_1 + ring Me
11.12	π_1	10.5	π_1 + ring Me	13.1		13.2	
11.52	Ring σ	12.8					
12.2							
13.6							
16.5							

Source: Ref. 178.

	Ionic state[a]			
	$^2A_{1g}$ (I_1)	$^2E_{1g}$ (I_2)	$^2E_{1u}$ (I_3)	$^2E_{1g}$ (I_4)
$(m\text{-}F_3CC_6H_4CF_3)_2Cr$ (1)	6.70	7.72	11.01 (broad)	
$(p\text{-}FC_6H_4CF_3)_2Cr$ (2)	6.59	7.46	10.20	10.66
$(p\text{-}FC_6H_4F)_2Cr$ (3)	6.38	7.18	10.00	10.56
$(m\text{-}ClC_6H_4Cl)_2Cr$ (4)	6.20	7.03	9.83 (broad)	
$(C_6H_5F)_2Cr$ (5)	5.91	6.71	9.85	10.15
$(C_6H_5Cl)_2Cr$ (6)	5.90	6.81	9.65	10.18
$(C_6H_5CO_2CH_3)_2Cr$ (7)	5.77	6.80	10.16 (broad)	
$(p\text{-}ClC_6H_4CH_3)_2Cr$ (8)	5.76	6.70	9.31	10.03
$[(C_6H_5)_2O]_2Cr$ (9)	5.52	6.36	8.73	9.25
$(C_6H_6)_2Cr$ (10)	5.40	6.40	9.6 (broad)	
$(CH_3C_6H_5)_2Cr$ (11)	5.31	6.24	9.18	9.71 (shoulder)
$(o\text{-}H_3CC_6H_4CH_3)_2Cr$ (12)	5.21	6.18	9.10 (broad)	
$[C_6H_5Si(CH_3)_3]_2Cr$ (13)	5.22	6.32	9.59 (broad)	
$[C_6H_5CH_2CH(CH_3)_2]_2Cr$ (14)	5.23	6.19	9.24	9.56
$[1,2,3\text{-}(CH_3)_3C_6H_3]_2Cr$ (15)	5.04	5.96	8.90	9.18 (shoulder)
$[1,3,5\text{-}(CH_3)_3C_6H_3]_2Cr$ (16)	4.97	5.85	8.87	9.22 (shoulder)
$[1,2,4,5\text{-}(CH_3)_4C_6H_2]_2Cr$ (17)	4.85	5.65	8.49	8.90

[a]Even though the substituted arenes possess lower symmetries, D_{6h} labeling of states and orbitals is used.
Source: Ref. 179.

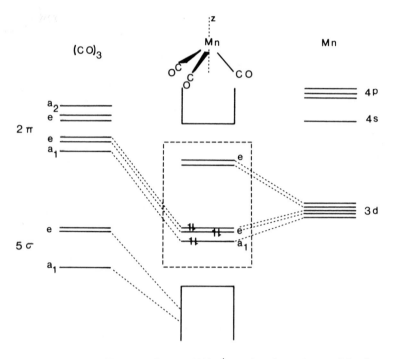

Figure 16   MO diagram for $Mn(CO)_3^+$. The frontier orbitals are in the box.   (From Ref. 58.)

The He(I) PE spectrum of $[CpMn(CO)_3]$ (Fig. 18) shows two bands in the region 8-12 eV [54].   The first ionization band occurs between 8.0 and 8.5 eV and is assigned to ionizations from the predominantly metal d levels.   This band is similar in IE value to the first IE value of $[Cr(CO)_6]$.   Although evidence from cross-section variation is lacking, this assignment is confirmed by comparison with the analogous rhenium complex [54].   The He(I) spectrum of that complex shows a very clear splitting of the first band, which probably originates from spin-orbit coupling.   The ordering of the metal a_1 and e ionizations has been determined using gaussian analysis.   Although such an analysis is never evidence itself, it can, in combination with other assignment criteria, give positive information concerning the ordering of the ionization bands.   Lichtenberger

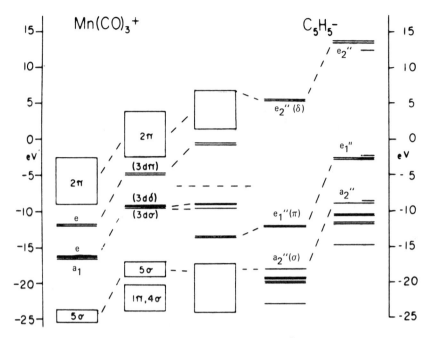

Figure 17   Molecular orbital diagram for [(η⁵-C₅H₅)Mn(CO)₃]. The outside columns represent the orbital eigenvalues of the isolated fragments $Mn(CO_3)^+$ and $C_5H_5^-$. In the case of $C_5H_5^-$, the eigenvalues of the ab initio calculation are also indicated by the shorter horizontal lines. The second and fourth columns represent the fragment orbital energies in the molecular environment, and the center column represents the orbital energies of [(η⁵-C₅H₅)Mn(CO)₃]. (From Ref. 54.)

and Fenske have used this technique in conjunction with a detailed and elegant analysis of the spin-orbit coupling in [CpRe(CO)₃]. On this basis they came to the conclusion that the a_1 ionization occurs at 8.5 eV and the practically unsplit e ionization at 8.0 eV. The second band, at about 10.0 eV, shows a distinct shoulder on the high-energy side. This band has been assigned to ionizations from the cyclopentadienyl unit. A splitting is still under discussion. Lichtenberger and Fenske suggested that it is vibrational fine structure. The separation of 0.39 eV corresponds to 3140 cm^{-1}, which is in fair agreement with the experimental ν_{CH} of 3116 cm^{-1}.

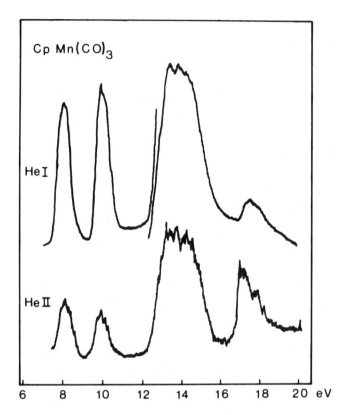

Figure 18   [CpMn(CO)$_3$]; He(I) and He(II) spectra.   (From Ref. 59.)

Disturbing for this interpretation, however, is the fact that only two components of the progression are visible, particularly in view of the rather high intensity of the second component.   It could be demonstrated using, for instance,   [((C$_5$(CH$_3$)$_5$)Mn(CO)$_3$] whether or not this is a vibrational progression, but at the moment the PE spectrum of that compound is unknown.

The splitting can also be interpreted as originating from re-moval of degeneracy of the two π MOs, owing to different interac-tions with the [Mn(CO)$_3$] fragment.   As mentioned earlier, the symmetry of [CpMn(CO)$_3$] is rather low.   The difference in intensity of the two components can be explained keeping in mind that the high-energy component has more metal character. Since it is known that the cross section of MOs containing considerable metal 3d character is generally lower than that containing a large amount of carbon 2p character, the observed difference is supported by the increase in intensity of the high-energy part with respect to the low-energy component of the corresponding band in the rhenium complex. This is the so-called "heavy-atom" effect.

The admixture of metal character in the second band is clearly shown by the small intensity change upon going from manganese to rhenium. The absence of a clear heavy-atom effect suggests considerable delocalization of metal character onto the ligand. The delocalization in this type of molecules is also seen in the absence of very large He(I)/He(II) effects in $[CpMn(CO)_3]$ [59] and in an analogous molecule $[CpCo(CO)_2]$ [60].

The He(I) spectra of complexes in which one of the CO ligands has been substituted by either dinitrogen or ammonia have been obtained [55]. The general features of these spectra resemble those of $[CpMn(CO)_3]$. The major differences appear in the ionizations associated predominantly with the metal d levels where shifts in IE values and loss of degeneracy reflect the differences of bonding of the nitrogen and carbonyl ligands with the metal center. The IE values measured are listed in Table 18.

$[CpMn(CO)_2N_2]$ is a very interesting molecule, owing to the coordination of the N_2 molecule and possible implications for nitrogen fixation. The He(I) spectrum of $[CpMn(CO)_2N_2]$ resembles strongly the spectrum of $[CpMn(CO)_3]$. Both spectra exhibit a broad, intense band in the binding energy range 12.5-15.5 eV, which has been attributed to ionizations from 5σ and 2π carbonyl orbitals and σ orbitals of the other ligands. Once more, two well-separated bands are found at about 8 and 10 eV.

The band near 8 eV is again attributed to ionizations from levels which are primarily metal d in character. The shape of this band in the spectrum of $[CpMn(CO)_2N_2]$ is substantially different

Table 18 Ionization

			Ionization Energies (eV) and Assignments				
Compound	Metal d	Conf.	Cyclopenta-dienyl	Other Ligand	MO calcula-tions used	Ref.	Remark
CpMn(CO)$_3$	8.05 (e) 8.40 (a$_1$)	d^6	9.90 10.29	-	Fenske-Hall	54	
CpRe(CO)$_3$	8.13 8.52 8.76^a	d^6	10.18 10.59	-	Fenske-Hall	54	Spin-orbit coupling
CpMn(CO)$_2$CS	7.81 8.00 8.23^a	d^6	9.71 10.07		Fenske-Hall	56	
CpMn(CO)$_2$N$_2$	7.54 7.89 8.07	d^6	9.78 10.17		Fenske-Hall	55	
CpMn(CO)$_2$NH$_3$	6.63 6.99 7.36	d^6	9.15		Fenske-Hall	55	
MeCpMn(CO)$_3$	7.97 8.22	d^6	9.62 (9.92)		-	59	He(I)/He(II)
CpMn(CO)$_2$C$_3$H$_4$O (acrolein)	8.11	d^6	9.82 10.29	9.4 10.6	-	59	He(I)/He(II)
MeCpMn(CO)$_2$C$_3$H$_4$O (acrolein)	(7.65) 8.02	d^6	9.5 -10.2^a	9.5 - 10.2	-	59	He(I)/He(II)
C$_6$H$_7$Mn(CO)$_3$	8.06	d^6		8.59 10.25 (π) [C$_h$H$_7^-$]	Fenske-Hall	63	

Compound		d^n		Calculation	He(I)/He(II)
$C_7H_9Mn(CO)_3$	7.86 8.10	d^6	8.67 9.97(π) [$C_7H_9^-$]	Fenske-Hall	63
$C_7H_7Mn(CO)_3$	7.66 7.86 8.33	d^6	10.33(π) [$C_7H_7^-$]	Fenske-Hall	63
$CpCo(CO)_2$	(7.5) 7.92 8.69 9.35	d^8	9.90	Ext. CNDO	60
$CpMo(CO)_3CH_3$	7.78 (6a')	d^4	9.7 10.0 (12.2) [CH_3] 9.07 [M-C-]	-	62
$CpW(CO)_3CH_3$	(7.6) 7.77 (3a'')	d^4	9.9 10.2 (12.3) [CH_3] 9.26 [M-C-]	-	62
$CpFe(CO)_2CH_3$	7.78 8.53	d^6	9.90 9.15 [M-C]	Fenske-Hall	61
$CpRu(CO)_2CH_3$	8.13 8.29 8.96	d^6	9.98 10.51 9.48 [M-C]	-	62
$CpFe(CO)_2CH_2CN$	8.29 8.90 9.45	d^6	10.25 11.14 [M-C] 11.89 12.27 [CN]	-	62
$CpFe(CO)_2Cl$	8.99 9.90 10.17	d^6	10.5 - 11.1 8.00 [Cl] 8.38 [M-Cl]	-	54[a]
$CpFe(CO)_2Br$	8.89 9.57 9.78	d^6	10.4 - 10.8 7.93 [Br] 8.30 [M-Br]	-	54[a]
$CpFe(CO)_2I$	9.18 9.37 10.03	d^6	10.40-10.76 7.77, 8.17 [I] 8.73 [M-I]	-	54[a]

[a] Assignments uncertain.

from that of the corresponding band of [CpMn(CO)$_3$]. Two distinctly
separate ionization bands are observed. The low-binding-energy
peak is approximately half as intense as the other peak. However,
three separate bands of about identical shape and amplitude appeared
by fitting this feature, as shown in Fig. 19. In this fit the low-
binding-energy peak is followed by two peaks that are close in
energy.

The ionization band near 10 eV displays a definite shoulder on
its high-energy side. This characteristic band-shape was also found
for [CpMn(CO)$_3$] and other Cp-metal complexes, being associated with
ionizations from the Cp e$_1''$ orbitals.

The shifts in the PE spectra upon substitution of dinitrogen
for a carbonyl group were predicted surprisingly well by the Fenske-
Hall method. Using the calculated differences in eigenvalues between [CpMn(CO)$_3$] and [CpMn(CO)$_2$N$_2$] as a correction to the observed
IE values of CpMn(CO)$_3$, the IE values of [CpMn(CO)$_2$N$_2$] were accurately predicted. This indicated that Koopmans' defects were of the same
order in both complexes.

CPMN (CO) 2N2 BAND ONE

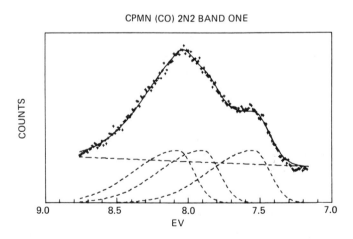

Figure 19   An expansion of the first band (He I) of CpMn(CO)$_2$N$_2$.
The plus signs are the data values. The dashed lines are the
curve-fit gaussian peaks and baseline, and the solid line is the fit
sum. (From Ref. 54.)

The trend in IE suggests that N_2 is a worse π-back-bonding ligand than CO, which is, of course, what could have been expected. The small change in IE also suggests that the σ-donating ability of N_2 is also somewhat poorer. The Fenske-Hall calculations confirm this view.

For $[CpMn(CO)_2NH_3]$ the reported spectrum shows severe decomposition into $CpMn(CO)_3$ and NH_3 [55]. Using spectral subtraction techniques the spectrum of a complex having three distinct ionization peaks at ~7 eV and an asymmetrical band at 9.2 eV in the low-energy region was obtained. This spectrum has been ascribed to $[CpMn(CO)_2NH_3]$. The assignment of these two bands is similar to that of the previous complexes.

As with $[CpMn(CO)_2N_2]$, the ionization energies of $[CpMn(CO)_2\text{-}NH_3]$ may be predicted from the calculations on $[CpMn(CO)_2NH_3]$ and $[CpMn(CO)_3]$ and the observed IE values of $[CpMn(CO)_3]$. In this case, however, serious discrepancies have been found and these were ascribed, by analogy with ab initio work on $[Cr(CO)_6]$ and $[Cr(CO)_5\text{-}NH_3]$, to Koopmans' defects. Thus it is assumed that relaxation and correlation effects are not of the same order in these related complexes. This is an important conclusion showing that great care should be taken in interpreting IE shifts and spectra of mixtures.

The isoelectric and isostructural compounds $[CpMn(CO)_3]$ and $[CpMn(CO)_2CS]$ have been studied by Lichtenberger et al. [55]. They concluded from the shifts in the IE values and their Fenske-Hall calculations that CS is not only a better π-back-bonding ligand but also that there is a larger interaction of the filled CS π orbitals with the metal electrons. This is reflected in the lower metal IE values in the thiocarbonyl complex. This same conclusion was reached in studies on $[Cr(CO)_5X]$ (X = CO, CS, CSe) [56].

The PE spectra of related, again isoelectronic complexes $[CpCr(CO)_2NO]$ and $[CpCr(CO)_2NS]$ have recently been reported [57]. The spectra are shown in Fig. 20.

The main ionization features are easily assigned by comparison with $CpMn(CO)_3$ and derivatives (see above). The bands between 7 and

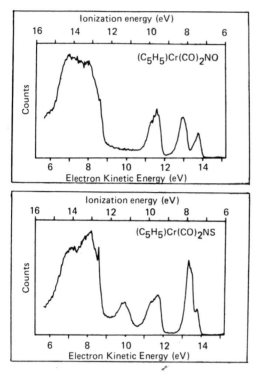

Figure 20 He(I) valence photoelectron spectra of [CpCr(CO)$_2$NO] and [CpCr(CO)$_2$NS]. (From Ref. 57.)

9 eV are associated with ionizations from metal d orbitals. The ionization band between 9 and 10 eV in each spectrum corresponds to the Cp e$_1''$ orbitals which interact with the metal. The NS complex has an additional band at ∿11.5 eV just before the onset of the broad, intense σ band. No particular assignment was given, but in view of the results for [CpMn(CO)$_2$CS] it was ascribed to an ioniza-tion from the NS fragment. Detailed cross-section studies should be carried out to reveal the exact nature of this band.

Assuming that Koopmans' defects are of the same order in [CpCr(CO)$_2$X] complexes, the differences in NO and NS orbital inter-actions with the metal are shown in Fig. 21. Just as in the [CpMn(CO)$_3$] ↔ [CpMn(CO)$_2$CS] comparison, the π* orbital of NS is

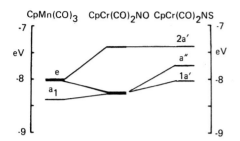

Figure 21 Changes in the ionization energies from [CpCr(CO)₃], [CpCr(CO₂NO], and [CpCr(CO)₂NS]. The symmetry labels indicated by the calculations. (From Ref. 57.)

lower in energy than the one of NO and accepts more electron density from the metal. A surprising feature in Fig. 21 is that even though the electronic interactions of NS and NO are appreciably different, the ionization associated with the 2a' orbital which is largely of S symmetry with respect to the ligand and which will consequently re- flect the effect of total charge distribution around the metal, does not significantly shift from the NO to the NS complex. The Fenske- Hall calculations on the ground states of these molecules agree with this observation and indicate that stabilization caused by removal of metal electron density by π back-bonding is offset by the greater electron density on nitrogen (sulfur is less electronegative than oxygen) and decreased metal back-bonding to the carbonyls.

Four independent reports [54,61,52] have appeared on [CpFe- (CO)₂X]-type systems in which X has been Cl, Br, I, CH_2CN, CH_3, and C_3H_5. Using substituent effects, spin-orbit couplings, metal vari- ation, and results from MO calculations, satisfactory assignments could be made and these are listed in Table 18.

In these d^6 systems the ionizations are well separated and the ordering of, for instance, [CpFe(CO)₂CH₃] is well established. At low IE values the metal d ionizations are found first, then the M-C ionizations, and finally the two nearly degenerate Cp ionizations. Symon and Waddington [61] have given another ordering reversing a metal ionization and the M-C ionization. This assignment is now

Table 19   Calculated Properties of Valence MOs of C_5H_5NiNO (a.u.)

Orbital	$<r^2>$	Calculated relaxation energy (eV)
$8e_1$	16.6	0.5
$7e_1$	9.7	1.9
$4e_2$	6.0	6.8
$15a_1$	5.5	6.6
$3e_2$	11.8	0.9
$14a_1$	9.6	1.0

Source: Ref. 64.

known to be incorrect since both comparisons with the other complexes [62] and intensity arguments [54] can be used to show that the third ionization must originate from the M-C orbital.

The various assignments of Symon and Waddington are partly based on an incorrect assignment for ferrocene and thus they may be expected to be incorrect in some details. In Ref. 62 a warning was given concerning the validity of the PE spectrum of $[Fe(CO)Cp]_4$ which can be attributed to decomposition products.

Complexes related to $CpMn(CO)_3$ have been investigated by Whitesides et al. using He(I) radiations and MO calculations [63]. In this study the cyclopentadienyl ring was replaced by other η^5 coordinating ring systems, such as $C_6H_7^-$, $C_7H_7^-$, and $C_7H_9^-$. The results are listed in Table 18. An elegant study by Evans et al. [64] on [CpNiNO] using ab initio techniques and He(I) PE spectroscopy represents an excellent example of a case where one needs guidance from accurate MO calculations. Severe breakdown of Koopmans' theorem was found. The ordering of the PE spectrum could be reproduced only by direct calculations on the hole states (ΔSCF technique). Larger orbital relaxations are associated with the localized metal orbitals rather than with the relatively delocalized ligand MOs.

Table 20   Ionization Energies and Assignments for $CpM(NO)_2X$ Complexes[a]

	M		
X	Cr	W	Assignment
Cl	8.17	8.03	12a''
	8.39	8.29	18a'
	9.18	9.05	17a'
	9.70	9.95	16a', 11a''
	10.26	10.63	10a'', 14a'
	10.72	11.61	15a'
Br	8.16	8.02	12a''
	8.41	8.34	18a'
	9.21	9.18	17a'
	9.66	9.75	16a'
	9.66	10.21	11a''
	10.31	11.00	15a', 10a'', 14a'
I	7.86	7.87	12a''
	8.22	8.24	18a'
	9.28	9.09	16a'
	9.28	9.34	17a'
	9.28	9.66	11a''
	9.88	10.44	15a'
	10.33	10.99	10a'', 14a'

[a]Estimated errors are ±0.05 eV.
Source: Ref. 180.

In an attempt to obtain a semiquantitative relationship between the spatial extent of a MO and the relaxation energy, they have computed expectation values of the second moment operator $<r^2>$ for the occupied MOs of the molecular ground state. In Table 19 it is shown that there is a very good correlation with the computed relaxation energy.

A. Recent Developments

Hall and co-workers have reported the He(I) spectra for $(\eta^5-C_5H_5)$-
$M(NO)_2X$, where $M = Cr$, W and $X = Cl$, Br, I. Assignments were made
using the Fenske-Hall MO method, spin-orbit couplings, and comparisons with related complexes. The IE values are listed in Table 20.
Although the complexes are formally d^6 [$M(0)$], it is proposed
--based on the similarity of the IE values of the Cr complexes to
those of the isoelectronic $(\eta^5-C_5H_5)Fe(CO)_2X$ complexes--that the
"metal" electrons are highly delocalized. The Fenske-Hall calculations support this view. Trends in reactivity were in agreement
with differences in the ionization energies.

Complexes of the type $[\eta^5-C_5H_{5-n}(CH_3)_n]M(CO)_3$, where $n = 0$, 1,
5 and $M = Mn$, Re have been published by Calabro et al. [181]. In
combining the use of core and valence photoelectron data a good description of bonding could be given. It is shown clearly that methyl
substitution of the cyclopentadienylring not only gives rise to
charge redistribution, but also that different valence-orbital overlap interactions are important. Extensions of the ring in (arene)-
$Cr(CO)_3$ complexes have been the subject of a study in Ref. 182.

VI. BENT BIS$(\eta^5$-CYCLOPENTADIENYL)ML$_n$ COMPLEXES

The rich chemistry of the bent bis$(\eta^5$-cyclopentadienyl)ML$_n$ complexes
provides us with many different types of molecules bearing ligands
such as NO, CO, olefines, alkyl and allyl groups, halides, and
hydrogen with a large variety of metals. There are several reports
on the PE spectra of the aforementioned molecules [65-72] and results from MO calculations are also available for several of them
[66,49]. From these studies it has become apparent that a unified
bonding scheme can account for bonding in these complexes. For the
description of bonding in these complexes, a molecules-in-molecules
approach was used by Lauher and Hoffmann [49]. These authors have
studied various classes of bent sandwich complexes on the basis of

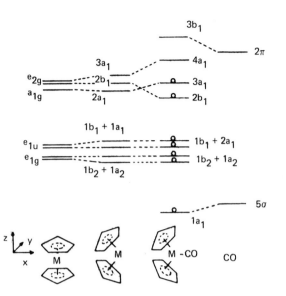

Figure 22   MO scheme for [Cp$_2$MoCO]. (From Ref. 65.)

Extended Hückel Type (EHT) MO calculations. Some aspects of their work, of relevance to the molecules treated here, will be discussed.

The molecules-in-molecules approach starts with the bending of a D$_{5d}$ metallocene and on letting the frontier orbitals thus created interact with the ligands. An example of this is shown in Fig. 22 for Cp$_2$MoCO.

The e$_{1g}$, e$_{1u}$ sets of Cp orbitals split to some extent (in C$_{2v}$ symmetry), yielding (b$_1$,a$_1$) and (b$_2$,a$_2$) combinations. This qualitative MO approach gives a fairly good account of bonding in these complexes.

The ordering of the metal orbitals and the orientation of the a$_1$ orbital was deduced from electron paramagnetic resonance (EPR) and crystallographic data [66]. From these latter data on d^0, d^1, and d^2 Cp$_2$ML$_2$ complexes, it appeared that the LML angle closed upon occupation of the lowest-lying metal orbital, and based on elementary electron repulsion considerations, it was concluded that the electrons came in an orbital that was orientated along the y axis.

EPR measurements on d^1 complexes gave a good characterization of
the singly occupied molecular orbital (SOMO), which can be regarded
as a d_{y^2} orbital [66]. Excellent agreement was found between these
results and the results from a nonparametrized Fenske-Hall MO calculation [66].

A large number of Cp_2ML_2 complexes have been studied with UPS
and the results are tabulated in Tables 21, 22, and 33. The assignments have been mostly made using cross-section arguments, except
for earlier work. A few examples of this class of complexes will
be treated here.

The most simple complexes to start with are the hydrides.
Green et al. [65] have published the He(I) spectra of Cp_2ReH,
Cp_2MoH_2, Cp_2WH_2, and Cp_2TaH_3. In these complexes the hydrogens are
assumed to lie in the yz plane and the molecules are assumed to
have C_{2v} symmetry. The symmetry-adapted combinations of H(1s)
orbitals appropriate for bonding to the Cp_2M unit are a_1 for H,
$a_1 + b_1$ for H_2, and $2a_1 + b_1$ for H_3. A correlation diagram for
these complexes is given in Fig. 23, which shows that the Re complex has two occupied d orbitals, Mo and W have only one and Ta has
none. This is clearly visible in the spectra (Fig. 24; Table 22).

The bands at very low IE values in the rhenium, molybdenum,
and tungsten complexes should originate from the metal, which is
concluded from their IE values and from the absence of these bands
in the d^0 complexes. The bands at 8-11 eV must in part be due to
ionization from the mainly Cp MOs. The varying complexity of these
bands in the different molecules indicates that ionization from the
M-H bonding orbitals also occurs in this region. This was also seen
on comparing analogous metal complexes.

Detailed assignments are not possible at the moment, since
He(II) spectra are lacking. Using cross-section variations it will
probably be very easy to distinguish between the Cp and the M-H
ionizations since it is known from other studies that the M-H orbitals have substantial H(1s) character. Thus a large intensity decrease is expected for the M-H orbitals.

Table 21 Vertical Ionization Energies (eV) of the Carbonyl, Olefin, and Allyl Complexes

[Cp₂MoCO]	[Cp₂Mo(C₂H₂)]	[Cp₂W(C₂H₂)]	[Cp₂W(C₂H₂)]	[Cp₂Nb(C₂H₂)]	Assignment C$_{2v}$	Assignment C$_2$
5.9	6.0	6.0	5.9	5.7	$3a_1$	$4a'$
6.8	6.9	7.1	7.0	8.0	$2b_1$	$3a''$
8.8	8.8	9.0	8.9	8.6	$2a_1 + 1b_2$	$2a' + 3a'$
9.3	9.2	9.3	9.5	9.2	$+ 1b_1 + 1a_2$	$+ 1a'' + 2a''$
9.6		9.5				
11.3	11.3	11.3	11.0		$1a_1$	$1a'$
12.6	12.6	12.5		13.0		
13.6	13.2	13.0	13.2	15.0		
16.8	17.0	16.7	16.9	16.9		

Source: Ref. 65.

Table 22 Vertical Ionization Energies (eV) of the Hydride and Methyl Complexes

[Cp$_2$ReH]	[Cp$_2$MoH$_2$]	[Cp$_2$WH$_2$]	[Cp$_2$TaH$_2$]	[Cp$_2$MoMc$_2$]	[Cp$_2$WMe$_2$]	Assignment
6.4	6.4	6.4	8.1	6.1	6.0	3a$_1$
7.0	8.9	8.9	8.7	8.3	8.3	2b$_1$
8.8	9.5	9.6	9.6	8.9	8.8	1a$_1$ + 1b$_2$
9.2					9.0	+ 2a$_1$ + 1b$_1$
9.9						
			10.6			
				9.6	9.6	1a$_1$
				11.3	11.3	CH$_2$
12.6	12.5	12.6	12.7	12.6	12.6	
13.4	13.5	13.7	13.5		13.3	
17.0	16.8	17.0	16.9	17.1	17.1	

Source: Ref. 65.

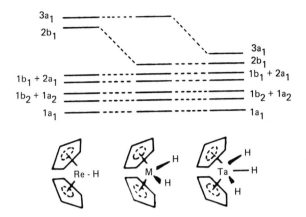

Figure 23   MO correlation diagram for $[Cp_2ReH]$, $[Cp_2MoH_2]$, and $[Cp_2TaH_3]$. (From Ref. 65.)

In the same paper Green et al. published the He(I) spectra of a series of carbonyl and olefin complexes: $[Cp_2Mo(CO)]$, $[Cp_2Mo-(C_2H_4)]$, $[Cp_2W(C_2H_4)]$, $[Cp_2W(C_3H_5)]$, and $[Cp_2Nb(C_3H_5)]$, which are reproduced in Fig. 25. The two metal d orbitals are again found at very low IE values. The first band is assigned to electron loss from the $3a_1$ orbital, its sharp profile indicating the nonbonding nature of the orbital. The second band has a shape indicating bonding character and is assigned to the $2b_1$ orbital. The stabilization of this orbital is ascribed to the π-back-bonding interaction of this orbital with empty $π^*$ orbitals on the CO and olefin ligands. Again the Cp ionizations are found in the region 8-10 eV. For the olefin complexes the assignments were based on comparison with the carbonyl complex. A new band at ∿11 eV is clearly seen in the ethylene complexes, which shifts to lower IE values upon methylation, and it is therefore tempting to assign this band to the π(C=C) orbital. However, this assignment contradicts the behavior found for the metal-olefin complexes [71], in which π back-bonding is very important. In these complexes the observed IE values of the π(C=C) orbitals are generally lower in the complex than in the free ligand. This is, of course, expected. π Back-bonding increases the charge

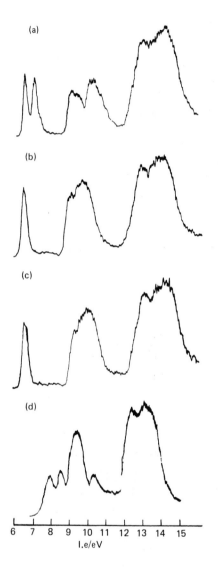

Figure 24   PE spectra of (a) [Cp$_2$ReH], (b) [Cp$_2$MoH], (c) [Cp$_2$WH$_2$], and (d) [CpTaH$_3$].   (From Ref. 65.)

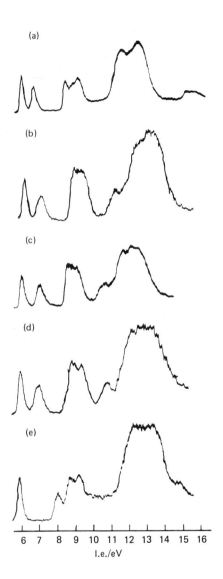

Figure 25   PE spectra of (a) $[Cp_2Mo(CO)]$, (b) $[Cp_2Mo(C_2H_4)]$, (c) $[Cp_2W(C_2H_4)]$, (d) $[Cp_2W(C_3H_5)]$, and (e) $[Cp_2Nb(C_3H_5)]$. (From Ref. 65.)

on the ligand, and thus the ligand MOs are destabilized (assuming
the validity of Koopmans' theorem). It must therefore be concluded
that the band at ∿11.0 eV does not originate from the $\pi(C=C)$ ionization. It probably is a $\sigma(CH)$ ionization which is strongly destabilized (12.40 → 11.0 eV in ethylene). The $\pi(C=C)$ ionization is
probably hidden under the Cp ionizations. Evidence for this is
found when we compare the CO and ethylene complexes. A distinct
intensity increase is seen in the Cp region upon going from the CO
to the C_2H_4 complex. Further evidence comes from a study on Cp_2Nb
and Ta carbonyl and olefin complexes in which by using substituent
effects and He(I)/He(II) cross-section changes, unambiguous assignments could be made [71]. The spectra of some of the complexes that
were studied are reproduced in Figs. 26 to 29.

The shifts upon methylation and variation of the metal are
small, but consistent assignments could be made using the following
presuppositions: First, it is assumed that methylation of the Cp
rings will mostly affect the Cp rings, while the other ligand orbitals are less influenced. Second, the other ligand orbitals are more
sensitive to metal variation than the Cp orbitals. These presuppositions appear, of course, self-evident, but in view of the small

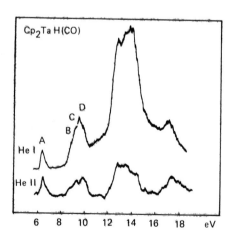

Figure 26 He(I) and He(II) spectra of $[Cp_2TaH(CO)]$. (From Ref. 71.)

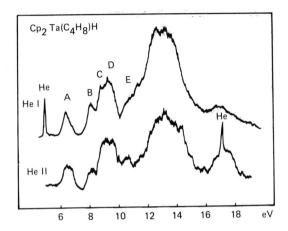

Figure 27   He(I) and He(II) spectra of $[Cp_2Ta(C_4H_8)H]$.   (From Ref. 71.)

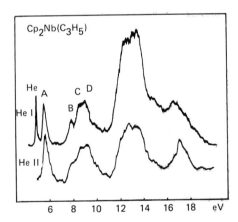

Figure 28   He(I) and He(II) spectra of $[Cp_2Nb(C_3H_5)]$.   (From Ref. 71.)

differences in IE between the complexes, only a few tenths of an electron volt, other assignment criteria should also be used. Thus in this study extensive comparisons with related complexes and He(I)/He(II) intensity differences were also used. Schematic MO interaction diagrams are shown in Fig. 30.

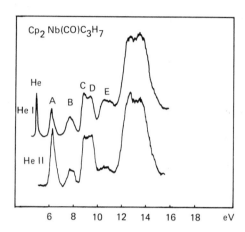

Figure 29   He(I) and He(II) spectra of $[Cp_2Nb(CO)(C_3H_7)]$. (From Ref. 71.)

Using the assignments listed in Table 33, several aspects of bonding in these complexes could be elucidated. It appears that π back-bonding is of very great importance in the carbonyl and olefin complexes. The $3a_1$ orbital (of Cp_2M in C_{2v} symmetry) can interact with the empty π^* orbitals of CO and the olefins, yielding a stabilization of the former orbital. Comparing the allyl complexes with the olefin (hydride) and carbonyl (alkyl) complexes the a_1 IE value is ~1 eV higher in the latter complexes, indicating that π back-bonding is of less importance in the allyl complexes. Regarding the alkyl complexes (Fig. 29), it is obvious that the metal d ionizations are at very low IE values. Then ionization occurs from the metal-alkyl ionization and then very nicely separated from the other ionizations are the $1b_1$ and $1b_2 + 1a_2$ cyclopentadienyl combinations. MO calculations predict that these latter orbitals have more metal character. This is confirmed by the He(I)/He(II) cross-section variation. The band at 6.1 eV in $[Cp_2TaC_3H_7(CO)]$ increases in intensity with respect to the 7.9-eV band on going from He(I) to He(II).

Cauletti et al. [69] have published He(I) and He(II) PE spectra of Cp_2MX_2-type systems. Observing the spectral variations on going

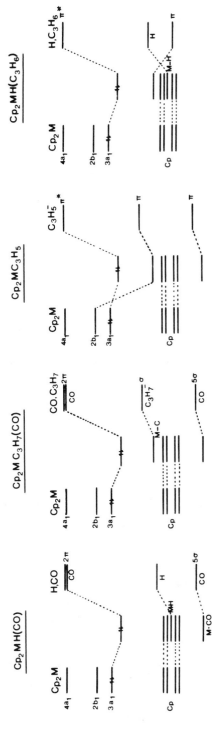

Figure 30 Correlation diagram for bent Cp_2ML_n complexes. (From Ref. 71.)

Table 23   Photoelectron Spectral Data of $Cp_2Ti(CO)_2$

IE (eV)	Assignment
6.35	Ti 3d
(6.63)	
(6.88)	
9.15	Cp π
12.67	Cp a_1 π
13.19	Cp σ(C-H)
13.61	Cp σ(C-C)
14.01	CO 5σ, 1π
16.87	Cp σ(C 2p)
17.30	
19.63	Cp σ(C 2s)
21.77	CO 4σ
23.91	-

Source: Ref. 72.

from He(I) to He(II), it appeared that halide and cyclopentadienyl π ionizations were sometimes strongly mixed, thus preventing detailed assignments.

Going further back in the first transition metal series, titanium can also form bent Cp_2MX_2 complexes. The UV-PE spectrum of the complex with X = CO has been published by Fragala et al. [72]. The assignment was straightforward using He(I)/He(II) differences and comparing analogous spectra. The data are shown in Table 23.

A.   Recent Developments

Böhm [183] has investigated the PE spectra of a series of bis(cyclopentadienyl)titanium dicarbonyl and dihalide complexes using a perturbational expansion based on the Green's function formalism within a semiempirical CNDO/INDO formalism. The theoretically determined "ionization energies" were compared with the available experimental data. Satisfactory assignments could be made using an

MO model which takes into account the interaction strength between the Cp π orbitals and the halide lone pair and σ coordinations (see Table 24).

In contrast to previous experience, it was found that Koopmans' theorem is a sufficient approximation for the assignments of the outer-valence ionization events. Using the theoretical scheme a reorganization energy for the occupied "Ti 3d" MO in $Cp_2Ti(CO)_2$ is found which is similar to the observed Koopmans' defects for the delocalized ligand orbitals.

This is in contrast with the findings on the extreme right of the 3d series (Fe, Co, Ni, and Cu), where the 3d orbitals are very localized, having very little metal-ligand overlap. Going to the left of the first transition series, the metal d orbitals appear to become more delocalized, leading to a situation where Koopmans' theorem can be used again. Green et al. have published the He(I) and the He(II) spectra for a large series of bis(η^5-cyclopentadienyl)-vanadium(III) halides, alkyls, and aryls $V(\eta^5\text{-}C_5H_5)_2X$, where X = Cl, Br, I, Me, CH_2SiMe_3, CH_2CMe_3, C_6F_5, C_6H_5, o-C_6H_4Me, m-C_6H_4Me, and 2,6-$C_6H_3Me_2$ [184]. Assignments (see Table 25) were based mainly on He(I)/He(II) intensity differences, trends in IE values, and a generalized MO scheme. Assignments were reasonably straightforward using these assignment criteria and in accordance with previous assignments on Nb and Ta complexes [65,68].

VII. METAL β-DIKETONATES AND RELATED COMPLEXES

Several studies of the PE spectra of metal β-diketonate complexes have been published. The complexes can be divided rather naturally into complexes with one, two, and three chelating groups, and these will be treated separately.

A. Metal Tris(β-Diketonates)

He(I) photoelectron spectra have been reported by Evans et al. [73, 74] for a variety of tris-chelates of the form ML_3, where L is commonly hexafluoroacetylacetone and M = Al, Ga, Sc, Ti, V, Cr, Co,

Table 24 Vertical Ionization Energies and Assignments[a] for Some bis(η^5-Cyclopentadienyl) Titanium Complexes

$Cp_2Ti(CO)_2$		Cp_2TiF_2		Cp_2TiCl_2		Cp_2TiBr_2	
6.62	Ti 3d$_{y^2}$	8.1	Cp(π), Ti 3d$_{xz}$	8.50	Cl(n), Cp(π)		Br(n), Cp(π) ⎫
	Cp(π), Ti 3d$_{xz}$	8.7	Cp(π)	8.90	Cl(n), Cp(π)		Br(n), Cp(π)
	Cp(π), Ti 3d$_{yz}$		Cp(π), Ti 3d$_{xy}$	9.10	Cl(n), Cp(π)	8.8 (max.)	Br(n), Cp(σ) ⎬
9.15	Cp(π), Ti 3d$_{xy}$	9.4	Cp(π), Ti 3d$_{y^2}$	9.90	Cp(π), Cl(n)		Br(n), Ti 3d$_{y^2}$
	Cp(π), Ti 3d$_{x^2-y^2}$	13 (max.)	Cp(π)	10.20	Cl(n),		TiBr(σ), Ti 3d$_{yz}$ ⎫
12.67	Cp(π)		F(n)	10.70	TiCl(σ)Cp	9.60	TiBr(σ) ⎬
13.19	Cp(σ)		Cp(σ)		Cp(π), Cl(n)	10.0	Cp(π), Ti 3d$_{xz}$, Br(n) ⎫
13.61	Cp(σ), Ti 3d$_{xy}$						Cp(π), Br(n), Ti 3d$_{y^2}$
14.01	Cp(σ), Ti 3d$_{xz}$					10.50	Cp(π), Ti 3d$_{x^2-y^2}$ ⎫
							Cp(σ), Ti 3d$_{xy}$
						12.30	Cp(σ) ⎫
							Cp(σ)
						13.70 (max.)	σpσ

[a]The assignments are approximate descriptions of orbital character.
Source: Ref. 183.

Table 25 Vertical Ionization Energies, Relative Band, Intensities, and Assignments for Bis(η^5-cyclopentadienyl)vanadium(III) Halides, Alkyls, and Aryls

Band	IE (eV)	$\omega_{1/2}^a$	Intensity He(I)	Intensity He(II)	Intensity ratio, He(I)/He(II)	Assignment
1. (η^5-Cp)$_2$VCl						
A'	6.80	0.36	1.07	1.03	0.96	$3b_1$
	7.42	0.28	0.93	0.97	1.04	$3a_1$
A"	8.29	0.42	4.1	0.95	0.23	Cl pπ
	9.47					
	9.81		22.4		0.41	Cp π + Cl pσ
	10.35					
B	12.8		64	32.6	0.51	Cp σ + Cp π
	13.2					
C	17.5					Cp σ
D	20.7					
	22.1					
2. (η^5-Cp)$_2$VBr						
A'	6.81	0.33	1.08	0.89	0.82	$3b_1$
	7.43	0.25	0.92	1.11	1.21	$3a_1$

Table 25 (Continued)

Band	IE (eV)	$\omega_{1/2}$	Intensity He(I)	Intensity He(II)	Intensity ratio, He(I)/He(II)	Assignment
A''	8.14	0.37	3.9	1.3	0.34	Br pπ
	8.90					
	9.37		16.3	9.9	0.61	Cp π + Br pσ
	10.07					
B	12.9		47.6	28.5	0.55	Cp σ + Cp π
	13.5					
C	17.6					Cp σ
			3.	$(\eta^5$-Cp) VI		
A'	6.71	0.31	1.06	0.90	0.84	$3b_1$
	7.33	0.21	0.93	1.10	1.17	$3a_1$
A''	7.69	0.22	3.6	0.61	0.17	I pπ "$2b_2$"
	8.30	0.28	3.1	0.37	0.12	I pπ "$2b_1$"
	9.02		13.1	6.3	0.48	Cp π + I pσ
	9.34					
B	12.85		49.8	36.4	0.73	Cp σ + Cp π
	13.3					
C	17.4					Cp σ
D	21.1					

4. $(\eta^5\text{-Cp})_2\text{VPh}$

					Assignment
A'	6.52	0.86		~1	$2b_1$
	6.83	1.14		~1	$4a_1$
A''$_1$	7.67	3.19	2.49	0.78	V–C σ
A''$_2$	8.53	16.9	13.9	0.82	Ar π
A''$_3$	9.13				Cp π
A''$_4$	11.02	8.2	5.1	0.62	Ar π + Ar σ
B	12.6	64.8	38.9	0.60	Ar σ + Cp σ + Cp π
C	13.5				Ar σ + Cp σ
D	17.55				
	21.7				

5. $(\eta^5\text{-Cp})_2\text{V}(2\text{-MeC}_6\text{H}_4)$

					Assignment
A'	6.51	0.84		~1	$2b_1$
	6.86	1.16		~1	$4a_1$
A''$_1$	7.55	3.25	2.45	0.75	V–C σ
A''$_2$	8.23	6.0	4.1	0.68	Ar π
A''$_3$	8.99	12.9	10.3	0.80	Cp π
A''$_4$	10.83	8.4	5.3	0.63	Ar π + Ar σ

Table 25 (Continued)

Band	IE (eV)	Intensity		Intensity ratio, He(I)/He(II)	Assignment
		He(I)	He(II)		
B	12.6	79	45		Ar σ + Cp σ + Cp π + Me σ
	13.0				
C	15.4				Ar σ + Cp σ + Me σ
	17.2				
D	21.5				
6. $(\eta^5\text{-Cp})_2 V(3\text{-MeC}_6\text{H}_4)$					
A'	6.52	0.69	0.71	1.03	$2b_1$
	6.83	1.31	1.29	0.98	$4a_1$
A''_1	7.56	2.7	2.0	0.74	V–C σ
A''_2	8.18	5.5	3.1	0.57	Ar π
A''_3	8.99	12.6	9.2	0.73	Cp π
A''_4	10.83	8.0	4.4	0.55	Ar π + Ar σ
B	12.6				
B	13.1	124	47	0.38	Ar σ + Cp σ + Cp π + Me σ
C	15.6				Ar σ + Cp σ + Me σ
	17.2				
D	21.4				
	22.1				

[a]Full width at half height (eV).
Source: Ref. 184.

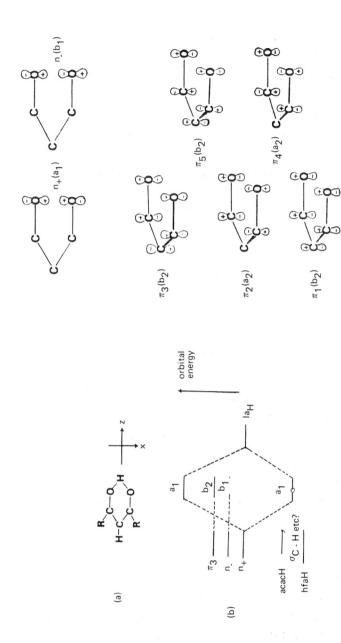

Figure 31 (Left) (a) Structure of the enol form of a β-diketone; (b) a molecular orbital diagram. (Right) π MOs and lone-pair combinations for the enol form. (From Ref. 73.)

Mn, Fe, and Ru. The spectra of some complexes with L = trifluoroacetylacetone and acetylacetone have also been published. It is
well known that acetylacetone (Hacac) exists in the vapor phase in
the enol form, which is approximately the same as in metal complexes.
The upper valence orbitals of which the ordering was determined with
UPS can thus be transferred to the metal complexes, and a simple MO
diagram can be constructed for the tris-chelates.

Relevant ligand orbitals for this bonding scheme are π_3, n_- and
n_+, of which pictorial representations are given in Fig. 31. In the
tris-chelates the ligand orbitals combine to new symmetry orbitals:

β-Diketonate orbital	Tris-chelate symmetry orbital
π^*	$e + a_2$
n_-	$e + a_2$
n_+	$e + a_2$

These orbitals can then combine with metal d orbitals of the appropriate symmetry Using a simple orbital interaction model, Evans et
al. (see Fig. 32) have rationalized bonding in these complexes.
According to their analysis the major source of bonding lies in the
interaction of $e(d_{x^2-y^2}, d_{xy})$ and the $e(n_+)$, $e(n_-)$ ligand symmetry
orbitals and only a small interaction is expected of the metal a_1
and $e(d_{xz}, d_{yz})$ orbitals with the ligands. Also, the interaction
between $e(\pi_3)$ and the $e(d)$ orbitals is expected to be very small.
It is obvious that the a_2 ligand orbitals cannot interact with the
metal orbitals.

Using this schematic MO approach and applying Koopmans' theorem
yielded very satisfactory assignments of most of the bands in the
lower IE regions of the spectra, the only matter of some controversy
remaining being the relative positions of the d bands and the ligand
bands in some of the complexes. Evans [73] and Brittain [75] have,
for instance, interpreted the PE spectra of Co(β-diketone)$_3$, with

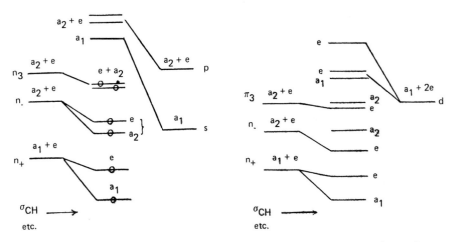

Figure 32   A molecular orbital diagram showing the interaction of the tris ligand system with metal s and p valence orbitals (left) or with metal d orbitals (right). [The metal d orbitals transform as $e(d_{x^2-y^2}, d_{xy})$, $e(d_{xz}, d_{yz})$, and $a_1(d_{z^2})$ in D_3 symmetry.]   (From Ref. 73.)

slightly different assignments. Both sets of assignments agree that the bands of $Co(acac)_3$ found at 8.99 eV and 9.54 eV are due to ionization from the n_- orbital combinations and that the band at 10.37 eV is due to n_+ orbital combinations. Both interpretations also assign the second band at 8.09 eV to a combination of metal d electrons and ligand-localized π_3 orbitals. Based on extrapolated trends in the PE spectra of the tris-chelates, Evans assigned the first band of $Co(acac)_3$ at 7.52 eV to a ligand-localized π_3 orbital and the third band at 8.55 eV to metal d ionization.

By comparison with several bis-chelates, Brittain [75] arrived at the reverse assignment. This controversy was solved when the He(I) and He(II) spectra of a limited series of ML_3 complexes were published [76] and it was concluded, on the basis of cross-section variations, that the main metal contribution was in the first band at 7.52 eV in $Co(acac)_3$ (Fig. 33). The He(II) spectra of $V(acac)_3$ and $Cr(acac)_3$ were also published as a check for the validity of the use of He(I)/He(II) intensity effects in this class of complexes.

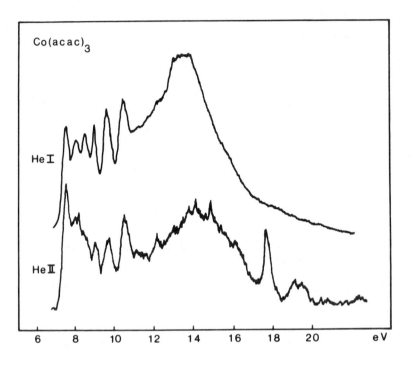

Figure 33   He(I) and He(II) spectra of Co(acac)$_3$.   (From Ref. 76.)

Brittain [75] has studied a series of cobalt acetylacetonates
in which the ring hydrogen "para" to the metal has been replaced by
Cl, Br, and NO_2 (see Table 26). This was done to probe the extent
of theoretically possible metal-to-ligand π bonding. It is well
known that chlorine and bromine are inductively withdrawing substituents while at the same time they can also donate π-electron density through a resonance interaction with the π system. The a_2 and
$e(\pi_3)$ orbitals are split by 0.46 eV in Co(acac)$_3$, but this gap widens
to 0.63 eV in the chlorine- and bromine-substituted analogs, showing
clearly the interaction of Cl with the ring π system. In the case
of a π interaction between the metal and the chelate ring, the IE of
the metal orbitals should decrease upon chlorine and bromine substitution, using the elementary principles mentioned above.

Table 26   Vertical Ionization Potentials for γ-Substituted
Acetylacetonate Complexes

Band	$Co(acac)_3$	$Co(acac-Cl)_3$	$Co(acac-Br)_3$	$Co(acac-NO_2)_3$
d	7.52	7.59	7.58	8.51
π	8.09	8.05	8.04	8.86
π	8.55	8.68	8.67	9.27
n_-	8.99	9.11	9.14	9.45
n_-	9.54	9.62	9.64	10.16
n_+	10.37	10.46	10.50	10.96
n_+	-	-	-	11.20
Halogen lone pair	-	11.44	10.50	-
Halogen lone pair	-	-	11.17	-

Source: Ref. 75.

The ionization energy of the d band found at 7.52 eV in
$Co(acac)_3$ is increased to $\sim$7.6 eV in the halogenated chelates. This
type of behavior resembles that of an orbital incapable of interaction with the ligand π system, and thus Brittain et al. concluded
that in the metal-chelate bonding, no strong π interactions are
present. This same conclusion was reached by ourselves in a study
on β-diketonate Rh and Ir carbonyl and olefin complexes [77]. From
extended CNDO/2 calculations on model complexes it could be concluded that the energy gap between the metal and the ring orbitals is
too large for significant interactions.

B.   Metal (β-Diketonate)$_2$ Complexes

A large number of divalent metal β-diketonates have been reported
with a variety of β-diketones (e.g., tetramethylheptanedione,
acetylacetone, trifluoroacetylacetone, hexafluoroacetyleacetone,
and various sulfur analogs). Metals used were Be, Mg, Al, Cr, Co,
Ni, Cu, and Zn [78-81]. Brittain and Disch [78] have done CNDO/2

calculations on $Mg(dfm)_2$ (dfm = diformylmethanideanion) both in tetrahedral (D_{2d}) and square-planar (D_{2h}) symmetry. Cotton et al. [82] have done Extended Hückel Type (EHT) calculations on the model compounds $Ni(dfm)_2$ and $Cu(dfm)_2$ (D_{2h} symmetry). These calculations give results which are in qualitative agreement with each other. They are also in general agreement with results from a qualitative MO approach similar to the one presented for the ML_3 complexes, of which the results are given in Fig. 32. The main difficulty remains in predicting the relative ordering of some of the levels. Unfortunately, the experimental results published in the literature help very little in solving this difficulty. There are several spectra of, for instance, $Ni(acac)_2$ in the literature, but they hardly resemble each other, and furthermore the cross-section variations upon changing from He(I) to He(II) radiation, which have been published by two groups [80,81], change in each paper. Both agree that the first ionization originates from a ligand orbital, and Cauletti et al. [80] assign the second band partly to metal d ionizations. Fragala [81], however, claims that metal d ionizations should occur in the region 11-12 eV. (This is based partly on an erroneous interpretation of his CNDO results.) It has been shown throughout the literature that relaxation of localized metal d orbitals can be as large as $\sim$10 eV and the use of a fixed correction of 3 eV is therefore incorrect.

However, it is also possible, based on the (poorly reproduced!) spectra, to come to the conclusion that the first band also contains a significant amount of metal character. Therefore, the assignments for these complexes are unreliable, and we only give the measured IE values in Table 27 without any assignment. In Ref. 185 the He(I) and He(II) spectra of a series of $M^{II}(sacac)_2$en complexes were published (see Table 28).

C. Other Metal β-Diketonates

Only a few examples of mono-β-diketonate complexes have appeared. Evans [73] have published the He(I) spectrum of $[(hfa)Mn(CO)_4]$ (hfa = hexafluoroacetylacetone) and van Dam et al. [77] have published He(I) and He(II) spectra of an extensive series of β-diketonate ML_2

Table 27   Ionization Energy Data (eV) for Some Bis(β-Diketonate) Complexes[a]

Compound									
AAH					9.1_5	9.7_5			
Ni(AA)$_2$	7.4_0	7.9_0	8.1_5	8.4_0	8.7_5	9.2_5		10.0_5	
Ni(AAS)$_2$	7.0_0	(7.5_5)	7.6_5	8.4_5	8.8_5	9.4_5		9.8_5	
Ni(AAS$_2$)$_2$	6.9_0	(7.6_5)	7.7_5	8.3_0	8.9_0	9.2_5	9.7_0	10.0_5	
Cu(AA)$_2$	8.3_5				8.7_0	9.3_0	(9.9_5)	10.4_0	(10.7_0)
Cu(AAS)$_2$	7.6_5				(8.6_5)	9.1_5	(9.5_5)	10.7_5	
Cu(TAA)$_2$	8.9_5				9.4_0	9.9_5	(10.8_5)	11.1_5	(11.5_0)
Cu(HAA)$_2$	10.2_0				10.6_0	11.1_0		12.2_0	
Co(AA)$_2$			8.5_0			9.9_0	10.5_5	10.8_5	
Co(AAS)$_2$	7.5_0				8.7_0	9.5_5		10.7_5	
Co(AAS$_2$)$_2$	7.2_0		7.6_5	(8.2_0)	8.4_5	(9.5_0)	9.7_0	10.2_5	
Co(TAA)$_2$			9.3_5				10.5_0	11.2_5	(11.7_5)
Al(TAA)$_3$					9.22	10.35		11.49	
Ni(TAA)$_2$	8.25	(8.75)			8.92	9.30	9.65	10.05	10.98
Ni(TAAS)$_2$	7.80		8.51		9.28	9.58	10.33	10.88	
Ni(TAAS$_2$)$_2$	7.65	(8.38)	8.58		9.08	9.38	9.98	10.36	10.68

[a]Shoulders in parentheses. AA, acetylacetone; AAS, monothioacetyl-acetone; AAS$_2$, dithioacetylacetone; TAA, trifluoroacetylacetone; TAAS, monothiotrifluoroacetylacetone; TAAS$_2$, dithiotrifluoroacetyl-acetone.
Source: Ref. 80.

complexes in which M = Rh, Ir and L = CO, ethylene, propylene. The latter alkene complexes will be treated in Sec. VIII (olefin com-plexes).

The He(I) spectrum of $(CO)_4Mn(hfa)$ [73] is shown in Fig. 34. The assignment of this complex is very simple, band Y is assigned, based on both its IE and intensity, to the metal 3d orbitals (correlating with t_{2g}^6 in octahedral symmetry) and bands A, B, and C must be assigned to the π_3, n_-, and n_+ ionizations, respectively, from the hfa ligand. The ordering is based on the ordering in the free ligand.

Table 28   Vertical Ionization Energies (eV) of Some N,N'-Ethylenebis(thioacetone-iminato) Complexes[a]

Complex	Ionization energy									
$H_2[(sacac)_2en]$					7.6_0		9.5_5	11.3_5		13.7_0
$Ni[(sacac)_2en]$	6.5_5	7.3_0	7.8_0	8.1_5	(8.5_5)	8.8_5	9.7_0	10.6_0	12.3_0	13.2_0
$Pd[(sacac)_2en]$	6.7_0	7.5_5	7.9_5	8.3_5	8.6_5	9.1_0	(10.0_5)	11.1_5		13.7_5
$Co[(sacac)_2en]$	6.5_0	7.1_5	(7.5_0)	7.8_0	(8.6_0)	9.1_0	(9.3_5)	10.7_5	12.3_5	13.5_0
$Cu[(sacac)_2en]$	6.3_5	7.0_0		7.5_0	8.1_0	9.0_5	9.6_5	11.3_5	12.6_5	13.5_0

[a]Shoulders in parentheses.
Source: Ref. 185.

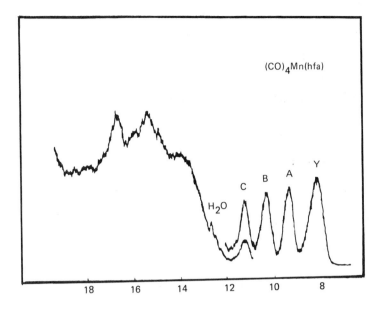

Figure 34   PE spectrum of $(CO)_4Mn(hfa)$.   (From Ref. 73.)

D. Recent Developments

Kitigawa et al. [186] have made assignments using the metal dependence of the IE values in a series of $M(acac)_2$ complexes (M = Mn, Co, Ni, Cu, and Zn). They found the order $d < \pi_3 < n_- < n_+$ (IE) to hold for all complexes measured.

VIII. OLEFIN COMPLEXES

Metal π complexes continue to be of interest both because of their theoretical interest and of their practical applications. Metal olefin complexes are involved in homogeneous and heterogeneous catalytic processes such as hydrogenation, isomerization, polymerization, and so on, of olefins. Excellent reviews have appeared on this subject [83]. For an understanding of catalytic behavior, detailed information concerning bonding is of crucial importance. Especially the fundamental study of model systems, small molecules with resemblance to postulated intermediates, has proved fruitful [83a].

Also from a theoretical point of view, bonding in metal-olefin complexes is very interesting. Until 1951 there was no satisfactory explanation for bonding between the olefinic ligand and transition metals. Then Dewar [84] showed that interaction between antibonding orbitals on the olefin and orbitals on the metal is mainly responsible for the surprising stability of silver-olefin complexes. Chatt and Duncanson [85] applied Dewar's description to Zeise's salt, and their account of the bonding between platinum and the ethylene molecule is now generally accepted.

Overlap between the filled ethylene π orbital and one of the vacant platinum $5d6s6p^2$ hybrid orbitals results in σ bonding between the metal and the olefin. The resultant charge flow from olefin to metal is then compensated by a π back-donation of electrons to the olefin π^* orbital (π back-donation).

Bonding in a number of metal-olefin complexes has been investigated using molecular orbital (MO) calculations and ultraviolet photoelectron spectroscopy (UPS). In particular, iron tetracarbonyl olefin complexes have received attention. Baerends et al. [86] published the DV-X_α results for $Fe(CO)_4 C_2 H_4$. In Ref. 87 the correct He(I) spectrum has been published. Now very good agreement is shown to exist between experiment and the results from the DV-X_α calculations (see Table 29).

Flamini et al. [88] have published the He(I) PE spectra of $Fe(CO)_4$(acrylonitrile) and $Fe(CO)_4$(acrolein). The spectrum of the latter complex, which was totally different from that published in Ref. 89, in reality originates from benzene, which was probably used as a solvent.

Hill et al. [90] have published the He(I) spectrum of $Fe(CO)_4$-tetramethylallene. An assignment was given, based on comparisons with $Fe(CO)_3$(diene) complexes. Four ionizations are found, at 7.84 8.24, 8.5, and 9.28 eV, of which the first two are assigned to ionizations originating from the metal atom. The last two are assigned as ionizations from the tetramethylallene ligand. The assignment should be viewed with caution. It is based on only one

Table 29   Ionization Potentials and Assignments of $Fe(CO)_4$ethylene

DV-X_α [86]	IP[a] (eV)	Assignment
7.6, 8.0	8.38	$3d_{xy}$, $3d_{x^2-y^2}$
8.8, 9.1		
	9.23	$3d_{xz}$, $3d_{yz}$
10.1	10.56 (10.51)	$\pi(C=C)$
10.1	12.48 (12.45)	$\sigma(CH)$
11.9	14-16	CO and olefin orbitals

[a]The values in parentheses are for free ethylene.
Source: Ref. 87.

He(I) spectrum and a comparison with $Fe(CO)_3$(diene)-type molecules, and it is in contrast with results from an extensive series of iron tetracarbonyl olefin complexes which have been investigated thoroughly using He(I) and He(II) radiation (see below). It would be the only case where a stabilization of the olefin levels on complexation is observed [which is normal for $Fe(CO)_3$(diene)-type molecules], where in all other cases destabilizations are observed. Recently, Böhm [196] reinterpreted this spectrum using INDO calculations.

The He(I) and He(II) photoelectron spectra of a series of iron tetracarbonyl olefin complexes [89] and some corresponding olefins have been reported [91]. The spectra of the olefins are assigned using He(I) and He(II) cross-section variations, the application of a localized orbital sum rule, vibrational progressions, and substituent effects [89]. A comparison was made of results from several MO schemes for acrolein and as a result of this, the CNDO/S scheme was selected for the interpretation of the spectra of all the olefins. Using all the aforementioned assignment criteria, assignments could be given for most of the bands.

Using results of this study, the spectra of the iron tetracarbonyl olefin complexes were interpreted as shown in Table 30. In general, destabilizations were found of the olefin levels upon

complexation and this was interpreted in terms of important π-
back-bonding contributions. Extended CNDO calculations confirmed
this view and a relationship was found between the calculated charge
on the olefin and CO stretching frequencies which are held to be a
measure of the amount of M → CO π back-bonding. It this appears
that changes in metal-olefin π back-bonding are compensated by
changes in metal-carbonyl bonding, while the metal is hardly affected. The CNDO/2 scheme worked surprisingly well in predicting the
destabilizations of the various levels upon coordination.

In Ref. 77 some aspects of the bonding in (β-diketonate)Rh(I)
and Ir(I) bis-carbonyl and bis-olefin complexes are discussed.
He(I) and He(II) PE spectra of a large series of complexes were
recorded and several regular trends emerged which were interpreted
in terms of bonding interactions (Tables 31 and 32). In these complexes π back-bonding to the olefin is of considerable importance.
Upon the introduction of a substituent into a ligand, the electronic
effect of the substituent affects the whole molecule. CNDO/S calculations suggest that this is caused by low-lying orbitals which are
delocalized over the entire molecule. The stabilization of the
ligand orbitals on going from rhodium to iridium can indicate that
σ bonding becomes more important in the iridium complexes.

In Ref. 72 an analysis is given of bonding in bis(η^5-cyclo-
pentadienyl)niobium and tantalum olefin(hydride), alkyl(carbonyl),
carbonyl(hydride), and allyl complexes. For the IE values measured
see Table 33. The information obtained from comparing He(I) and
He(II) spectra proved of great importance in the probing of relative amounts of metal character. For the olefin complexes that have
been studied it has been concluded that π back-bonding is very important and the familiar σ bonding π back-bonding scheme should be
preferred above the alternative metallocyclopropane scheme. π Back-
bonding is very important in the olefin and carbonyl complexes,
whereas in the allyl complexes it is of less importance. Much work
has been done on $M(CO)_3$(diene) (M = Fe, Ru)-type complexes, especially in the period 1969-1976 [92,93]. In particular, the work on

$Fe(CO)_3$(butadiene), $Fe(CO)_3$(cyclobutadiene), and $Fe(CO)_3$(trimethyl-enemethane) has been of considerable interest. The assignments of these molecules were made using results from ab initio calculations [94-96] and here it seems that relaxation energies are underestimated using the ΔSCF method. Later, Green et al. [97] published the He(I) and He(II) PE spectra of a series of Fe and Ru diene complexes, verifying the earlier assignments.

Recently, Worley et al. have published the He(I) spectra of a series of $Fe(CO)_3$(diene) complexes, together with results for the free ligands [98]. Focusing especially on π perturbation energies upon complexation, estimates were made of the π IE values of the organic transient species cyclobutadiene (8.29 and 11.95 eV) and trimethylenemethane (8.36 and 11.79 eV), two novel molecules that have not been studied by UPS to date.

The He(I) PE spectra of several bis(1,3-diene)monocarbonyl iron complexes have been published by Böhm and Gleiter. The assignment of the first seven bands is based on INDO calculations using the ΔSCF procedure and the "transition operator" model. Relaxation energies up to $\sim$4 eV were found for the iron d states. Bonding in these complexes was discussed [99].

Böhm and Gleiter followed the same procedure, measuring the He(I) spectrum of tricarbonylcyclooctatetraene iron [100]. The first band arises mostly from 3d orbitals, the next two bands are from admixtures of COT π orbitals and 3d orbitals, and the last two bands are from orbitals located on the COT ligand.

A. Recent Developments

Recently, Böhm published results from INDO calculations on $Fe(CO)_3$-(norbornadiene) [187]. Large reorganization energies were found for the metal 3d orbitals, indicating a dramatic breakdown of Koopmans' theorem. $Fe(CO)_3(\eta^4$-cyclobutadiene) has been studied by Kostic and Fenske [188] using SW-X$_\alpha$ MO calculations for the interpretation of the spectra. A reasonable agreement with experiment was found using the transition-state half-electron method.

Table 30 Ionization Potentials and Assignments for Fe(CO)$_4$ Olefin Complexes[a,b,c]

	Olefin			
Assignment	Acrolein	Crotonaldehyde	Acrylic acid	Methyl acrylate
Fe 3d$_{xy}$	8.69	8.60	8.66	8.50
3d$_{x^2-y^2}$	9.42 (sh)	9.36 (sh)	9.36	9.28
3d$_{yz}$	9.24 (sh)	9.36 (sh)	9.36	9.28
3d$_{xz}$				
Olefin π (C=C)	10.76 (10.94)	10.35 (10.38)	10.57 (10.95)	10.80 (10.74)
n$_0$(a')	9.67 (10.11)	9.59 (9.73)	10.29 (10.78)	10.50 (11.20)
n$_0$(a'')			11.66 (12.00)	12.55
Various substituent orbitals	σ(CH) 12.9 (13.67)	σ(CH) 12.6 (13.06)	σ(CH) 12.9 (13.54)	σ(CH) 12.9 (13.39)

	Olefin			
Assignment	Dimethyl maleate	1,1-Dichloro-ethylene	trans-1,2-Dichloro-ethylene	trans-1,2,Dibromo-ethylene
Fe 3d$_{xy}$	8.68	8.82	8.72	8.74
3d$_{x^2-y^2}$				
3d$_{yz}$	9.31	9.51	9.49 (sh)	9.45 (sh)
3d$_{xz}$				

Olefin π(C=C)	$10.1\text{-}11.0^d$ (10.3-11.2)	9.98 (17.96)	9.7-9.9 (9.80)	9.61 (9.55)
Various substituent orbitals	$n_{Cl}(a')$ 11.05 (11.65)	$n_{Cl}(a')$ 11.45 (11.90)		$n_{Br}(a')$ 10.71 (11.04)
	$n_{Cl}(a')$ 11.56 (12.14)	$n_{Cl}(a'')$ 12.0^e (12.61)		$n_{Br}(a'')$ 11.28 (11.57)
	$n_{Cl}(a'')$ 12.05 (12.54)			σ(C-Br) 12.30 (12.90)
	σ(C-Cl) 13.28 (13.7)			$n_{Br}(a'')$ 12.63 (13.3)
	$n_{Cl}(a'')$ 13.91 (14.24)			

[a] Only assignments of the Fe 3d orbitals and some of the olefin bands are given.
[b] Symmetry annotations are for the corresponding orbitals in the free ligands [91].
[c] The values in parentheses are the ionization potentials for the free ligands.
[d] Unresolved bands; see the text.
[e] Uncertainty in IPs is due to partial decomposition.
Source: Ref. 89.

Table 31 Vertical Ionization Energies of (β-Diketonate) RhL_2 ($L = CO$, C_2H_4, C_3H_6)[a]

	Metal d orbitals				Diketonate orbitals			Olefin orbital
	$14a_1$	$5b_2$	$13a_1$	$4a_2$	$4b_1(\pi_3)$	$11b_2(n_-)$	$12a_1(n_+)$	
(tmh)Rh(CO)₂		8.27	(9.4)		9.4		(10.8)	
(acac)Rh(CO)₂		8.52	(9.5)		(9.84)	10.01	11.22	
(tfa)Rh(CO)₂		9.04	(9.6)			10.50	11.74	

	$6b_1$	$14a_1$	$5a_2$	$13a_1$	$5b_1(\pi_3)$	$10b_2(n_-)$	$12a_1(n_+)$	$9b_2$
(tmh)Rh(C₂H₄)₂	7.50	7.94			8.93		(10.5)	10.01
(acac)Rh(C₂H₄)₂	7.54	8.11			8.94	9.33	10.76	10.22
(tfa)Rh(C₂H₄)₂	7.96	8.56	(8.7)	(8.8)	9.44	9.79	11.21	10.64
(hfa)Rh(C₂H₄)₂	8.34	9.06			9.94	10.32	11.78	11.07
(tmh)Rh(C₃H₆)₂	7.27	7.76			8.70		10.18	9.68
(acac)Rh(C₃H₆)₂	7.43	7.92			(8.8)	9.13	10.51	9.85

[a]Symmetry assignment and numbering are taken from the CNDO calculations on the [acacCo(CO)₂] and [acacCo(C₂H₄)₂] complexes; shoulders in the spectra are indicated by the parenthetical values.
Source: Ref. 77.

Table 32   Vertical Ionization Energies of (β-Diketonate)IrL$_2$ (L = CO, C$_2$H$_4$, C$_3$H$_6$)[a]

	Metal d orbitals				Diketonate orbitals			Olefin orbital
	14a$_1$	5b$_2$	13a$_1$	4a$_2$	4b$_1$(π_3)	11b$_2$(n$_-$)	12a$_1$(n$_+$)	
(tmh)Ir(CO)$_2$	8.20	8.48	9.09	9.62	9.89		(11.3)	
(acac)Ir(CO)$_2$	8.42	8.69	9.25	9.94	9.94	10.34	11.63	
(tfa)Ir(CO)$_2$	8.75	9.17	9.71	10.45	10.97		12.31	
(hfa)Ir(CO)$_2$	9.14	9.26	10.17	(10.9)	10.91	11.42	12.69	
	6b$_1$	14a$_1$	5a$_2$	13a$_1$	5b$_1$(π_3)	10b$_2$(n$_-$)	12a$_1$(n$_+$)	9b$_2$
(tmh)Ir(C$_2$H$_4$)$_2$	7.32	7.76	8.17	8.79	9.12		n.o.[b]	(10.3)
(acac)Ir(C$_2$H$_4$)$_2$	7.36	7.83	8.37	8.86	(9.35)	9.51	11.24	10.41
(tfa)Ir(C$_2$H$_4$)$_2$	7.70	8.17	8.80	9.25	9.79	10.05	11.54	10.90
(acac)Ir(C$_3$H$_6$)$_2$	7.15	7.60	8.15	8.59	(9.05)	9.29	10.56	10.01
(tfa)Ir(C$_3$H$_6$)$_2$	7.57	7.99	8.61	8.99	9.54	9.71	11.01	10.36

[a]Symmetry assignment and numbering are taken from the CNDO calculations on the [acacCo(CO)$_2$] and [acacCo(C$_2$H$_4$)$_2$] complexes; shoulders in the spectra are indicated by the parenthetical values.

[b]Not observed due to severe crowding of orbitals.

Source: Ref. 77.

Table 33   Ionization Energies

(a)

	$Cp_2HbC_3H_7(CO)$	$Cp_2IaC_3H_7(CO)$	$(MeCp)_2TaC_3H_7(CO)$	Assignment
A	6.2	6.1	6.0	Metal d, $[+ \pi^*(CO)]$
B	7.7	7.9	7.8	M-C
C	8.8	8.9	8.7	Cp
D	9.4	9.5	9.3	Cp
E	10.6	10.6	10.4	$C_3H_7 [\sigma(CH)]$
	(11.2)	(11.0)	(10.9)	

(b)

	$Cp_2TaH(CO)$	Assignment
A	6.3	Metal d
B	(8.8)	Cp
C	(9.4)	Cp, M-H
D	9.6	

(c)

	$Cp_2TaH(C_3H_6)$	$Cp_2TaH(C_4H_8)$	$(MeCp)_2TaH(C_4H_8)$	Assignment
A	6.5	6.4	6.3	Metal d $[+ \pi^*(C=C)]$
B	8.2	8.0	8.0	$\pi(C=C)$
C	9.0	8.8	8.6	Cp

				Cp, M-H
D	9.5	9.4	9.2	
E	(9.6)	(9.5)	(9.4)	

(d)

	Cp$_2$Nb(C$_3$H$_5$)	(MeCp)$_2$Nb(C$_3$H$_5$)	Cp$_2$Ta(C$_3$H$_5$)	(MeCp)$_2$Ta(C$_3$H$_5$)	Assignment
A	5.5	5.5	5.6	5.5	Metal d
B	7.8	7.8	(8.0)	(7.9)	Allyl n.b. π
C	8.6	8.3	8.6	8.4	Cp
D	9.1	8.9	9.2	8.9	Cp
E	(9.4)	(9.5)	(9.6)	(9.7)	Allyl

(e)

	Cp$_2$NbCl$_2$	(MeCp)$_2$NbCl$_2$	Cp$_2$TaCl$_2$	(MeCp)$_2$TaCl$_2$	Assignment
A	6.8	6.5	6.4	6.2	$a_1 d^1 (a_1)$
B	(8.7)	(8.5)	(8.8)	(8.6)	Cp, M-Cl
C	9.0	8.9	9.2	9.0	
D	10.2	9.8	10.1	9.8	Cp
E	(10.5)	(10.4)	(10.5)	(10.5)	n_{Cl}, M-Cl
F	10.9	10.9	11.1	11.1	

Source: Data from Ref. 72.

The description of bonding in (cyclobutadiene)Fe(CO)$_3$ that
emerges from this study and from the previous Hartree-Fock study
[96] differ in two respects: the high-lying MOs, crucial for bonding, are significantly more delocalized in the SW-Xα calculations
than in the Hartree-Fock calculations and the SW-Xα eigenvalues of
these MOs lie within 1.0 eV, whereas corresponding Hartree-Fock
eigenvalues constitute two sets separated by 4.6 eV.

The UV photoelectron spectra of Mo(butadiene)$_3$ and W(butadiene)$_3$
have been recorded [189] and assigned with the assistance of extended
Hückel calculations. Substantial metal-to-ligand electron transfer
is indicated. Using the He(I)-He(II) cross-section considerations,
it is indicated that the highest occupied MOs are delocalized on the
ligands. Extensive back-donation should lead to an equalization of
the C-C distances in the coordinated ligands. A structure determination confirms this effect [189].

The He(I) PE spectra of several norbornadiene complexes have
been published by Worley and Webb [190]. Varying the metal from Fe
to Mo and Cr hardly affected the olefin IE values. Also, the He(I)
spectra for Cr(CO)$_3$mesitylene and Mo(CO)$_3$mesitylene were published
[190].

The He(I) PE spectra of the endo, exo, endo-exo, and di-exo iron
tricarbonyl complexes of 2,3,5,6-tetrakis(methylene)-7-oxabicyclo-
[2.2.1] heptane have been studied by Granozzi et al. [191]. The
spectral evidence indicates that there is a stronger interaction between Fe(CO)$_3$ and the butadiene moiety in the endo isomer than in
the exo isomer. This might be attributed to electrostatic interactions between the oxa bridge and the Fe(CO)$_3$ unit. Calabro and
Lichtenberger have published the He(I) and He(II) PE spectra of [η^5-
C$_5$H$_{5-n}$(CH$_3$)$_n$]Mn(CO)$_2$L (n = 1 and 5; L = C$_2$H$_4$ and C$_3$H$_6$) [229].
Interpretations were based on comparisons with the corresponding
tricarbonyl complexes [181], Fenske-Hall calculations, and substitution effects. The shift to lower energy of the olefin orbitals is
interpreted by taking charge redistributions, effects of decrease in
bond order of the coordinated olefin, and effects of metal olefin

overlap energy into consideration. Using the same kind of reasoning, the XPS spectra of $Fe(CO)_4$ethylene have been interpreted [230]. It was concluded that there is a very important σ interaction in the metal-olefin bond.

Böhm et al. published a study on a series of dipentadienyl iron complexes [192]. These can be seen as "open ferrocenes" and interpretations were based on analogies with these complexes. Predictions concerning the geometry of these complexes were based on PE data. Again, strong reorganization effects were found for the metal-centered MOs. Bis(π-pentadienyl)dinickel was also studied by Böhm [193]. A detailed study of Koopmans' defects, as observed using an INDO-type MO method, of this complex as a function of parametrization showed reorganization energies of up to 4 eV for the metal-centered orbitals.

IX. π-ALLYL COMPLEXES

Bis(π-allyl)nickel has always been one of the classical examples of the breakdown of Koopmans' theorem. The initial papers [101] showed large disagreement between the theoretical calculations and the PE results. ΔSCF calculations pointed out that relaxation was very important upon ionization from the localized metal d orbitals. Still the assignment of the He(I) spectra remained uncertain. Attempts to use only substitution effects [102] gave ambiguous results [2].

More recently, the spectra using He(I)/He(II) intensity differences, substituent effects, and MO calculations gave the key for definite assignments. Also, the metal was varied from Ni to Pd and Pt [103,104]. The He(I) spectra of bis(π-allyl)nickel (1a), bis(π-methallyl)nickel (1b), and the corresponding palladium (2a, resp. 25) and platinum (3a, resp. 3b) analogs are shown in Fig. 35. The assignments are in agreement with the MO diagram presented in Fig. 36 and are based on the aforementioned assignment criteria [104] (see Table 34).

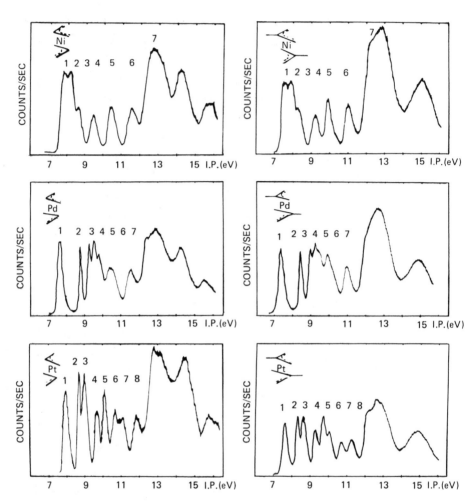

Figure 35   PE spectra of bis(π-allyl)M and bis(π-methallyl)M (M =
Ni, Pd, Pt).   (From Ref. 103.)

A. Methyl Substitution

For the compounds bis(π-allyl)nickel, bis(π-methallyl)nickel, bis(π-
crotyl)nickel, and bis(π-1,3-dimethylallyl)nickel, two effects could
be demonstrated: first, a destabilization of 0.2 eV per methyl
group regardless of its location, and second, a specific shift for
each band depending on the Hückel coefficients squared.

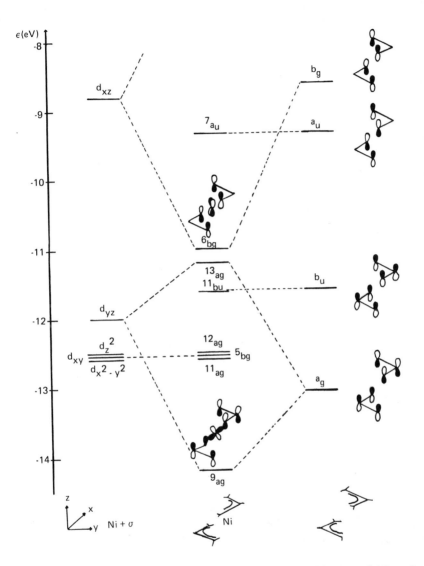

Figure 36 Interaction diagram between the 3d orbitals of Ni and the π orbitals of the allylic moieties of bis(π-allyl)Ni. (From Ref. 103.)

Table 34 Vertical Ionization Potentials ε and Calculated Orbital Energies (eV) of a Series of Bis(π-allyl)M Derivatives (M = Ni, Pd, Pt)

Orbital	MO type	Calculated[a] IE	Percent Ni	Percent π-diallyl	Percent σ-diallyl	Peak no. (Fig. 35)	1a	1b	2a	2b	3a	3b
$7a_u$	$a_2\pi_L$	8.75		99		1	7.76	7.53	7.56	7.33	7.91	7.65
$13a_g$	Ni $3d_{yz}$	8.91	67	22	11	2	8.19	7.91	8.72	8.45	8.64	8.37
$5b_g$	Ni $3d_{xy}$	9.19	96		4	2						
$12a_g$	Ni $3d_{z^2}$	9.21	96	2	2	3						
$11a_g$	Ni $3d_{x^2-y^2}$	9.47	93	4	3	3	8.58	8.32	9.25	8.97	8.95	8.68
$6g_b$	$3d_{xz} + \pi_L$	10.07	46	42	12	4	9.40	9.22	9.51	9.25	9.65	9.37
$11b_u$	$b_1\pi_L$	10.88		93	7	5	10.38	9.86	9.78	9.45	10.14	9.81
$9a_g$	$b_1\pi_L$	12.16	26	63	6	6	11.55	10.93	10.45	9.93	10.73	10.12
$6a_u$	$CC\sigma_L$	13.02			100							
$10a_g$	$CC\sigma_L$	13.05	6	8	86	7	12.70	12.20	11.57	11.01	11.15	10.80
$10b_u$	$CC\sigma_L$	13.09		5	95							
$4b_g$	$CC\sigma_L$	13.25	13	1	86							

[a]Calculated IP values beyond Koopmans' approximation with the one-particle Green's function approach.
Source: Ref. 103.

B. He(I)/He(II) Intensity Variation

Comparison of the bands in the He(I) and He(II) spectra shows a
drastic enhancement of the intensity of bands 2, 3, and 4 compared
to ligand bands 1, 5, 6, and 7 in both bis(π-allyl)Pd and bis(π-
methallyl)Pd. This gives the location of the metal d orbitals.

C. The Ni-Pd-Pt Comparison

The authors assign bands 1, 5, and 6 on the basis of variation of
the central metal atom from Ni to Pd to Pt. The ligand IE values
vary less than the metal IE values.

D. Comparison with the Allyl Radical

The first peak in the allyl radical is found at 8.13 eV. In the
bis(π-allyl) complexes the allyl part is negatively charged (-0.4e),
so the resulting first IP must be lower than 8.13 eV. The first
peak in the complex is the only possibility. Agreement between the
experimental values of the IPs with their assignment and the calculated ones via the Green's function approach by Böhm and Gleiter
[103] is very good.

Green and Seddon [105] measured and assigned the He(I) and
He(II) photoelectron spectra of $Cr(\eta^3-C_3H_5)_3$, $Cr(\eta^3-C_3H_5)_4$, and
$Mo_2(\eta^3-C_3H_5)_4$. The spectra are shown in Fig. 37. The bands above
12 eV belong to ionizations from allyl σ orbitals. He(I)/He(II)
intensity ratios do not alter very much, so a large amount of mixing must exist. In agreement with the assignments of the UP spectra of other metal-metal-bonded species, the first band (A) is
attributed to ionization from the M-M δ orbital (see Sec. XI and
Refs. 125, 126, 150, 151, and 165).

This band is relatively more intense in the Mo than in the Cr
spectrum, which indicates a high degree of metal d character giving
rise to larger cross sections going from 3d to 4d ionizations. The
next two bands must contain a mixture of the ligands a_2 levels and
M-M, π, and σ orbitals. A complete assignment could not be given.

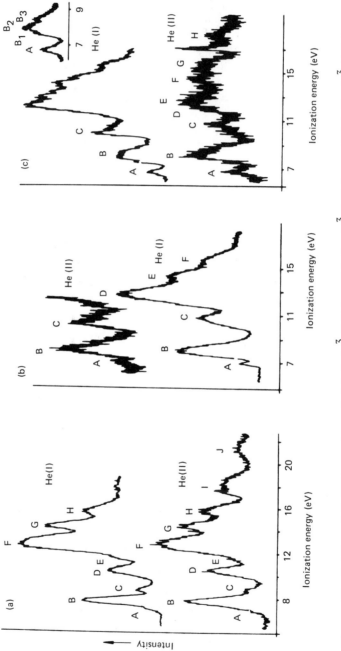

Figure 37   He(I) and He(II) spectra of (a) $Cr(\eta^3-C_3H_5)_3$, (b) $Cr_2(\eta^3-C_3H_5)_4$, and (c) $Mo_2(\eta^3-C_3H_5)_4$. (From Ref. 105.)

Table 35   Ionization Energies (eV) and Assignments for Some η^3-Allyl Manganese, Molybdenum, and Tungsten Complexes

$(\eta^3\text{-}C_3H_5Mn(CO)_4$	$(\eta^3\text{-}2\text{-}CH_3\text{-}C_3H_4)Mn(CO)_4$	Assignment
(8.05)	(8.03)	Mn (3d)
8.48	8.37	Mn (3d)
9.03	8.95	π_2 allyl
11.13	10.58	π_1 allyl

$(\eta^5\text{-}C_5H_5)\,(\eta^3\text{-}C_3H_5)M(CO)_2$		
M = Mo	M = W	Assignment
7.14	7.08	Metal d
7.67	7.65	Metal d
8.71	8.80	π_2 allyl
9.52	9.66	π Cp
9.75	9.97	π Cp
10.71	10.75	π allyl

Source: Ref. 194.

E.   Recent Developments

Worley et al. published the He(I) spectra of $(\eta^3\text{-}C_3H_5)Mn(CO)_4$, $(\eta^3\text{-}2\text{-}CH_3C_3H_4)Mn(CO)_4$, $(\eta^5\text{-}C_5H_5)\,(\eta^3\text{-}C_3H_5)Mo(CO)_2$, and $(\eta^5\text{-}C_5H_5)\,(\eta^3\text{-}C_3H_5)W(CO)_2$ [194]. The assignments for these complexes are straight-forward (see Table 35). Most of the ionizations are relatively insensitive to changes in the metal or ligand. The largest shift is seen in the allyl π_1 IE value upon methylation. This orbital has maximum orbital density at the point of substitution. The second allyl π orbital has a node at this position, so a small shift is expected and observed. Louwen et al. [195] have published the He(I) and He(II) PE spectra of a series of iron tricarbonyl(π-allyl)halide complexes. In this study large differences in bonding of the allyl ligand to the transition metals are indicated. The assignments and IE values are listed in Table 36.

Table 36 Ionization Energies

Compound	Metal 3d[a]	Halogen	Allyl[b]			
			n.b.	b.	σ_{CH}	CO
[Fe(CO)₃C₃H₅Cl]	8.96(d)	9.45	10.18	10.38	11.02	11.63	~13.5	~15
[Fe(CO)₃C₄H₇Cl]	9.15(d)	9.26	10.15	10.40	11.17	11.17	~13.5	~15
[Fe(CO)₃C₃H₅Br]	8.69(d)	9.43	9.64	10.03	10.53	11.60	~13.5	~15
[Fe(CO)₃C₄H₇Br]	8.89(d)	9.46	9.61	10.09	10.54	11.14	~13.5	~15
[Fe(CO)₃C₃H₅I]	9.46(d)	9.84	8.36	8.60	10.29	11.62	~13.5	~15
[Fe(CO)₃C₄H₇I]	9.15(d)	9.68	8.19	8.49	10.07	11.04	~13.5	~15
[Co(CO)₃C₃H₅]	7.73	8.43			9.73	11.17	~13.0	~14
	8.70	9.02						

[a]d, double.
[b]n.b., nonbonding; b., bonding.
Source: Ref. 195.

Böhm and Gleiter have studied the heavy-atom effect in $M(\eta^3$-allyl)$_2$ (M = Ni, Pt) and $M(CO)_4(\eta^3$-allyl) (M = Mn, Re) [197]. On going from Ni to Pt and from Mn to Re, large splittings in the metal d ionization bands were observed. This was attributed to larger interaction between the metal and the organic ligands by which differences in these interactions are "magnified."

X. TRANSITION METAL COMPLEXES WITH ALKYL, BORANE, OR WITH O-, N-, OR S-DONOR LIGANDS

Several papers have appeared recently dealing with these classes of compounds. Green et al. [106a] presented the spectra of the series $W(CH_3)_6$, $Re(CH_3)_6$, $Ta(CH_3)_5$, $ReO(CH_3)_4$, and $ReO[CH_2Si(CH_3)_3]_4$. Chisholm et al. [106b] published the He(I) spectra of $Cr(N-i-Pr_2)_3$, $Cr(NEt_2)_4$, $Mo(NMe_2)_4$, $Mo(NEt_2)_4$, $Nb(NMe_2)_5$, and $Ta(NMe_2)_5$ in combination with SCF-Xα-SW calculations.

One example of the excellent He(I)/He(II) spectra of Ref. 106a is shown in Fig. 38. The assignments could be given only on the

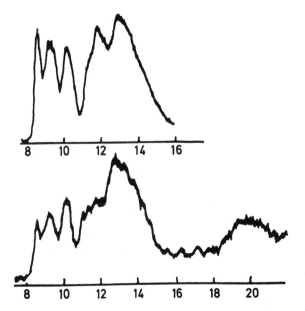

Figure 38 He(I) and He(II) spectra of $W(CH_3)_6$. (From Ref. 106a.)

basis of localized bond orbitals, in which case local symmetry was assumed. The spectra could be divided in three regions: below 11 eV for the M-C bonding orbitals, from 11 to 16 eV for the $\sigma_{C(2p)-H}$ bonding orbitals, and at higher IE values for the $\sigma_{C(2s)-H}$ bonding orbitals.

In $W(CH_3)_6$ the local symmetry is O_h, in which the six W-C bonding orbitals transform like $a_{1g} + t_{1u} + e_g$. Assignment following the naive 1:3:2 intensity ratio rule of these bands was impossible. Good assignments could only be made using He(I)/He(II) intensity ratios and cross-section rules. Thereby the following combinations with the metal orbitals were assumed: 5d - $e_g + t_{2g}$, 62 - a_{1g}, and 6p - t_{1u}. The data and the assignments are shown in Table 37.

In the region 11-16 eV the bands assigned to ionizations from $\sigma_{C(2p)-H}$ orbitals ($t_{1g} + t_{2u} + 2t_{1u} + t_{2g}$) show substantial splitting, similar to that found in neopentane, where the effect was explained by steric compression of the methyl groups. The splitting of the bands and the He(I)/He(II) intensity variations are in complete agreement with this explanation.

The spectrum of $Re(CH_3)_6$ could be assigned following the same reasoning. The ground state $^2T_{2g}$ would, however, be expected to be split by spin-orbit coupling into $^2U'$ and $^2E''$, of which the thermal population provides the asymmetry of the leading edge of the first band.

The transformation of the M-C bonding orbitals in $Ta(CH_3)_5$ [106a] and their combination with metal orbitals is different: d-($a_1' + e' + e''$), s-a_1', and p-($a_2'' + e'$). The behavior of the He(I)/He(II) intensity changes leads to the proposed assignment.

The spectrum of $ReO[CH_2Si(CH_3)_3]_4$ could be assigned similarly.

The He(I) spectra of the five amino complexes as published by Chisholm [106b] are found in Fig. 39. The He(II) spectra are lacking for complete proof of the proposed assignment. In the SW-Xα calculation the transition-state method is included, from which the results demonstrated the breakdown of Koopmans' theorem. The

Table 37 Ionization Energies (eV) of $W(CH_3)_6$, $Re(CH_3)_6$, $Ta(CH_3)_5$, and $ReO[CH_2Si(CH_3)_3]_4$, and the Proposed Assignment

$W(CH_3)_6$	$Re(CH_3)_6$	$Ta(CH_3)_5$	$ReO(CH_3)_4$	$ReO[CH_2Si(CH_3)_3]_4$
O_h	O_h	D_{3h}	C_{4v}	
	7.89		8.86	
	(d')		(d' = b_2)	
8.59	8.47	8.83	9.5	8.46
(t_{1u}-WC)	(t_{1u}-ReC)	(a_2''-TaC)	(e-ReC)	(ReC)
9.33	9.77	9.25	9.95	8.93
(a_{1g}-WC)	(a_{1g}-ReC)	(a_1'-TaC)	(b_1-ReC)	(ReC)
10.17	10.48	10.10		
(e_g-WC)	(e_g-ReC)	(e'-Tac)		
11.55	11.14	11.14		10.2
(c_{2p}-H)		(a_1'-TaC)		(Si-C)
11.97	12.2	12.07	13.0	12.9
(C_{2p}-H)	(C_{2p}-H)		(a_1-ReC)	
			(π-ReO)	
			(σ-ReO)	
			(σ-CH)	
13.14	13.4	13.51		
(C_{2p}-H)	(C_{2-}-H)			
20.8				
(C_{2s}-H)				

Source: Ref. 106a.

measured IE values, together with the calculated IE values and the assignment, are presented in Table 39.

Detailed assignment of the UV PE spectra of paramagnetic transition metal systems is generally complicated because of the large number of ionic states. Based on the peak intensities in He(I) spectra, the first and second IE values of $Cr(N-i-Pr_2)_3$ are attributed to Cr(3d) orbitals with a_2 and e symmetry, respectively. The agreement with the SW-Xα calculation is good, as shown in Table 41.

The tetracoordinate dialkylamides are paramagnetic, $Cr(NEt_2)_4$, or diamagnetic, $Mo(NMe_2)_4$ and $Mo(NEt_2)_4$. An explanation for this difference cannot be given. Probably it is a reflection of the spin-pairing energies being in the order Cr > Mo and the ligand field energies being in the order Mo > Cr. The IE values measured together with the assignment of the closed-shell amino complexes, are given in Table 39.

Striking are the almost identical spectra of $Nb(NMe_2)_5$ and $Ta(NMe_2)_5$, although both possess a completely different structure

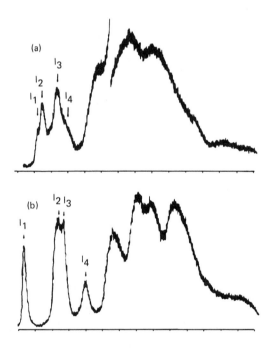

Figure 39 He(I) UVPES of (a) $Cr(N-i-Pr_2)_3$; (b) $Mo(NMe_2)_4$; (c) $Mo(NEt_2)_4$; (d) $Cr(NEt_2)_4$, and (e) $Ta(NMe_2)_5$. (From Ref. 107.)

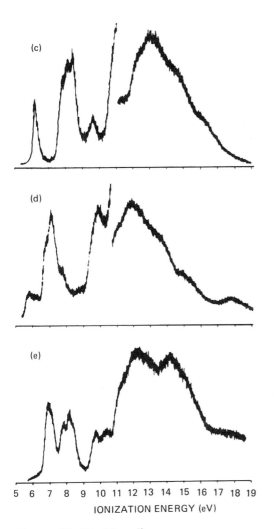

(c)

(d)

(e)

5   6   7   8   9   10 11 12 13 14 15 16 17 18 19
IONIZATION ENERGY (eV)

Figure 39 (Continued)

Table 38   Computed and Measured IE Values of Tricoordinate Amino
Compounds

	$Cr(NH_2)_3$:Calculated (SW-Xα)	$Cr(N-i-Pr)_3$:Experimental
$4a_1$	6.76	6.3
$6e$	7.01	6.53
$3a_2$	7.52	7.38
$5e$	8.57	7.9
$4e$		9.9
$3a_1$		

Source: Ref. 107a.

Table 39   Experimental IE Values of Closed-Shell Amino Complexes

$Mo(NMe_2)_4$	$Mo(NEt_2)_4$	$Nb(NMe_2)_5$	$Ta(NMe)_5$
5.30	5.3		
$(^2B_1 = d_{x^2-y^2})$	$(^2B_1 = d_{x^2-y^2})$		
7.34 $(^2E = n_N)$	7.0; 7.3 (^2E)	6.77 (n_N)	6.89 (n_N)
		6.9 (n_N)	7.1 (n_N)
7.70 $(^2B_2 = n_N)$	7.56 $(^2B_2 = n_N)$	7.63 (n_N)	7.78 (n_N)
9.01 $(^2A_1 = n_N)$	8.7 $(^2A_1 = n_N)$	8.21 (n_N)	8.35 (n_N)
10.7 (M-N)		9.7 (M-N)	9.7 (M-N)
		10.2 (M-N)	10.4 (M-N)

Source: Ref. 106b.

in the solid phase (square pyramidal and trigonal bipyramidal,
respectively). This might be evidence for structural similarity
of these molecules in the gas phase. However, without MO calculations or He(II) spectra, it is difficult to draw definite conclusions in this series.

The PE spectra of some Ti(IV)methyl derivatives with the overall formula $TiR_{4-x}X_x$ (R = Me; X = Cl, OR, NR_2, Cp) have been published [106c]. The assignment is based on CNDO/2 calculations, as shown in Table 40 for $TiMeCl_3$.

However, relaxation energies have not been taken into account, nor have He(II) spectra been measured. Substitution effects in the spectra of $TiMe(OR)_3$, $Ti(OMe)(OR_3)_3$, $TiMeCp(OR)_2$, $TiMe(NR_2)_3$, $TiCpCl_3$, and $TiCp_2Cl_2$ are discussed.

Ulman et al. [107a] could give a characterization of the ferroboranes $C_2B_3H_5Fe(CO)_3$, $C_2B_3H_7Fe(CO)_3$, $B_4H_8Fe(CO)_3$, $B_5H_9Fe(CO)_3$, and $B_5H_3Fe(CO)_5$ by He(I) and Ne(I) photoelectron spectra. As an example, the assignment of $C_2B_3H_5Fe(CO)_3$ is given in Table 41.

Two papers on dithiocarbamate complexes have been published recently by Cauletti et al. [107b,c]. First the diethyldithiocarbamates of Cr^{III}, Fe^{III}, Ni^{II}, Cu^{II}, and Zn^{II} are reported and a tentative assignment given. The absence of He(II) spectra, however, led to some confusion in the assignment in the d-orbital region since the Cu- and Fe-3d orbitals, contrary to the Ni-, Cr-, and Co-3d orbitals, seemed to be hidden under the ligand orbitals. The

Table 40 Experimental and Calculated IE Values (eV) of $TiMeCl_3$

Band	Experimental	Calculated	Orbital character
$5a_1$	10.8	13.77	Ti-C
$1a_2$	11.7	14.57	Cl
5e		14.65	Cl
4e	12.7	15.36	Cl
$4a_1$	13.1	15.75	Cl + Ti
3e	13.5	16.16	Cl + Ti
$3a_1$	13.9	16.35	Cl

Source: Ref. 106c.

Table 41   Vertical Ionization Energies and Band Assignments

Molecule	IP (eV)	IP per band	Assignment[a]
$C_2B_3H_5Fe(CO)_3$	8.6	1	F
	9.1	2	F
	9.9	1	S, R
	11.2	2	S, RP
	11.9	2	Ex, R
	12.7	1	Ex, P
	14.7	10	F
	13.8 sh		

[a]F, $Fe(CO)_3$ fragment; S, surface orbital; Ex, exopolyhedral orbital;
R, ring orbital; RP, ring-polar interaction orbital.
Source: Ref. 107a.

Table 42   Ionization Energies (eV) of Some Diethyldithiocarbamato
Complexes

Complex	3d		Ligand S_{3p}				3d
$[Ni(S_2CNEt_2)_2]$	6.95		7.13	7.84	8.10	8.66	9.07
$[Cr(S_2CNEt_2)_2]$		7.02	7.48	8.15		8.42	8.83
$[Co(S_2CNEt_2)_3]$	6.67		7.35		8.25		9.45
$[Cu(S_2CNEt_2)_2]$			7.36	(7.93)			8.13
$[Fe(S_2CNEt_2)_3]$			7.75		8.19		8.39
$[Zn(S_2CNEt_2)_2]$				8.13		8.31	9.41

Source: Ref. 107b.

suggested $3d^{10}$ band in the Zn compound at 9.41 eV is unlikely compared to PE spectra of other Zn compounds (see Table 42).

The second paper reports the spectra of $Fe(S_2CNR_1R_2)_2$ complexes
in the gas phase originating from the $Fe(S_2CNR_1R_2)(CO)_2$ compounds.
Here also the first corresponding IE arises at ∿7.6 eV. From the
splitting between the orbitals assigned to Fe(a) and Fe(e), the

structure of the cluster could be deduced. The results are compared
with calculated results published earlier [107d].

A. Recent Developments

Bancroft et al. [198] have published the He(I) and He(II) spectra of
AuMe(PMe$_3$). The assignments were made using cross-section arguments,
analogous with $(CH_3)_2Hg$ data and a SW-Xα calculation.

Using the calculated correction for the HOMO (transition-state
method) for all the levels, large discrepancies were found between
theory and experiment. The observed energy difference between the
HOMO (calculated to be the Au-C orbital) and the first metal d MOs
[unambiguously assigned using He(I)/He(II) arguments] is ∿1.6 eV,
while the calculation gives 4.5-5 eV. So it seems here also that
large differences in AO composition lead to differential effects.

The observed IE values, together with their assignments, are
listed in Table 43.

From the same group a paper appeared on the He(I) and He(II) PE
spectra of three Au(III) complexes [AuMe$_3$L] (L = PMe$_3$, PMe$_2$Ph, and
PMePh$_2$) [199]. Assignments were made using results from Ref. 198
and cross-section considerations. The IE values are listed in Table
44, together with their assignments.

Table 43 Photoelectron Data for [AuMe(PMe$_3$)]

IE (eV)	Assignment
8.24	Au-C
9.22	Au-P
9.84	Au $d_{5/2}$
10.55	Au d_σ
11.33	Au $d_{3/2}$
12.00	P-C
12.7-15	C-H

Source: Ref. 198.

Table 44   Ionization Energies (eV) for Some $AuMe_3(PRR_2^*)$ Complexes

Assignments	$AuMe_3(PMe_3)$	$AuMe_3(PPhMe_2)$	$AuMe_3(PPh_2Me)$
Au-C	7.76	7.68	7.61
	8.59	8.49	8.31
Ph π		9.45	9.32
Au 5d	9.87	9.88	9.73
5d	10.10	10.18	10.06
5d	10.63	10.57	10.50
Au-P	10.99	10.95	10.92
P-C	11.89	11.63	11.59

Source: Ref. 199.

Surprisingly large Au-P stabilization energies are involved to assign the spectra. Deconvolution techniques are used extensively in this paper. It is not impossible that the metal-phosphorus bonding orbital is hidden under the rather complicated metal d bands.

Furlani et al. [200] have published the PE spectra of a series of organomercury compounds with aromatic and alkynyl ligands. Assignments could be made using He(I)/He(II) intensity differences (see Table 45). Ionizations from the d shell were observed at IE values of >15 eV, with very high intensities in the He(II) spectra.

Cauletti and Zanoni have published UPS and XPS data for the d^2 complex tetramesitylmolybdenum [201]. A doublet was found for the $4d^2$ ionization. This doublet was assigned to a low-symmetry split configuration corresponding to $e^2T_d \rightarrow a_1^1b_2^1D_{2d}$. The $T_d \rightarrow D_{2d}$ symmetry lowering is generally found for these complexes.

The He(I) and He(II) PE spectra of a large series of metal silylamido complexes have been published by Green et al. [202]. Detailed assignments could be given by using large variations in the metal ion (ranging from Na, Mg, and Al, to transition metals, the lanthanides, and Zn, Hg, etc.).

Table 45   Ionization Energies (eV) for Some Aryl-Mercury Compounds

Compound	$(\pi_{phen} + \sigma_{Hg-C})$	σ_{Hg-C}	$(\sigma + \pi)_{phen}$	σ_{phen}	σ	$^2D_{5/2}$	σ	$^2D_{3/2}$
$(C_6H_5)_2Hg$	9.03	10.98	11.60	12.81	14.01	14.75	16.29	16.68
$(p\text{-}CH_3C_6H_4)_2Hg$	(8.53) 8.94	10.82	11.36	12.38	13.74	14.63		16.48

Compound	π_{phen}	σ_{Hg-C}	π_{Cl}	$\pi_{phen} + \sigma$	σ	$^2D_{5/2}$	σ	$^2D_{3/2}$
C_6H_5HgCl	9.46 (9.73)	(10.36) 10.82	(11.91) 12.38	13.48	14.75	15.59	16.79	17.52
$p\text{-}CH_3C_6H_4HgCl$	9.10 (9.50)	(10.32) 10.76	(11.96) 12.38	13.08	14.24	15.59		17.48

Source: Ref. 200.

Gleiter and co-workers have published a study on the electronic structure of (cyclopentadienyl)(1,4-dimethyl-1,4-dibora-2,5-cyclo-hexadiene)cobalt, a "mixed sandwich" type of complex using UPS and results from INDO calculations [203]. $(\eta^5-C_5H_5)Fe(CO)_2B_2H_5$ was studied by DeKock et al. [204] using He(I) and Ne(I) radiation and Fenske-Hall calculations. A detailed comparison between the Fe-B interaction in this complex and the Fe-C interaction in $Fe(CO)_4C_2H_4$ was made, of which the PE spectra were published before [87]. This comparison demonstrated that the B_2H_5 fragment can be considered as a $B_2H_4^-$ bound side-on to the metal, with a proton in the π lobe opposite the metal. The Fe-B interaction was described as a closed three-center two-electron interaction, where the Fe-B bonding densi-ty is inside the FeB_2 triangle, while in $Fe(CO)_4C_2H_4$ it was found to be largely outside the FeC_2 triangle, stressing the importance of π^* interactions in this complex.

Ciliberto et al. have published the PE spectra of some diethyl-dithiophosphato complexes [205]. Use was made of correlations in the series and of some preliminary He(II) work to make the assign-ments (see Table 46).

Louwen et al. published the He(I) and He(II) spectra of a series of zinc and aluminium diazabutadiene complexes [206]: $Et_2Al(tBu-DAB)$, MeZn(tBu-DAB), and EtZn(tBu-DAB) (tBu-DAB = 1,4-ditertiarybutyl-1,4-diazabutadiene) [206]. This bidentate ligand has a very low lying π^* LUMO, which can easily accept electrons. It could be concluded (also using ESR arguments) that the radical elec-tron that is present in these complexes resides mainly in the DAB π^* orbital. A low-intensity band at around 6 eV was assigned to ioniza-tion from this orbital. MNDO calculations on these molecules failed to agree with the experimental results. The N,N',C-2,6-bis-[(dimethylamino)methyl]phenyl moiety (abbreviated L) was used as a ligand in a study of a series of LMX (M = Ni, Pd, Pt; X = Cl, Br, I) complexes [207]. These complexes are very interesting, not only be-cause little information is present on the UPS of bivalent group VIII transition metal complexes, but also because of their unusual

Table 46   Pertinent IE Data of $M(dtp)_3$ Complexes (eV)

Complex	IE	Assignment
$In(dtp)_3$	8.3	$e(n_-)$
	8.75	$a_2(n_-)$, $e(\pi_-)$, $a_1(\pi_-)$
	9.43	$e(\pi_+)$, $a_2(\pi_+)$
	10.59	O 2p lone pairs
$Cr(dtp)_3$	7.71	Metal d
	8.45	$a_2(n_-)$, $a_1(\pi_-)$, $e(\pi_-)$
	9.10	$e(\pi_+)$, $a_2(\pi_+)$
	9.35	$e(n_-)$
	9.9 ⎫	O 2p lone pairs +
	10.4 ⎭	n_+ ligand orbitals (?)
$Co(dtp)_3$	7.95	Metal d
	8.63	$a_2(n_-)$, $a_1(\pi_-)$
	9.0	$e(\pi_+)$, $a_2(\pi_+)$
	9.56	$e(\pi_-)$, $e(n_-)$
	10.58	O 2p lone pairs
$Rh(dtp)_3$	7.70	Metal d
	8.22 ⎫	Ligand n_-, π_-, π_+
	9.33 ⎭	
	10.6	O 2p lone pairs

Source: Ref. 205.

chemistry. He(I) and He(II) spectra were measured and intensity differences were used extensively to assign the various ionizations. (For the IE values and assignments, see Table 47.)   A representative spectrum is shown in Fig. 40.

The electronic differences between the nickel, palladium, and platinum complexes are clearly reflected in the spectra.   From these results it was concluded that a strong π interaction exists between the metal d orbitals and the π levels of the phenyl moiety.   In Ref. 208 another series of square-planar divalent nickel triad complexes is studied.   In that paper a series of bis-triethylphosphine

Table 47   Ionization Energies[a] of [LMX] and [LInMe$_2$] (eV)

MX/level	$\pi_{b_1}^-$	σ^-	d_{z^2}	$X_{nonbonding}$	d_{xz}, d_{xy}	π_{a_2}	C^+	$\pi_{b_1}^+$	n_N
NiCl	7.16	7.70	(8.72)	9.44	(8.72)	9.03	10.47	10.06	(11.18)
NiBr	7.22	7.75	(8.66)	8.66	(8.66)	(8.66)	(10.27)	(10.27)	(11.22)
NiI	7.07	7.54	(8.75)	8.07/8.29	(8.75)	9.10	(10.00)	(10.00)	(11.12)
PdBr	7.65	7.79	8.15	8.75	(8.75)	(8.75)	9.34	(10.12)	(10.12)/(11.08)
PtCl	7.16	7.78	8.05	9.01	(8.90)	(8.90)	9.66	10.14	10.42/(11.30)
PtBr	7.29	7.87	8.05	8.32	(9.02)	(9.02)	9.48	10.19	10.53/11.34
PtI	7.12	7.57	8.06	8.21/8.54	(8.96)	8.76	9.33	10.05	10.58/11.13
InMe$_2$ [21]	(8.58)	8.03	-	-	-	(8.58)	9.26	-	-

[a]Values are correct within 0.02 eV; values in parentheses are approximate values, taken as the maximum of an overlapping band.
Source: Ref. 206.

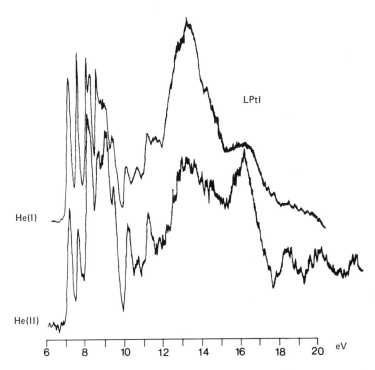

He(I)

He(II)

LPtl

6   8   10   12   14   16   18   20   eV

Figure 40   He(I) and He(II) spectra of [LPtI].   (From Ref. 206.)

acetylide and cyanide complexes of Pd and Pt is published and
assignments were made using the same assignment criteria as in the
previous paper [207], together with results from HFS-Xα calculations.
Relativistic effects were taken into consideration in this scheme.

The ionization energies, together with the assignments, are
listed in Table 48.

There is evidence for a strong π interaction between the metal
and the filled acetylide or cyanide ligand orbitals, both in and out
of plane. However, no indications were found for metal-ligand π
back-bonding.

Generally, a strong similarity exists between observed energy
levels for corresponding Pd and Pt complexes, and this is reflected
in the HFS calculations. Also, for the Pt complexes, relativistic

Table 48   Vertical Ionization Energies for $[(PEt_3)_2M(C\equiv X)_2$ (eV)[a]

M:	Pd	Pt	Pd	Pt	Pd	Pt
X:	C-H	C-H	C-CH$_3$	C-CH$_3$	N	N
π_{op}^{-}	7.98	7.49	7.43	7.05	9.07	8.99
π_{ip}^{-}	7.98	7.93	7.43	7.38	9.52	9.43
π_{ip}^{u}	7.98	8.26	7.68	7.89	9.97	9.99
d_z^2	8.33	8.26	8.05	8.01	9.23	8.77
π_{op}^{u}	9.03	9.02	8.36	8.46	-	-
d_{yz}	9.31	9.16	9.21	8.99	10.19	10.33
σ_{M-C}^{u}	9.64	-	9.21	9.67	8.71	8.86
n_p^{u}	9.51	9.29	9.21	9.14	-	-
π_{op}^{+}	$\sim$10.3	$\sim$10.	$\sim$9.8	$\sim$9.9	11.50	11.40
π_{ip}	$\sim$10.3	$\sim$10.	$\sim$9.8	$\sim$9.9	11.50	11.40
n_N	-	-	-	-	10.81	10.82

[a]For assignments refer to text; op, out of plane; ip, in plane;
+(-), (anti)bonding between fragments; u, ungerade.
Source: Ref. 208.

corrections to be applied to the nonrelativistic results appear to
be very small.

XI. METAL-METAL BONDED COMPLEXES

The study of compounds with metal-metal bonds became one of the more
important topics in UPS research some 20 years ago with the description of a quadruple bond in $Cr_2(O_2CCH_3)_4 \cdot 2H_2O$ [108] in 1964 by
Cotton. For the bonding scheme of these quadruple bonds a δ component had to be postulated in addition to the more classical σ- and
two π-orbital contributions in triple bonds, leading to the descrip-
tion $|(\sigma)^2(\pi)^4(\delta)^2|$ [109].

A crystal structure determination of $Cr_2(O_2CCH_3)_4 \cdot 2H_2O$ [110] and also of $K_2Re_2Cl_8 \cdot 2H_2O$ [111] revealed extremely short metal-metal bonds, suggesting a high bond order. Since then hundreds of papers and several reviews have appeared about the metal-metal bonds with single, double, triple, and quadruple bond orders. The considerations about the bond order in metal-metal complexes in inorganic textbooks and in most of the papers are based on the purely formal 18-electron rule.

Attempts to correlate quantitatively these formal bond orders with observables such as the metal-metal distances, the infrared metal-metal stretching frequencies (c.q., the force constants), and the Raman intensities, grosso modo, failed. Even quantitatively the bond orders correlate with the metal-metal distances only in some restricted series of related complexes. So at this stage the polynuclear metal complexes are still a challenge to the theoretical chemist and also to the UV photoelectron spectroscopist.

The earliest quantitative molecular orbital calculation of a complex with a quadruple bond was of the extended Hückel type and was presented by Cotton and Harris [112] in 1967. The results of these calculations were in agreement with the original qualitative picture [113]. This picture has been confirmed by SCF-Xα calculations on various compounds with triple and quadruple bonds [114-117]. However, recent SCF-Xα-SW calculations performed on Mo_2-$(O_2CH)_4$ and $Mo_2Cl_8^{4-}$ [118-120] suggested that some metal-metal bonding character is mixed into molecular orbitals that are largely ligand in character, leading to partially filled δ orbitals and to lower bond orders.

The analogous carboxylato-bridged chromium dimers have been a subject of even greater controversy with respect to an adequate description of the metal-metal bond orbitals. The first publication on this topic in 1976 was an ab initio MO calculation, together with the He(I) photoelectron spectrum of $Cr(O_2CCH_3)_4$ in the gas phase, exhibiting an amazing ground-state configuration [i.e., $|(\sigma)^2, (\delta)^2, (\sigma^*)^2, (\delta^*)^2|$] and hence pointing to no net bonding between the two chromium atoms [121]. The first reactions to this statement came from Benard and Veillard [122,123] and in an extension of the method described in Ref. 121 to other chromium dimers by Guest [124]. All these calculations were consistent with the absence of Cr-Cr bonding--that is, before the inclusion of a limited configuration interaction completely altered the initial ground-state configuration. However, for the Cr-Cr distance in $Cr(O_2CH)_4$, the quadruple bonding determinant $|(\sigma)^2(\pi)^4(\delta)^2|$ was calculated to contribute only 16% in the CI ground-state wavefunctions, while for the corresponding longer Mo-Mo quadruple bond, this percentage is as much as 66%.

Correlation effects are expected to be especially important in the dichromium complexes, which have rather longer metal-metal bonds than the dimolybdenum complexes, due to the inability of the single determinantal method to describe dissociation correctly. Both correlation and, as will be shown in Fe and Co clusters [125,126], relaxation effects are of crucial importance.

Some dispute also exists about the pure carbonyls of Fe, Co, and Mn. The 18-electron rule requires a direct metal-metal bond in all of the three cases, $Mn_2(CO)_{10}$, $Fe_2(CO)_9$, and $Co_2(CO)_8$. Heyser et al. [127,128] found by using the HFS-DV-Xα scheme that in Mn_2-$(CO)_{10}$ the two $Mn(CO)_5$ fragments are linked by a single Mn-Mn bond, but that neither in $Fe_2(CO)_9$ nor in $Co_2(CO)_8$ is a direct metal-metal bond present. Whether this is a true or a false picture of reality will surely be the subject of more research in the near future.

A. The Metal-Metal Bond in Dinuclear Complexes of Group VI Metals

In this type of complex the controversy about the bond order and hence about the assignment of the UV photoelectron spectra was the most profound. In three recent papers this question has been treated thoroughly [129-131]. In Ref. 129 a new assignment has been proposed following the commonly assumed ordering of the metal orbitals (i.e., $\sigma_{d_{z^2}} < \pi_{d_{xz,yz}} < \delta_{xy}$).

The earlier assignment using SCF-Xα-SW calculations [116,119], suggesting for $Mo_2(O_2(O_2CH)_4$ that the low-energy bands at 7.6, 9.4, and 12.7 eV correspond to the δ, π, and σ metal-metal bonding orbitals, has become obsolete. The He(I) and He(II) spectra of a series of Cr and Mo complexes are shown in Figs. 41 to 47. The ionization energies and the relative intensities of the bands for the metal carboxylates are presented in Tables 49 and 50. For molecules of this size, neither minimal-basis ab initio [131] nor SCF-Xα-SW calculations can claim to give the decisive answer in the assignment controversy. For $[Mo_2(O_2CH)_4]$ as an example, a large number of MO calculations have been performed. The various assignments suggested in the literature for this specific molecule are tabulated in Table 51.

Unfortunately, on the available experimental evidence it is impossible to make a proper decision among assignments II, II, and IV. The main objection to assignment II is that the σ ionization ($4a_{1g}$), which is mainly metal localized, is far too high. The π-σ separation is much larger than the measured separation of 0.7 eV in Mo_2-$(OCH_2CMe_3)_6$ [114]. Moreover, the intensity ratios of the first two peaks are found to be 1:5.5-3.0 in He(I) and 1:2.8-3.3 in He(II) spectra, suggesting that peak B contains both σ and π ionizations.

Ab initio calculations lead to a σ-π separation that is too small and SCF-Xα-SW calculations predict a separation of 3.2 eV, arising from the assignment of peak E to the Mo-Mo σ-bonding orbital, which is too large. Another possibility, namely that the Mo-Mo σ orbital is hidden under peak C, leads to a reasonable π-σ separation of 1.6 eV.

In conclusion, it seems reasonable to suggest that the δ, π, and σ metal-metal bonding electrons all contribute to the first band in $Cr_2(O_2CH)_4$ and that the corresponding spectra of other chromium and molybdenum complexes can be assigned similarly. This is not in conflict with electron diffraction density measurements obtained from low-temperature diffraction data and with unrestricted

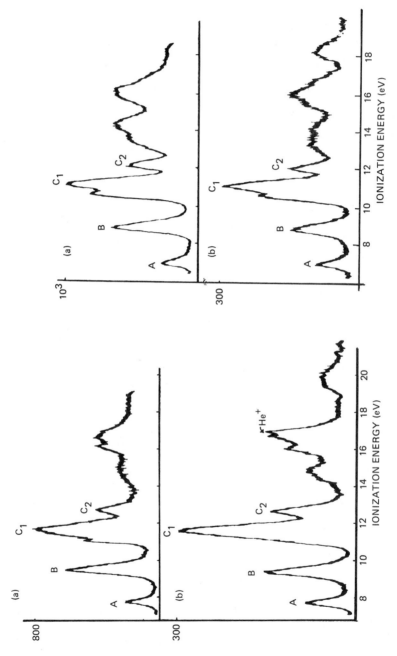

Figure 41 He(I) and He(II) spectra of
$[Mo_2(O_2CH)_4]$. (From Ref. 130.)

Figure 42 He(I) and He(II) spectra of
$[Mo_2(O_2CMe)_4]$. (From Ref. 130.)

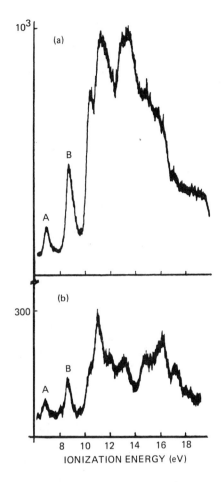

Figure 43 He(I) and He(II) spectra of $[Mo_2(O_2CCMe_3)_4]$. (From Ref. 130.)

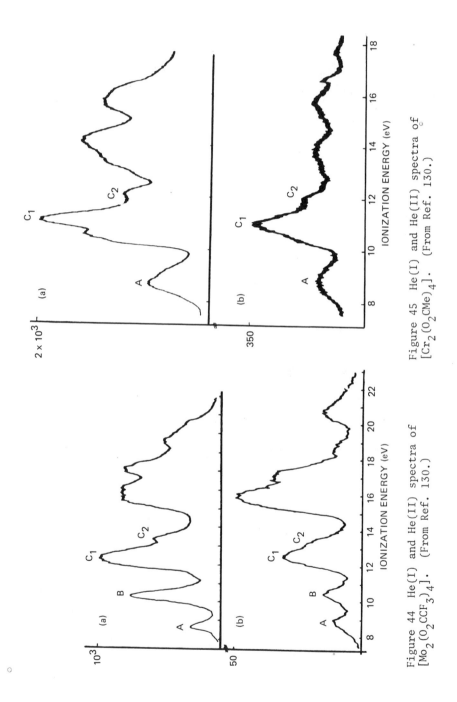

Figure 45 He(I) and He(II) spectra of $[Cr_2(O_2CMe)_4]$. (From Ref. 130.)

Figure 44 He(I) and He(II) spectra of $[Mo_2(O_2CCF_3)_4]$. (From Ref. 130.)

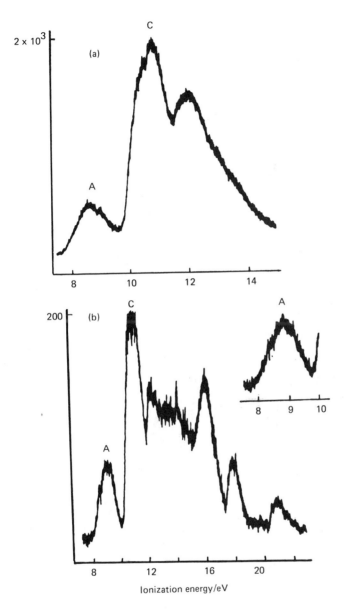

Figure 46   He(I) and He(II) spectra of $[Cr_2(O_2CEt)_4]$.   (From Ref. 129.)

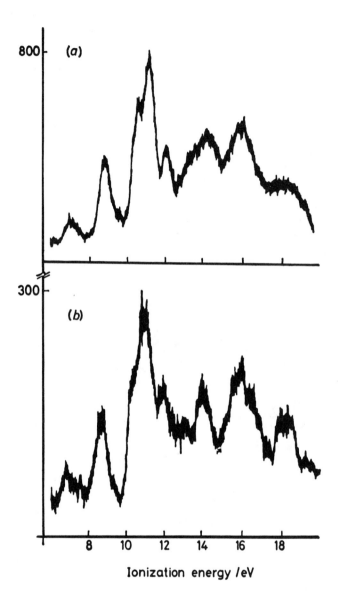

Ionization energy /eV

Figure 47 He(I) and He(II) spectra of $[CrMo(O_2CMe)_4]$. (From Ref. 130.)

Table 49 Ionization Energies (eV)

Region	$[Mo_2(O_2CH)_4]$	$[Mo_2(O_2CMe)_4]$	$[Mo_2(O_2CCMe_3)_4]$	$[Mo_2(O_2CCF_3)_4]$	$[CrMo(O_2CMe)_4]$[a]
A	7.60	6.92	6.75	8.67	7.06
B	9.37	8.77	8.54	10.44	8.82
C_1	10.95, 11.56, 11.89 (sh)	10.47, 10.94	10.22, 10.97, 11.61	12.59	10.59, 11.12
C_2	12.69, 14.92	11.99, 13.31	13.14, 14.48	13.53, 15.95	12.08, 13.31
D	16.16, 16.68	14.09, 15.56[b], 15.93[b]	15.74, 17.25	17.21, 18.63	14.16, 15.83
E	19.68[b]	16.57[b], 18.15[b]		20.78[b]	18.20[b]

Region	$[Cr_2(O_2CMe)_4]$	$[Cr_2(O_2CEt)_4]$	CF_3CO_2H
A	8.65, 9.10 (sh)	8.104[b] (sh), 8.55, 8.92 (sh)	
C_1	10.2, 10.51, 11.04	10.50, 10.80	12.08, 13.17
C_2	12.08, 13.33	12.04, 16.06[b]	14.85, 15.84, 16.59, 17.41
D	14.11, 15.68[b], 16.21[b], 18.43[b]	17.96[b], 21.08[b]	17.84, 19.7[b], 20.8[b], 22.6[b]

[a]See text for discussion on nature of vapor-phase species.

[b]Value obtained from He(II) spectrum.

Source: Ref. 130.

Table 50 Relative Intensities of Bands for Metal Carboxylates

Region	$[Mo_2(O_2CH)_4]$		$[Mo_2(O_2CMe)_4]$		$[Mo_2(O_2CCMe_3)_4]$		$[Mo_2(O_2CCF_3)_4]$		$[CrMo(O_2CMe)_4]$	
	He(I)	He(II)	He(I)	He(II)	He(I)	He(II)	He(I)	He(II)	He(I)	He(II)
A	0.18	0.38	0.21	0.36	0.32	0.43	0.31	0.60	0.33	0.37
B	1	1	1	1	1	1	1	1	1	1
C	3.17	4.26	3.92	4.21			3.51	3.48	4	

Region	$[Cr_2(O_2CMe)_4]$	
	He(I)	He(II)
A	1	1
C	5.5	4.8

Source: Ref. 130.

Table 51 Suggested Assignments for the PE Spectrum of $[Mo_2[O_2CH]_4]$

Experimental (eV)	i.e.	(I)	(II)	(III)	(IV)
7.6	A	$2b_{2g}$ (δ)	$2b_{2g}$ (δ)	$2b_{2g}$ (δ)	$2b_{2g}$ (δ)
9.37	B	$6e_u$ (π), $4e_g$, $1a_{1u}$	$6e_u$ (π)	$5a_{1g}$ (σ), $6e_u$ (π)	$6e_u$ (π)
10.95	C$_1$	$5e_u$, $5a_{1g}$, $3e_g$, $3a_{2u}$	$4e_g$, $1a_{1u}$	$1a_{1u}$, $4e_g$	$4e_g$, $1a_{1u}$, $5a_{1g}$ (σ)
11.56	C$_1$	$3b_{2u}$, $1b_{1u}$	$5e_u$, $5a_{1g}$, $3e_g$, $3a_{2u}$, $3b_{2u}$	$5e_u$, $3e_g$, $3b_{2u}$, $3a_{2u}$, $1b_{1u}$	$5e_u$, $3e_g$, $3a_{2u}$, $3b_{2u}$
11.89	C$_1$	$4b_{1g}$	$1b_{1u}$		$1b_{1u}$
12.69	C$_2$	$4a_{1g}$ (σ), $1a_{2g}$, $4e_u$	$4a_{1g}$ (σ), $4b_{1g}$	$4b_{1g}$, $4a_{1g}$	$4b_{1g}$, $4a_{1g}$
14.92	D	$1b_{2g}$	$1a_{2g}$, $4e_u$, $1b_{2g}$	$1a_{2g}$, $4e_u$, $2e_g$	} as (II)
16.16	D	$3b_{1g}$, $2e_g$, $3a_{1g}$, $3e_u$	$3b_{1g}$, $2e_g$, $3a_{1g}$, $3e_u$	$1b_{2g}$	
16.68	D	$2a_{2u}$, $2b_{2u}$	$2a_{2u}$, $2b_{2u}$	$2b_{2u}$, $2a_{2u}$, $3b_{1g}$, $3e_u$, $3a_{1g}$	
19.68	E		$2e_u$, $2b_{1g}$, $2a_{1g}$	$2e_u$, $2b_{1g}$, $2a_{1g}$	

Source: Ref. 130 and references therein.

Hartree-Fock and limited configuration interaction calculation as described by Benard et al. [132].

Special emphasis has been given to the $M_2(mhp)_4$ complexes, where M = Cr, Mo, Rh, and mhp stands for 6-methyl-2-oxopyridine. Several groups have studied this type of complex [133-137] with UPS and theoretical calculations. However, uncertainties in the spectral interpretation persist, in particular there is concern about the assignment of the σ-bonding metal-metal orbital. $Cr(mhp)_4$ and $Mo(mhp)_4$ are of special interest in view of the very short metal-metal distance in the chromium complex [133].

Bursten et al. [136] made the assignment of the He(I) spectra of a series of five homologous compounds, $MM'(mhp)_4$ ($MM' = Cr_2$, CrMo, Mo_2, MoW, and W_2) only with guidance from SCF-Xα-SW calculations. The suggested order of the orbitals is $\delta_{MM'}$, $\pi_{MM'}$, $\pi_{1(lig)}$, $a_2(lig)$, $\pi_{2(lig)}$, σ'_{MM}, as shown in Table 52 and Fig. 48.

Peak E in particular has been assigned by Bursten et al. to the σ metal-metal bonding orbital because of consistent trends in the strength of the metal-metal bond, the force constants from the Raman frequencies, and the broadness and intensity of these peaks

Table 52   Photoelectron Data for the $M_2(mhp)_4$ Molecules

$M_2(mhp)_4$	Vertical ionizations (eV)						
	A	X	B	C	D	E	F
	$\delta_{MM'}$	$\pi_{MM'}$	$\pi_{1(lig)}$	$a_2(lig)$	$\pi_{2(lig)}$	σ'_{MM}	
Cr-Cr	6.8		7.75	8.1	9.8	10.2	11.1
Mo-Cr	6.0		7.73	8.15	9.7	10.5	11.2
Mo-Mo	5.89		7.69	8.20	9.6	10.5	11.2
W-Mo	5.60		7.70	8.15	9.6	(10.4 - 11.2)[a]	
W-W	5.3	7.30	7.70	8.0	9.6	10.6	11.3

[a]Not able to resolve distinct peaks.
Source: Ref. 136.

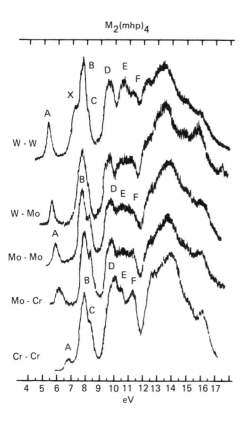

Figure 48   He(I) photoelectron spectra for the series of MM'(mhp)4 compounds.   Hatch marks on the top correspond to the integral eV values at the bottom.   (From Ref. 136.)

going through the series.   Objections can be made by the fact that only He(I) spectra have been measured, and that this peak is some-times hidden in the spectrum.

The assignment of Garner et al. [134] based on He(I) and He(II) spectra is different with respect to this σ orbital.   The He(I) spectra are shown in Fig. 49.   The vertical ionization potentials and the relative intensities are shown in Tables 53 and 54.

By analogy with the PE spectra of the $M_2(O_2Cr)_4$ (M = Cr, Mo) complexes, peak A in both spectra is assigned to the ionization from δ-bonding orbital.   The bands higher in energy than peak B have

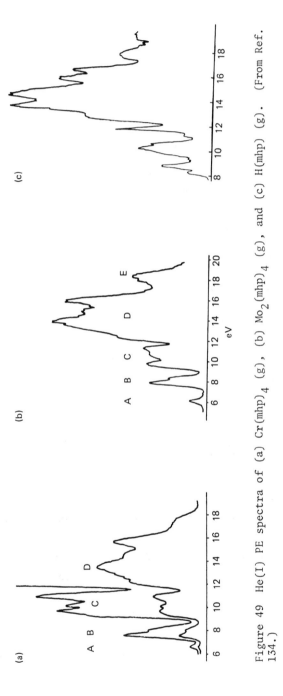

Figure 49 He(I) PE spectra of (a) Cr(mhp)$_4$ (g), (b) Mo$_2$(mhp)$_4$ (g), and (c) H(mhp) (g). (From Ref. 134.)

Table 53   Ionization Energies[a] of MM'$(mhp)_4$-type Complexes

$Cr_2(O_2CCF_3)_4$	Region[b]	$Cr_2(mhp)_4$	$Mo_2(mhp)_4$
10.04(2)	A	6.70(3)	5.84(3)
12.57(6)	B	7.74(2)	7.59(3)
		8.15(3)	8.02(3)
		9.51(5)	9.47(4)
16.00(7)	C	9.78(3)	
		10.27(3)	10.40(6)
17.32(5)		11.06(3)	11.01(4)
		12.40(10)	12.18(5)
20.8(1)	D	13.68(4)	13.58(6)
		14.70(5)	14.70(6)
		15.85(4)	15.70(6)
	E[c]	19.05(10)	18.65(10)

[a]In eV with estimated error in parentheses.
[b]See Figs. 48 and 49.
[c]Measured from He(II) spectrum.
Source: Ref. 134.

Table 54   Relative Intensities of Bands in
the PE Spectra of $M_2(mhp)_4$ Complexes

region	$Cr_2(MHP)_4$		$Mo_2(MHP)_4$	
	He(I)	He(II)	He(I)	He(II)
A	0.05	0.06	0.11	0.11
B	1.0	1.0	1.0	1.0
C	5.1	3.2	3.4	3.1

Source: Ref. 134.

similar relative intensities for both complexes and are thus assigned to ionizations from predominantly ligand orbitals. The intensity of A is significantly lower for $Cr_2(mhp)_4$ that for Mo_2- $(mhp)_4$, consistent with a lower photoionization cross section for chromium 3d compared to Mo 4d orbitals. A similar pattern in relative intensities is observed for peaks B and C. Therefore, it must be concluded that peaks A, B, and C possess considerable metal character.

Peak B contains ionizations from σ and π metal-metal bonding orbitals as well as ligand contributions. Peak C represents mainly ionizations from orbitals with ligand character together with contributions from metal-nitrogen and metal-oxygen bonds.

The situation in the $Rh_2(mhp)_4$ dimer is completely different. There is some controversy about the metal-metal bond in this dimer. It is suggested to be a triple bond by Cotton [110,138] and Richman [139] or a single bond by Norman [140].

Berry et al. [141] report, in an x-ray diffraction study of this compound, the shortest Rh-Rh bond length (2.359 Å), together with the He(I) and He(II) photoelectron spectra, which are shown in Fig. 50. The ionization energies are listed in Table 55.

The assignments (Table 55) are made under the following assumptions:

1. The metal-metal bonding orbitals are at higher bonding energy than the corresponding antibonding orbitals.

2. The relative peak areas are directly related to the degeneracy of the levels.

Objection against the first assumption is that "counter-intuitive" orbital mixing might be possible. The second assumption is a very doubtful one, owing to the cross-section differences. The assignment that the lowest IE values are attributed to electrons in the Rh-Rh δ^* and π^* orbitals is in agreement with a $(\sigma)^2(\pi)^4(\delta)^2(\pi^*)^4-$ $(\delta^*)^2$ configuration, corresponding with a metal-metal single bond as suggested by Norman [140]. The metal-metal triple bond

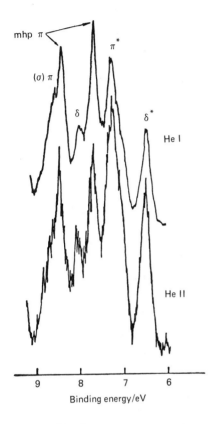

Figure 50   Lower-energy regions of the He(I) and He(II) spectra of $Rh_2(mhp)_4$.   (From Ref. 141.)

configuration $(\sigma)^2(\pi)^4(\delta)^2(\delta^*)^2(p_{z_1})^2(p_{z_2})^2$ is inconsistent in every way with the photoelectron spectral features.

B.   Metal Halogen Dimers

Much attention has recently been paid to the complex dichlorotetra-carbonyldirhodium(I).   Many differences in the assignments of two recent UPS papers [142,143] and two theoretical papers [144,145] can be recognized.   Many large discrepancies are found due to the orbital relaxations, even between calculations of the same type

Table 55   Ionization Energies for $Rh_2(mhp)_4$

Peak	Ionization energy/eV	Assignment	Orbital character[a]
A	6·49(2)	Rh–Rh δ*	a₂
B	7·25(2)	Rh–Rh π*	e
C	7·64(2)	mhp π	b₁,e
D	8·00(2)	Rh–Rh δ	b₁
E	8·37(2)	mhp π	a₂
F	8·53(3)	Rh–Rh π (σ)	e(a₁)

[a] In D_{3d} symmetry.

Source: Ref. 141.

(SW-Xα in Refs. 143 and 144), since one has been performed without and the other with the transition-state procedure. The agreement between the bands in the measured spectra and those calculated with the last procedure is good, as shown in Table 56.

The first three bands, A, A', and A'', gain in intensity upon changing from He(I) to He(II), although the enhancement of A'' is doubtful, as already mentioned by Dickson et al. [142]. So the first two bands can definitely be assigned to predominantly Rh-4d orbitals. In the orbitals belonging to the third band, some Cl character must be present. The next bands, B, B', and B'', change drastically in relative intensity [He(I)/He(II)], incidating considerable Cl character. By comparison with UPS of other carbonyl complexes, the bands C and C' are unambiguously assigned to carbonyl orbitals. Striking are the large differences between the two spectra of the same compound [142,143] in peak positions and in the shapes of the bands.

Comparing $Rh_2Cl_2(CO)_4$ with $Rh_2Cl_2(PF_3)_4$, Nixon could conclude that PF_3 has an overall greater electron-withdrawing power than CO, a conclusion that is now well established. Generally, the spectra and the He(I)/He(II) intensity ratios agree with the bent (C_{2v}) structure of the molecule in the gas phase and with the theoretical calculations indicating some minor redistributions of charge in the

Table 56   Detailed Assignments for $Rh_2Cl_2(CO)_4$ from Xα-SW Calculations

exptl label	C_{2v} level	% Rh	main character	calcd ionization energy,[a] eV	exptl ionization energy, eV	calcd density	approx. obsd intens
A	9b₁	92	Rh 4d	10.1	9.01	2	1
	11a₁	90		10.2			
	10a₁	67		10.7			
A'	8b₁	74	Rh 4d	10.7	9.77	3	3
	9b₂	70		(10.8)			
	7a₂	86		(11.1)			
A''	9a₁	72	Rh 4d	11.2	10.66	3	2
	7b₁	86		(11.2)			
B	8b₂	7	Cl 3p	12.1	11.29	1	2
	6b₁	14		(12.4)			
B'	7b₂	18	Cl 3p	(12.6)	12.39	4	5
	8a₁	23		12.8			
	6a₂	9		(12.8)			
B''	7a₁	16	Cl 3p	13.3	13.41	1	1
	6b₂	0		(14.0)			
	5a₂	1		(14.0)			
	4a₂	7		(14.2)			
	5b₂	8	CO 1π	(14.2)	15.0 sh		
	5b₁	7		14.3			
C	6a₁	8		(14.3)			
	5a₁	15		(14.6)			
	4b₁	13		(14.6)			
	4a₁	33	CO 5σ	(16.6)			
	3b₁	33		16.7			
					16.08		
	3a₂	43	CO 5σ	(17.3)			
	4b₂	45		(17.3)			
	2a₂	2		(19.5)			
C'	3b₂	3	CO 4σ	(19.5)	18.93		
	3a₁	1		19.6			
	2b₁	1		(19.6)			
	2b₂	3	Cl 3s	(24.3)	b		
	2a₁	2		(24.5)			

[a]Energies in parentheses are estimated from the ground-state eigenvalues and the explicitly calculated relaxation of levels of similar type.   The accuracy of this procedure is estimated to be ca. 0.1 eV.

[b]Outside range.

Source: Ref. 143.

complex. Hence the atoms are almost neutral, indicating that no
direct Rh-Rh bond exists, while strong Rh-Cl interactions dominate
the structure.

Completely different is the bonding in the pure halogen metal-
metal compounds of molybdenum, $[Mo_2Cl_8]^{4-}$, and rhenium, $[Re_2Cl_8]^{2-}$
and Re_3Cl_9. The quadrupole molybdenum-molybdenum bond (2.138 Å)
with the formal description $\delta_{xy}^2(\pi_{xz,yz})^4\sigma_{z^2}^2$ has been supported by
x-ray emission [146] and x-ray photoelectron spectroscopy [147]
measurements. Comparison of these spectroscopic results with both
the theoretical treatments of this molecule, an ab initio calculation [123], and an Xα calculation [120] showed for the former agreement in the Mo-Mo bonding region but disagreement for the Mo-Cl
bonds, while in the latter the separations between the Mo-Cl, σ, π,
and δ orbitals appeared to be too low. The overall picture seems
to be the same, however.

From the rhenium clusters, structural and vibrational studies,
as well as two different photoelectron studies, have been published
[148]. The results of Trogler et al. are rather unexpected, since
in the calculations the orbitals originating from Re(5d) and Cl(3p)
are randomly spread over approximately 8 eV (6.55-14.27 eV; observed
8.85-13.85 eV). Unfortunately, the He(I) spectrum is not of good
quality, and no He(II) spectrum was available, so that no sound
assignment could be given. The main cause of the disagreement with
the results of Bursten et al. [149] is the fact that only for the
HOMO has a transition-state calculation been performed, and it was
assumed that all other orbitals would have the same relaxation
shifts. For several transition metal complexes it has been shown
that this procedure is erroneous [125,126]. The assignments of
Bursten et al. are completely different, being based on He(I)/He(II)
intensity differences with the assistance of SCF-Xα-SW and Fenske-
Hall molecular orbital calculations.

The He(I) and He(II) photoelectron spectra are shown in Fig.
51. In Table 57 the ionization energy values are tabulated, together
with the relative band intensities. Here the first two ionizations

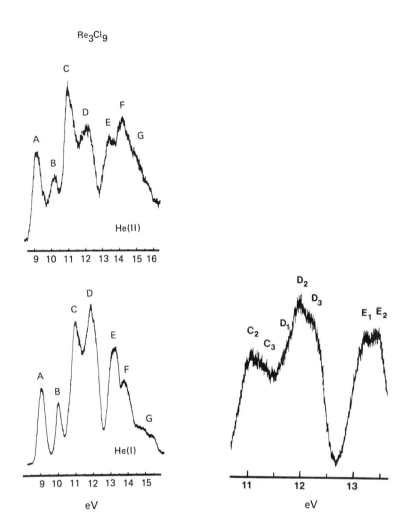

Figure 51   He(I) and He(II) spectra of Re_3Cl_9.   (From Ref. 149.)

Table 57   He(I)/He(II) Intensity Ratios in the PE Spectrum
of Re_3Cl

peak	energy[a]	intensity He(I)	He(II)
A	9.15	2.1	3.4
B	10.10	1.6	2.0
C_1	10.78 (sh)		
C_2	11.07	6.0	7.1
C_3	11.26 (sh)		
D_1	11.67 (sh)		
D_2	11.93	9.3	6.3
D_3	12.11 (sh)		
E_1	13.18	6.6	4.5
E_2	13.35		
F	13.88	4.6	4.7
G_1	14.92	2.9	5.4
G_2	15.43		

[a]Energies are in eV; sh, shoulder.
Source: Ref. 149.

are from metal-metal π-bonding orbitals. The calculated rhenium
contributions (69% for peak A and 45-50% for peak B) are consistent
with the He(I)/He(II) intensity ratios. The normalized He(I) intensity for peak C and the He(II) intensity change points to the same
assignment that the calculation indicates (i.e., several terminal
chlorine orbitals and the Re-Re σ-bonding orbital). Peaks D and E
are principally Cl in character. Peaks F and G finally may be
assigned to ionizations from the metal-metal bonding and metal
ligand bonding MOs.

The He(I) and He(II) PE spectra of Re_3Br_9 are shown in Fig. 52.
The He(I) spectra of Re_3Br_9 and Re_3Cl_9 appear to be quite similar,
particularly if one takes into account the lower electronegativity
of Br, thus suggesting that the electronic structures of both compounds are quite similar.

The He(I)/He(II) spectra, however, illustrate that the ordering of the molecular orbitals in Re_3Br_9 is rather different from

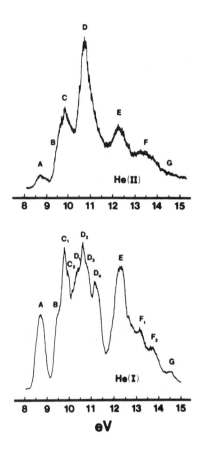

Figure 52   He(I) and He(II) spectra of Re_3Br_9.   (From Ref. 149.)

that of Re_3Cl_9.   In Re_3Br_9 the first three peaks seem to be composed of ligand orbitals.   The main difference is that the terminal
Br levels are now above the e" and a_2'' Re π bonds.   The metal orbitals are shifted into the lower ML π-bonding orbital region.   Peak A
originates from a ligand e" level which is destabilized by a ReBr
antibonding interaction, the weaker band of the a_2'' ligand level for
shoulder B.   The terminal and bridging Br lone pairs give rise to
peaks C and E.   D is a mixture which is in agreement with He(I)/
He(II), while F and G are mainly from Re-Re and Re-Cl π-bonding MOs.

The $[Re_3Cl_{12}]^{3-}$ ion is derived from Re_3Cl_9, which possesses acceptor properties for three more ligands. The electronic structure of the Re_3Cl_9 is obviously, but only slightly, perturbed by the addition of three axial Cl^- ions.

C. Metal-Metal Bonds in Transition Metal Clusters

Recently, the photoelectron spectra of several polynuclear complexes of the type $M_x(CO)_yL$ with metal-metal bonds have been published [125,126,150,151]. For the first time bands in the photoelectron spectra of clusters have been assigned to IPs of the metal-metal orbitals. MO calculations have also been performed on several of these molecules, leading to a confirmation of these assignments. The metal-metal bonding orbital seems always to be the highest occupied molecular orbital, according to calculations. The calculations of Anderson [152] with a modified extended Hückel scheme for $[Fe_2(CO)_6(acetylene)]$ and $[Co_2(CO)_6(acetylene)]$ and of Thorn and Hoffmann [153] with extended Hückel for $M_2(CO)_6L$ (M = Fe, Co) complexes also point to this conclusion. Heyser [127] has published HFS-DV-Xα calculations for $Fe_2(CO)_9$ and $Co_2(CO)_8$. He came to the unexpected conclusion that no net metal-metal bond exists in these complexes and that bonding occurs via the bridging carbonyls. This was in contrast to the computational result for $Mn_2(CO)_{10}$, where the two $Mn(CO)_5$ fragments are bonded by a single Mn-Mn bond.

More or less along the same line are the calculations via the Fenske-Hall scheme for $Co_2(CO)_8$ [154], indicating that bonding is best considered as multicentered bonds delocalized over the metal and the bridging carbonyls. In contrast with this are results for $Fe_2(CO)_6LL'$, also with the Fenske-Hall scheme [155], indicating that the bonding characteristics of the $Fe_2(CO)_6$ dimers are markedly different from those of $Co_2(CO)_8$. For the $Fe(CO)_6LL'$ dimers a distinct "bent" metal-metal bond was calculated.

This feature was also found in the recently published CNDO/2 and ab initio calculations for a series of $Fe_2(CO)_6LL_1$ complexes (L = L' = S,i-propyl S, LL_1 = t-butyl NS). These results could be

used to get a proper assignment of the UV PE spectra [126]. The
UV PE spectra of these compounds all have roughly the same features,
as shown in Fig. 53. In the first region, between 8 and 10 eV, the
metal d orbitals could readily be assigned since the broad band increases strongly in intensity on going from He(I) to He(II) radiation. A distinct shoulder was found on the low-energy side of this
band in the spectra of most of these complexes, and was assigned
to the $5a_1$ metal-metal bonding orbital. The second region contains
bands from the bridging ligands. The bands attributed to ionizations from sulfur 3p orbitals are all much lower in intensity in the
He(II) spectra, as expected. The assignments of the spectra of
these complexes are tabulated in Table 58.

Satisfactory assignments of the PE spectra could also be made
on the basis of the various MO schemes. The results of the ab
initio ground state (A_1) calculation (using Koopmans' theorem), for
instance for $Fe_2(CO)_6S_2$, are shown in Table 59.

This result is in agreement with the Fenske-Hall calculation.
Six metal d orbitals $(1a_1, 1b_1, 2a_1, 1a_2, ab_1, 1b_2)$ form bonding
and antibonding combinations which are highly localized on the metal
atom. Only the uppermost $5a_1$ orbital (the bent Fe-Fe bonding orbital) does not have an occupied antibonding counterpart. This $5a_1$
orbital has only 53% metal d character and is greatly delocalized
over the carbonyl ligands. Experience with transition metal complexes over the last years has shown that the relaxation energy
associated with orbitals of substantial metal character is much
larger than that of the ligand orbitals [125,126,156,157]. In that
light, the very large spread of the calculated IE values in the
ground state is not unexpected. The only way to obtain accurate IE
values is to perform a series of SCF calculations of the ion states.

The ΔSCF procedure failed to yield satisfactory results.
Relaxation corrections of only a few electron volts were found for
the metal states. The disagreement between theory and experiment
has been ascribed to the physically unrealistic description of the
ionization process. For the lower-lying metal orbitals the removal

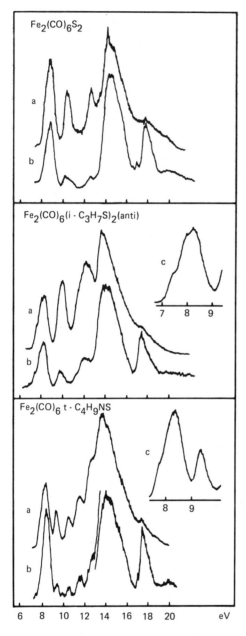

Figure 53 He(I) and He(II) spectra of $Fe_2(CO)_6S_2$, $Fe_2(CO)_6(i-C_3H_7S)_2-$ (anti), and $Fe_2(CO)_6(t-C_4H_9NS)$. (From Ref. 126.)

Table 58 Comparison of the MO Methods for the Bridging Ligand MOs for $Fe_2(CO)_6S_2$

Experiment	ab initio	Fenske-Hall	Ext. CNDO
10.28	10.0 (a_2)	11.55 (a_2)	12.35 (a_2)
	10.1 (b_2)	11.86 (b_2)	12.65 (b_2)
12.57	11.8 (a_1)	14.61 (a_1)	14.50 (a_1)
(13.5)	12.8 (a_1)	15.62 (a_1)	15.77 (a_1)
	12.9 (b_1)	15.68 (b_1)	16.60 (b_1)

Source: Ref. 126.

Table 59 Results of the MO calculation on $Fe_2(CO)_6S_2$ Using Koopmans' Theorem

Orbital	Koopmans' Theorem Ionization potential (eV)	Sulphur population 3s(%)	3p(%)	Carbonyl (%)	Iron population 4s(%)	3d(%)	Type
$5a_1$	6.0	0	1	48	12	41	Bent metal bond
$2a_2$	10.0	4	82	3	0	11	Sulphur π_g
$2b_2$	10.1	0	80	4	0	16	Sulphur π_g
$4a_1$	11.8	11	74	1	2	12	Sulphur σ_g
$3b_1$	12.8	0	66	6	0	28	Sulphur π_u
$3a_1$	12.9	0	75	10	2	13	Sulphur π_u
$1b_2$	14.8	0	1	15	0	84	M-M antibonding
$2b_1$	14.9	0	0	19	0	81	M-M antibonding
$1a_2$	15.3	1	2	14	0	83	M-M bonding
$2a_1$	15.4	5	5	20	0	70	M-M bonding
$1b_1$	16.0	0	20	15	0	65	M-M antibonding
$1a_1$	16.7	2	15	17	0	66	M-M bonding
-	17.7	-	-	-	-	-	1st Carbonyl

Note: Atomic charges are: for Fe, +0.74; S, -0.25; C(average), +0.12; O(average), -0.29.
Source: Ref. 126.

of an electron from the canonical MOs results in an ion with a charge of +0.5e on each iron atom. A better description of ionization, based on the long metal-metal distance, would be the description of ionization as a *localized* process. Herefor, wave functions with the metal and sulfur MOs localized using the Boys localization procedure [158] are required as a starting point for broken-symmetry calculations. The metal-metal bonding $5a_1$ orbital is unaffected by this localization procedure since the corresponding antibonding MO is unoccupied. The IE values calculated in this way showed large relaxation energies, of up to 10 eV.

Table 60 shows IE values and relaxation energies. It can be seen that all the metal 3d ionizations occur to lower energy than the ligand orbitals. These results indicate that using this broken-symmetry Hartree-Fock scheme, better agreement with experiment is obtained. It thus appears that, just as in the case of the "localization" of the corehole states in, for instance, nitrogen [159], the "repolarization" energy, the interaction of the hole with the surrounding electrons, is more important than the "delocalization" energy [160], even in the valence state! Thus it should always be kept in mind that in symmetrical molecules broken-symmetry HF solutions can be of help in the interpretation of spectral data. Examples of this can be found in, for instance, Refs. 159-164.

The spectra of $Fe_2(CO)_6B_2H_6$ and of $Fe_2(CO)_6S_2$ have been measured by Fehlner et al. [150] and the given assignments of the d

Table 60   ΔSCF and Relaxation Energies

MO	Orbital description	IE (eV)	Relative energy (eV)
84	$5a_1$ metal-metal σ	5.1	0.9
83	$2a_2$ sulfur π_g	8.8	1.2
82	$2b_2$ sulfur π_g	9.3	0.8
78	Iron lone pair d	8.1	6.7
75	Iron lone pair d	8.5	6.9

Source: Ref. 165.

bands are in agreement with the ab initio calculations as given in
Ref. 125. The spectra of a series of $Co(CO)_6C_2R_2$ complexes also
showed corresponding features: the metal-metal bonding orbital as
the HOMO, then the d-orbital bands of the metal, then a broad band
from the acetylene π orbitals not far shifted from those of the free
acetylene, and finally a broad region ionization from the π and σ
orbitals of the carbonyl ligands. The vertical IE values shown in
Table 61, demonstrate very clearly the influence of the substituents
of the alkyne ligand on the metal IE values. The electron-withdrawing and electron-donating capacities of R are directly reflected in
these IE values.

For a theoretical description of these systems, broken-symmetry
HF calculations were performed on $Co_2(CO)_6(C_2H_2)$, yielding qualitatively the same picture as for the iron dimers. The relaxation
energies of ionizations localized on the metal are again extremely
large, up to 10 eV, while those of the ligand orbitals are considerably smaller (1-2 eV). The ab initio calculation was found to be in
good agreement with the interpretation of the PE spectrum.

Mulliken population analysis yields a large positive charge
(+1.25e) on the metal atoms with a corresponding negative charge
(-0.62e) on the acetylene carbon atom. It is interesting to note
that the high negative charge on the acetylene ligand does not shift
the ligand IE values very much. The proximity of the two positive
cobalt atoms has a stabilizing effect.

The metal-metal bonded triangulo $Ru_3(CO)_{12}$ cluster has been
measured with UV PE spectra by Ajò et al. [166]. It is a pity that
in this paper only the He(I) PE spectrum is presented. He(I)/He(II)
intensity changes might confirm the assignment, now completely based
on CNDO calculations. The quoted expectation that Koopmans' theorem
will be valid for this complex is rather optimistic, as shown earlier in this chapter. Ajò et al. came to a calculated Ru-Ru bond
population of 0.304, suggesting a rather strong Ru-Ru bond. The
He(I)/He(II) spectra of Green et al. [167] recorded of the same compound each show two composite bands in the region 7-11 eV, as shown
in Fig. 54.

Table 61 Ionization Energies and Assignment for $Co_2(CO)_6(RC{\equiv}CR')$ [a]

	acetylene	4-methyl- -pentyn-2	4,4 dimethyl pentyn-2	3-hexyn	propargyl alcohol	2-methyl 3-butyn-2-ol
bent metal- -metal bond	(7.96)	(7.73)	(7.53	(7.8)	(7.89)	(7.87)
metal-d M.O.'s	8.74	8.4	8.4	8.6	8.7	8.7
π ligand	11.4(11.28)	10.40(9.55)	10.35(9.24) 10.59(9.46)	10.7(9.70)	10.82 $\begin{matrix}10.41\\10.64\end{matrix}$ 11.29(n_o)(11.21)	10.60 $\left(\begin{matrix}10.41\\10.61\end{matrix}\right)$ 10.98(n_o)(10.89)

[a]Values for the free ligands are in parentheses.
Source: Ref. 125.

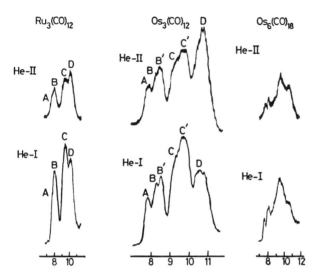

Figure 54   He(I) and He(II) spectra of $Ru_3(CO)_{12}$, $Os_3(CO)_{12}$, and $Os_6(CO)_{18}$.   (From Ref. 167.)

Each band could be subdivided into two parts.   In the paper
the starting point is that the measured intensity ratio between both
bands (1:3) suggests that the first band (A + B) account for 6 electrons and that the second band (C + D) arises from 18 electrons.
Then the band pattern strongly suggests that A and B account for a_1
and e symmetry, respectively, an interpretation that is consistent
with the spin-orbital splitting of the band B found in the corresponding osmium cluster.   Band C, as shown, gives an intensity de-
pletion in the He(II) spectrum, as expected from orbitals, which
give back-bonding to CO, relative to metal-metal bonding orbitals
[168].

Band D shows a relative increase in the He(II) spectrum which is
characteristic for orbitals with a high metal content.   This assignment is consistent with the EH calculations of Hoffmann et al. [169],
including the result that the 2a' orbital is the HOMO, and not 2e'.
In Table 62 the IE data are given for the Ru and corresponding Os
cluster as well as for the bicapped tetrahedral cluster $Os_6(CO)_{18}$.

Table 62   Ionization Energy Data for Metal Carbonyl Clusters (eV)

	$Ru_3(CO)_{12}$		$Os_3(CO)_{12}$	$Os_6(CO)_{18}$
A	7.7^a	A	7.83	7.50
B	8.0	B	8.28	8.09
		B'	8.50	9.47
C	9.4	C	9.24	10.44
		C'	9.60	
D	10.1	D	10.44	

[a]The error on these values is 0.2 eV, owing to spectral shift with time.
Source: Ref. 167.

These data indicate that the first IE value decreases only by 0.3 eV when the number of metal atoms is doubled. From the differences between the observed IE values and the work functions of the corresponding metal surfaces (4.71 eV for Ru and 4.87 eV for Os) it is concluded that the electronic characteristics differ significantly from those of the surfaces.

D. Carbonyl Clusters

To compare the osmium cluster $Os_3(CO)_{12}$ with the isoelectronic hydrido cluster $Re_3(CO)_{12}H_3$ and further with $Os_4(CO)_{12}H_4$ and $Os_3(CO)_{10}H_2$, Green et al. have measured the UV PE spectra [170]. The He(I) and He(II) photoelectron spectra are shown in Fig. 55. The metal d orbitals are easily assigned by comparing the He(I)/He(II) intensity ratios.

   In the same way the 12-eV band of $Re_3(CO)_{12}H_3$, showing a large decrease in He(II), is assigned to an orbital predominantly localized on the hydrogen bridging atoms, since the ionization cross section of a hydrogen is orbital is known to drop considerably, going from He(I) to He(II) emission.

   All these observed bands in the range 11.9-12.7 eV for $Re_3(CO)_{13}H_3$, $Os_3(CO)_{10}H_2$, and $Os(CO)_{12}H_4$ suggest that the M-H-M

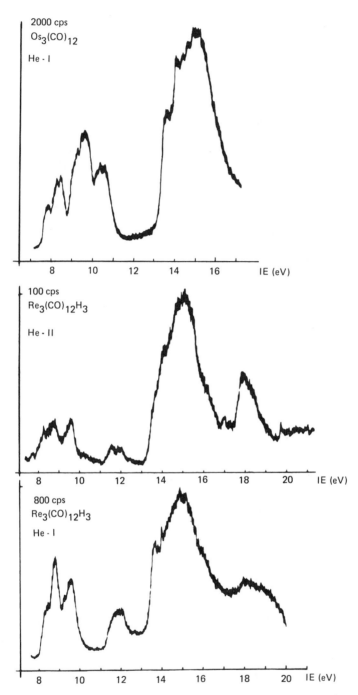

Figure 55   He(I) spectrum of $Os_3(CO)_{12}$ and the He(I) and He(II) spectra of $Re_3(CO)_{12}H_3$.   (From Ref. 170.)

bridging bonds are essentially of a localized nature. This is confirmed by the spectrum of $Ir_3(CO)_{12}$, which is isoelectronic with $Os(CO)_{12}H_4$ and in which this band has disappeared, while the remaining parts of the PE spectra are essentially identical.

A topological model, as proposed by Lipscomb [170a] for the boranes, was used for the description of the three-center two-electron bonds in these complexes.

Very recently in a He(I) PE study of $Co_3(CO)_9CY$ (Y = CH_3, F, Cl), Granozzi et al. [170b] could give an assignment of the bands. An extensive π interaction of the $Co_3(CO)_9C$ unit with the Y substituent was suggested.

Granozzi et al. [170c] also performed a PE study on μ-CH_2-$[(\eta^5$-$C_5H_5)Mn(CO)_2]_2$, which has a very short Mn-Mn interatomic distance [2.799 Å compared to 2.932 in $Mn_2(CO)_{10}$]. A comparison of the experimental data with the CNDO results is shown in Table 63. The assignment is consistent with He(I)/He(II) intensity changes.

In conclusion, the HOMO represents the direct Mn-Mn bonding interaction, while an orbital representing a large amount of Mn-CH_2-Mn π interactions contributes in the next highest band.

E.   Recent Developments

Much work has been done on metal-metal bonded binuclear complexes bridged with various ligands. Nixon et al. [209] studied $Rh_2X_2L_4$ (X = Cl, Br, I; L = CO, PF_3) and $IrCl_2(PF_3)_4$, using He(I) and He(II) spectra and UV spectroscopy, as an extension of the work reported in Ref. 142. The assignments were made using cross-section assignments and correlations with analogous complexes. Previous assignments [142] were confirmed. The IE values are listed in Table 64.

Granozzi et al. studied the electronic structure of $(\mu_2$-CO)-$[(\eta^5$-$C_5H_5)Rh(CO)]_2$ using UPS and CNDO calculations [210] and concluded using a comparison with results from Refs. 170c and 231 on $(\mu_2$-$CH_2)[(\eta^5$-$C_5H_5)MnCO)_2]_2$ that μ_2-CO is a worse π acceptor than μ_2-CH_2. It is indicated that the Rh-Rh and Rh $\overset{CO}{}$ Rh are the highest occupied MOs and that they are close in energy. $[Ni(\eta^5$-$C_5H_5)(\mu$-CO)]_2$

Table 63   Ionization Potentials of $\mu\text{-CH}_2[(\eta^5\text{-C}_5\text{H}_5)\text{Mn(CO)}_2]_2$

Experimental data (eV)	Eigenvalues CNDO	Assignment
6.8	-6.90	Mn-Mn bonding
7.1-7.7	-7.7	
	-7.89	3d Mn
	-8.10	
	-8.18	
8.5	-8.59	Mn CH_2-Mn σ bonding
9.3-9.9	-9.23	
	-9.45	π C_5H_5 + metal MOs
	-9.56	
	-9.58	
10.5	-12.16	CH_2 σ lone pair pointing toward center of the ring
	-12.72	
	-12.78	C_5H_5 σ MOs
	-12.93	
	-13.06	

Source: Ref. 170b.

was also studied by Granozzi et al. using He(I) and He(II) PE
spectroscopy [211]. Strong π back-bonding to the bridging carbonyls
was found and it is also indicated that no net Ni-Ni bonding interactions are present.

Vites and Fehlner studied the methylene-bridged complex:
$[(\mu\text{-CH}_2)\text{Fe}_2\text{(CO)}_8]$ using He(I) and Ne(I) PE spectra [212]. In this
study also the π back-bonding capacity of $\mu\text{-CH}_2$ was stressed. (μ-
Butatriene)hexacarbonyldiiron complexes (butatriene = C_4H_4 and
C_4Me_4) were studied [213]. Assignments were made in agreement with
results from previous work on related diironhexacarbonyl complexes
[126]. CNDO calculations indicate the presence of two strong Fe-C

Table 64 Ionization Energies (eV) and Assignments for $M_2L_2L_4$

Band Type:	A Metal orbitals								B Halogen orbitals						P	
									Localized	Bridging					M-P	
	$9b_1$	$11a_1$	$10a_1$	$8b_1$	$9b_2$	$7a_2$	$9a_1$	$7b_1$	$8b_2$	$6b_1$	$7b_2$	$8a_1$	$6a_2$	$7a_1$	σ
Complex															
$Rh_2Cl_2(CO)_4$	9.0	9.8					10.7		11.3		12.4			13.4	–
$Rh_2Br_2(CO)_4$	9.0	9.7						10.9			12.1			–	–
$Rh_2Cl_2(PF_3)_4$	9.0	10.0						11.2			12.4			13.3	14.5
$Rh_2Br_2(PF_3)_4$	8.9	9.7						10.8			12.1			–	14.2
$Rh_2I_2(PF_3)_4$	9.1						9.7		10.3		11.8			–	13.9
$Ir_2Cl_2(PF_3)_4$	8.9	9.5	10.3			11.1			11.5		12.8			13.9	15.3

Source: Ref. 209.

bonds accounting for the major $Fe_2(CO)_6$ butatriene interaction. Much work was also done on tri-, tetra-, and so on, metal complexes.

The He(I) photoelectron spectra of $[Co_3(CO)_9CY]$ (Y = H, F, Cl, Br, I, CH_3, or CF_3) and some He(II) spectra were reported and assigned [214]. Ionizations corresponding to the CY group can be assigned in all the compounds (Table 65).

Sherwood and Hall have published the He(I) spectra of a series of $[(\mu\text{-}H)_3Ru_3(CO)_9(\mu_3\text{-}CX)]$ complexes [215]. It is suggested that the Ru-H-Ru interaction is best described as a three-center two-electron bridge without direct Ru-Ru bonds. DeKock et al. published the He(I) and Ne(I) PE spectra for the related species $[(\mu\text{-}H_3Fe_3\text{-}(CO)_9(\mu_3\text{-}CCH_3)]$ and $Co_3(CO)_9(CCH_3)$ [219].

Costa et al. have also reported the PE spectra of $Co_3(CO)_9CH$ and $Co_3(CO)_9CCH_3$ [220]. The ionization from the CH and CCH_3 portions of these molecules are correlated with ionizations from species on a metal surface.

Chesky and Hall [232] have published the PE data for a series of mixed metal carbonyl sulfide clusters. In this study the variation in metal was very elegantly used to demonstrate the localized ion states arising from ionization from metal d levels. This was also invoked in theoretical studies on, for example, $Fe_2(CO)_6S_2$ [126]. Bonding in metal-acetylene complexes has been studied by various authors [216-218,221-223].

DeKock et al. [219] have studied a series of $R_2C_2Co_2(CO)_6$ complexes, focusing in particular on the nature of the highest occupied MO. Based on substituent shifts it is concluded that the HOMO is the b_1 bridging ligand-metal orbitals. This is in contrast with previous work done at our laboratory. In Ref. 127 it is suggested that the HOMO is the a_1 metal-metal bonding orbital based on all-electron ab initio calculations. In this study it was found that upon substitution the HOMO and the Co 3d band were influenced to the same extent by the substituent. The difference between these ionizations stays around 0.8 ± 0.1 eV. (No trend is visible; the spread is probably due to the experimental difficulties and alcohol

Table 65 Ionization Energies and Assignments for $Co_3(CO)_9(CY)$[a]

	Y						Assignment
CF_3	F	Cl	Br	I	H	CH_3	
8.38(3)	8.18(5)	8.11(5)	8.02	7.92	8.12(9)	7.99(8)	$Co_3(d)$
8.99(5)	8.83(3)	8.72(2)	8.53	8.50	8.77(2)	8.59(3)	$Co_3(d)$
10.54(2)	10.13(2)	9.85(6)	9.63	9.30	10.31(5)	9.95(1)	$(Co_3-C)e(\pi)$
			11.56(6)	10.81(2)			$X(np_\pi)$
		12.55(5)			12.62(9)		$\sigma(C-H)$
						12.93(4)	$(CH_3)e$
			12.70				$\sigma(C-Br)?$
				13-16			$CO(5\sigma + 1\pi)$
17.97	17.94	17.80	17.80	17.91	17.81	17.77	$CO(4\sigma)$

[a]Quantities in parentheses are standard deviations.
Source: Ref. 214.

groups on the acetylene ligand.) The evidence is not unambiguous
and more work should be done, perhaps using stronger substituent
effects, to clarify this matter.

In Ref. 217 Casarin et al. published the He(I) and He(II) spectra of $[(Ni(\eta^5-C_5H_5))_2(\mu-C_2R_2)]$ (R = H or CF_3). In these complexes
two ionizations at very low IE values "stand out of the crowd" of
the remaining metal d orbitals (the metal character of these bands
is, of course, verified using He(II) spectra). The IE values and
assignments for these molecules are listed in Table 66.

Again the first ionization band is assigned to the metal-metal
bonding orbital. This was also supported by ab initio calculations
on $[Ni(\eta^5-C_5H_5)]_2(\mu-C_2H_2)$ [233]. The importance of π back-bonding
in these molecules is stressed and a very delocalized electron
distribution is suggested for these molecular systems [217].

Deshmukh et al. have studied the influence of the number of
surrounding metal atoms on carbyne fragments using $[Co_2(CO)_6(C_6H_5-$
CCH)], $[Co_4(CO)_{10}(C_6H_5CCH)]$, and $[Co_3(CO)_9(C_6H_5C)]$ [218]. It is
concluded, in agreement with work cited above, that π back-bonding
from the metal to the ligand is very important in these complexes.

Table 66 Ionization Energies (eV) for $[(Ni(\eta-C_5H_5))_2(\mu-C_2H_2)]$ (1)
and $[(Ni(\eta-C_5H_5))_2(\mu-C_2(CF_3)_2)]$ (2)

(1)	(2)	Assignment
6.85	7.5	Ni-Ni bonding MO
7.17	7.77	Ni-alkyne back-bonding MOs
8.2	9.0	Ni 3d nonbonding levels
8.9	9.4	
9.2	9.9	Ni-C_5H_5 bonding MOs
9.8	10.6	
10.9	11.3	π -alkyne MOs

Source: Ref. 217.

Combining results from UPS, ^{13}C-NMR, and CNDO calculations, the alkyne-cluster interaction in $[(\eta^2\text{-EtC}_2\text{Et})\text{Fe}_3(\text{CO})_9]$ was studied by Granozzi et al. [221]. This group also studied a series of μ-hydrido-μ_3 alkynyl triangulo ruthenium and osmium compounds [222,223] and a series of "butterfly" $\text{Ru}_4(\text{CO})_{12}(\text{R-C}_2\text{-R})$ cluster complexes [224]. In these very complicated systems at present only some general assignments can be made with confidence which gives some understanding of their intricate electronic structures.

Louwen et al. studied complexes with metal-metal bonds in which a transition metal is bonded to a main group metal [225-227]. In Ref. 225 a series of $\text{M}[\text{Co}(\text{CO})_4]_2$, $\text{M}[\text{Mn}(\text{CO})_5]_2$ with M = Zn, Cd, Hg is studied. Metal-metal bonding orbitals were assigned. In this work the "broken trend" upon going from Zn to Cd to Hg is used as an assignment criterion. This broken trend is caused by relativistic effects which have to be taken into consideration in the interpretation of the spectra.

In Ref. 226 a series of $\text{L}_3\text{MCo}(\text{CO})_4$ complexes is studied (with M = Si, Ge, Sn, Pd and L = Cl, Br, CH$_3$). Fairly complete assignments could be given using He(I) and He(II) spectra and by taking into account relativistic effects. A series of $[\text{CpM}(\text{CO})_x]_2\text{Zn}$ complexes with M = Fe, Cr, Mo, W and x = 2, 3 was studied in [227].

XII. PORPHYRINS

The He(I) spectra of several metal-porphyrin complexes have been reported. Khandelwal and Roebber [171] have published spectra of some meso-tetraphenylporphyrin (TPP) metal complexes. The complexity of bands above 7 eV resulting from the phenyl π electrons make these complexes unsuitable for a detailed analysis.

Much better resolved spectra were published for the octaethylporphyrin (OEP) complexes of Mg, Fe, Co, Ni, Cu, Zn, and Pd [172] (Table 67). Only the first two bands can be assigned unambiguously. These bands are at 6.7 eV in all spectra and all have the same band shape. There is a slight metal dependence of these bands. These bands have been assigned a_u and b_{1u} MOs on the basis of ab initio

Table 67 Vertical Ionization Potentials[a] from the PE Spectra of Octaethylporphyrin and Metallooctaethylporphyrins

compd	band no.[b]									
	1	2	3	4	5	6	7	8	9	10
H_2OEP	6.39	6.83	7.55[c]	7.80[d]	8.13[d]	8.44[d]	9.82[d]			
MgOEP	6.19	6.57	7.42[c]	7.63[d]	8.30	8.92	9.33	9.50[d]	9.68[d]	9.82[d]
FeOEP	6.06	6.48	7.29[c]	7.65[d]	8.05[e]	8.21[e]	9.40[f]	9.70[f]		
CoOEP	6.09	6.58	7.43[f]	7.92[f]	8.16	8.25	9.92[d]			
NiOEP	6.38	6.88	7.15	7.80	8.16	8.42[d]	9.96[d]	10.24[d]		
CuOEP	6.31	6.72	7.46	7.78[f]	8.01[f]	8.40[e]	9.74[d]			
ZnOEP	6.29	6.72	7.71[e]	8.04[f]	8.15[f]	9.74[d]				
PdOEP	6.37	6.82	7.28	7.42	7.78	8.08	8.30	8.43	9.41[f]	9.85[f]

[a] Peak maxima in eV (±0.03 eV).
[b] The corresponding peaks among these compounds do not necessarily have the same band number.
[c] Shoulder peak.
[d] Error limit ±0.1 eV.
[e] Error limit ±0.07 eV.
[f] Error limit ±0.07 eV.
Source: Ref. 172.

calculations [173,174]. A MS-Xα calculation was performed on the Cu-porphine complex [175]. The calculated g and hyperfine coupling tensors were in good agreement with the experimental results. However, the predicted value of 9.1 eV for the first IE (via Slater's transition state) is much larger than the observed value of 6.31 eV. It is also strange that the one-electron eigenvalues are all higher than the IE values, the more so since it is claimed by Xα theorists, without exception, that these eigenvalues are always lower than the observed IE.

The ab initio calculation of Kashigawa et al. [174] yield much better quantitative results using a double zeta basis and ΔSCF calculations for several of the ion states. For Co-porphyrin the predicted first and second IE values are 6.51 and 6.57 eV, resulting from A_{4u} and A_{2u} states, respectively. These values are in very good agreement with the experimental values of 6.09 and 6.58 eV.

The remaining bands in the spectra cannot be assigned with certainty at this moment, owing to the fact that no ΔSCF calculations have been performed for higher-lying ion states and it has become apparent that Koopmans' theorem does not hold for these complexes. In the spectra some changed are seen in the region 7-10 eV upon variation of the metal, but assignments of the metal d orbitals cannot yet be given since no He(II) spectra have been published.

Some evidence for the presence of metal d character in the region 7-10 eV is presented by XPS measurements [176]. Using MgXα radiation the metal d orbitals, which have a rather large cross section, can be observed in this region. From this study it was concluded that the metal and porphyrin levels are nearly uncoupled in the copper and zinc porphyrins, but that the two kinds of levels interact more extensively in the cobalt complex.

Related molecules have been studied by Berkowitz [177]. He studied an extensive series of phthalocyanine metal complexes. Also using a combination of UPS and XPS, he identified the metal 3d levels.

XIII.   FUTURE PROSPECTS FOR UPS OF TRANSITION METAL COMPLEXES

UPS is rapidly coming to full growth in the study of transition
metal complexes. See Ref. 228 for another recent review of this
field. It is now routinely possible to do He(I) and He(II) measurements on all sorts of transition metal complexes. Interpretations
based on cross-section variations and semiempirical MO schemes are
relatively easy for diamagnetic mononuclear complexes.

However, the study of polynuclear metal complexes is much more
difficult. The metal-metal bond is very intriguing and it has become clear that we are close to the reliability limit of even the
most sophisticated MO schemes. UPS will therefore develop its full
potential only if MO schemes improve dramatically. It is, of course,
also clear that this development will go hand in hand with advances
in computer technology. Larger and faster machines are necessary to
cope with large-scale ab initio calculations, including CI and so on.
Vector-processing machines look very promising in this respect.
Developments in both computers and theory will thus yield a more
accurate description of chemical bonding. Relativistic effects will
be included, open-shell systems will be more easy to study, and so
on.

Another field where theory should be developed more is in the
description of the ionization process. A detailed description of
cross-section variation with different incident photon energy is
essential for the characterization of the various ion states. In
conjunction with more accurate cross-section calculations, PE
measurements using synchroton radiation will be of tremendous importance. As a last possible trend, photoion-photoelectron measurements will probably prove their importance in the field of transition
metal complexes.

REFERENCES

1. A. F. Orchard, Electronic States of Inorganic Compounds: New
    Experimental Techniques (P. Day, ed.), D. Reidel, Dordrecht,
    The Netherlands, 1975, p. 267.

2. M. H. Cowley, *Prog. Inorg. Chem.*, 26:45 (1979).

3. C. Furlani and C. Cauletti, *Struct. Bond. (Berlin)*, 35:119 (1978).

4. J. W. Rabalais, *Principles of Ultraviolet Photoelectron Spectroscopy*, Wiley, New York, 1977.

5. R. G. Parr, *The Quantum Theory of Molecular Electronic Structure*, McGraw-Hill, New York, 1970, p. 43.

6. A. Schweig and W. Thiel, *J. Chem. Phys.*, 60:951 (1974).

7. K. H. Johnson, *J. Chem. Phys.*, 45:3085 (1966); K. H. Johnson, *Adv. Quantum Chem.*, 7:143 (1973).

8. R. P. Messmer, in *Modern Theoretical Chemistry*, Vol. 7 (G. A. Segal, ed.), Plenum, New York, 1977, p. 105; T. N. Rhodin and G. Ertl, eds., *The Nature of the Surface Chemical Bond*, North-Holland, Amsterdam, 1979.

9. N. Rösch, W. G. Klemperer, and K. H. Johnson, *Chem. Phys. Lett.*, 23:149 (1973).

10. E. J. Baerends and P. Ros, *Int. J. Quantum Chem.*, S12:169 (1978), and references therein.

11. H. Sambe and R. H. Felton, *J. Chem. Phys.*, 62:1122 (1975).

12. J. Tylicki, R. J. Hood, G. A. Gallup, and C. J. Eckhardt, *J. Chem. Phys.*, 66:3745 (1977).

13. R. J. Hoffmann, *J. Chem. Phys.*, 39:1397 (1963).

14. J. A. Pople and D. L. Beveridge, *Approximate Molecular Orbital Theory*, McGraw-Hill, New York, 1970; J. Del Bene and H. H. Jaffé, *J. Chem. Phys.*, 48:1807 (1968); G. Klopman and R. C. Evans, in *Semi-empirical Methods in Electronic Structure Calculations* (G. A. Segal, ed.), Plenum Press, New York, 1977.

15. J. F. Labarre, *Struct. Bond. (Berlin)*, 35:1 (1978); H. van Dam and A. Oskam, *J. Electron Spectrosc. Relat. Phenom.*, 16:307 (1979); H. van Dam, G. Boxhoorn, D. J. Stufkens, and A. Oskam, *Inorg. Chim. Acta*, 53:L235 (1981).

16. D. R. Lloyd and E. W. Schlag, *Inorg. Chem.*, 8:2544 (1969).

17. J. C. Green, D. I. King, and J. H. D. Eland, *J. Chem. Soc., Chem. Commun.*, 1121 (1970).

18. I. H. Hillier, M. F. Guest, B. R. Higginson, and D. R. Lloyd, *Mol. Phys.*, 27:215 (1974).

19. E. J. Baerends, Ch. Oudshoorn, and A. Oskam, *J. Electron Spectrosc. Relat. Phenom.*, 6:259 (1975).

20. B. R. Higginson, D. R. Lloyd, P. Burroughs, D. M. Gibson, and A. F. Orchard, *J. Chem. Soc., Faraday Trans. II*, 69:1659 (1973).

21. B. R. Higginson, D. R. Lloyd, J. C. Green, and I. H. Hillier, J. Chem. Soc., Faraday Trans. II, 70:1418 (1974).

22. I. H. Hillier and V. R. Saunders, J. Chem. Soc., Chem. Commun., 642 (1971); Mol. Phys., 22:1025 (1971).

23. E. J. Baerends and P. Ros, Mol. Phys., 28:1735 (1975).

24. B. I. King, H. Adachi, and S. Imoto, J. Electron Spectrosc. Relat. Phenom., 11:349 (1977).

25. J. B. Johnson and W. G. Klemperer, J. Am. Chem. Soc., 99:7132 (1977).

26. Ref. 16 in H. van Dam, A. Terpstra, D. J. Stufkens, and A. Oskam, Inorg. Chem., 19:3445 (1980).

27. D. E. Sherwood, Jr., and M. B. Hall, Inorg. Chem., 19:1805 (1980).

28. B. C. Bursten, D. G. Freier, and R. F. Fenske, Inorg. Chem., 19:1805 (1980).

29. K. G. Caulton and R. F. Fenske, Inorg. Chem., 7:1273 (1968).

30. B. Rees and A. Mitschler, J. Am. Chem. Soc., 98:7918 (1975).

31. M. B. Hall, J. Am. Chem. Soc., 97:2057 (1975).

32. D. L. Lichtenberger and R. F. Fenske, Inorg. Chem., 13:486 (1974).

33. S. Cradock, E. A. V. Ebsworth, and A. Robertson, J. Chem. Soc., Dalton Trans., 22 (1973).

34. B. R. Higginson, D. R. Lloyd, S. Evans, and A. F. Orchard, J. Chem. Soc., Faraday Trans. II, 71:1913 (1975).

35. D. L. Lichtenberger, D. Seitmann, and R. F. Fenske, J. Organomet. Chem., 117:253 (1976).

36. M. A. Weiner, A. Gin, and M. Lattman, Inorg. Chim. Acta, 24:235 (1977).

37. M. A. Weiner and M. Lattman, Inorg. Chem., 17:1084 (1978); L. W. Yarbrough II and M. B. Hall, Inorg. Chem., 17:2269 (1978).

38. T. F. Block and R. F. Fenske, J. Am. Chem. Soc., 99:4321 (1977).

39. D. L. Lichtenberger and R. F. Fenske, Inorg. Chem., 15:2015 (1976).

40. A. M. English, K. R. Plowman, I. S. Butler, E. Diemann, and A. Müller, Inorg. Chim. Acta, 32:113 (1979).

41. J. L. Hubbard and D. L. Lichtenberger, Inorg. Chem., 19:3865 (1980).

42. H. van Dam, Ph.D. thesis, University of Amsterdam, Amsterdam, 1981.

43. H. Daamen and A. Oskam, *Inorg. Chim. Acta,* 27:209 (1978).

44. H. Daamen and A. Oskam, *Inorg. Chim. Acta,* 26:81 (1978).

45. H. Daamen, A. Oskam, D. J. Stufkens, and H. W. Waaijers, *Inorg. Chim. Acta,* 34:253 (1979).

46. H. Daamen, G. Boxhoorn, and A. Oskam, *Inorg. Chim. Acta,* 28: 263 (1978).

47. H. Daamen, A. Oskam, and D. J. Stufkens, *Inorg. Chim. Acta,* 38:71 (1980).

48. M. C. Böhm, J. Daub, R. Gleiter, P. Hofmann, M. F. Lappert, and K. Ofele, *Chem. Ber.,* 113:3629 (1980).

48a. O. Goscinski, B. T. Pickup, and G. Puruis, *Chem. Phys. Lett.,* 22:167 (1975).

49. J. W. Lauher and R. Hoffmann, *J. Am. Chem. Soc.,* 98:1729 (1976).

50. J. V. Brencic and F. A. Cotton, *Inorg. Chem.,* 8:2698 (1969).

51. C. Cauletti, J. C. Green, M. R. Kelly, P. Powell, J. van Tilborg, J. Robbins, and J. Smart, *J. Electron Spectrosc. Relat. Phenom.,* 19:327 (1980).

52. S. Evans, M. L. H. Green, B. Jewitt, A. F. Orchard, and C. F. Pygall, *J. Chem. Soc., Faraday Trans. II,* 68:1847 (1972) and 70:356 (1974).

53. J. W. Rabalais, L. O. Werme, T. Bergmark, L. Karlsson, M. Hussain, and K. Siegbahn, *J. Chem. Phys.,* 57:1185 (1972).

54. D. L. Lichtenberger and R. F. Fenske, *J. Am. Chem. Soc.,* 98:50 (1976).

55. D. L. Lichtenberger, D. Sellmann, and R. F. Fenske, *J. Organomet. Chem.,* 117:253 (1976).

56. D. L. Lichtenberger and R. F. Fenske, *Inorg. Chem.,* 15:2015 (1976).

57. J. L. Hubbard and D. L. Lichtenberger, *Inorg. Chem.,* 19:1388 (1980).

58. B. E. R. Shilling, R. Hoffmann, and D. L. Lichtenberger, *J. Am. Chem. Soc.,* 101:585 (1979).

59. H. van Dam and B. A. Roosendaal, unpublished work.

60. H. van Dam and A. Oskam, spectra available on request.

61. D. A. Symon and Th. C. Waddington, *J. Chem. Soc., Dalton Trans.,* 2140 (1975).

62. J. C. Green and S. E. Jackson, *J. Chem. Soc., Dalton Trans.,* 1698 (1976).

63. Th. H. Whitesides, D. L. Lichtenberger, and R. A. Budnik, *Inorg. Chem.*, 15:68 (1975).

64. S. Evans, M. F. Guest, I. H. Hillier, and A. F. Orchard, *J. Chem. Soc., Faraday Trans. II*, 70:417 (1974).

65. J. C. Green, S. E. Jackson, and B. Higginson, *J. Chem. Soc., Dalton Trans.*, 403 (1975).

66. J. L. Peterson, D. L. Lichtenberger, R. F. Fenske, and L. F. Dahl, *J. Am. Chem. Soc.*, 97:6433 (1975), and references therein.

67. G. Condorelli, I. Fragala, A. Centineo, and E. Tondello, *J. Organomet. Chem.*, 87:311 (1975).

68. J. P. Clark and J. C. Green, *J. Less Common Met.*, 54:63 (1977).

69. C. Cauletti, John P. Clark, J. C. Green, S. E. Jackson, I. L. Fragala, E. Ciliberto, and A. W. Coleman, *J. Electron Spectrosc. Relat. Phenom.*, 18:61 (1980).

70. I. L. Fragala, T. J. Marks, P. J. Fagan, and J. M. Manriquez, *J. Electron Spectrosc. Relat. Phenom.*, 20:249 (1980).

71. H. van Dam, A. Terpstra, A. Oskam, and J. H. Teuben, *Z. Naturforsch.*, 36B:420 (1981).

72. I. L. Fragala, E. Ciliberto, and J. L. Thomas, *J. Organomet. Chem.*, 175:C25 (1979).

73. S. Evans, A. Hamnett, A. F. Orchard, and D. R. Lloyd, *J. Chem. Soc., Faraday Discuss.*, 54:227 (1973).

74. S. Evans, A. Hamnett, and A. F. Orchard, *J. Coord. Chem.*, 2:57 (1972).

75. H. G. Brittain, G. Horozogh, and A. D. Baker, *J. Electron Spectrosc. Relat. Phenom.*, 16:107 (1979).

76. H. van Dam and A. Oskam, *J. Electron Spectosc. Relat. Phenom.*, 17:353 (1979).

77. H. van Dam, A. Terpstra, D. J. Stufkens, and A. Oskam, *Inorg. Chem.*, 19:3448 (1980).

78. H. G. Brittain and R. L. Disch, *J. Electron Spectrosc. Relat. Phenom.*, 7:475 (1975).

79. C. Cauletti and C. Furlani, *J. Electron Spectrosc. Relat. Phenom.*, 6:465 (1975).

80. C. Cauletti, C. Furlani, and G. Storto, *J. Electron Spectrosc. Relat. Phenom.*, 18:329 (1980).

81. I. Fragala, L. L. Constanzo, E. Ciliberto, G. Condorelli, and C. D'Arregio, *Inorg. Chim. Acta*, 40:15 (1980).

82. F. A. Cotton, C. B. Harris, and J. J. Wise, *Inorg. Chem.*, 6:909 (1967).

83. See, for instance, F. G. A. Stone and R. West, eds., *Catalysis and Organic Synthesis*, Advances in Organometallic Chemistry, Vol. 17, Academic Press, New York, 1979; G. N. Schrauzer, ed., *Transition Metals in Homogeneous Catalysis*, Marcel Dekker, New York, 1971.

84. M. J. S. Dewar, *Bull. Soc. Chim. Fr.*, 18:C79 (1951).

85. J. Chatt and L. A. Duncanson, *J. Chem. Soc.*, 2939 (1953).

86. E. J. Baerends, Ch. Oudshoorn, and A. Oskam, *J. Electron Spectrosc. Relat. Phenom.*, 6:259 (1975).

87. H. van Dam and A. Oskam, *J. Electron Spectrosc. Relat. Phenom.*, 17:357 (1979).

88. A. Flamini, E. Samprini, F. Stefani, C. Cardaci, G. Bellachioma, and M. Andreocci, *J. Chem. Soc., Dalton Trans.*, 695 (1978).

89. H. van Dam and A. Oskam, *J. Electron Spectrosc. Relat. Phenom.*, 13:273 (1978).

90. W. E. Hill, C. H. Ward, T. R. Webb, and S. D. Worley, *Inorg. Chem.*, 18:2029 (1979).

91. H. van Dam and A. Oskam, *J. Electron Spectrosc. Relat. Phenom.*, 16:307.

92. M. J. S. Dewar and S. D. Worley, *J. Chem. Phys.*, 50:654 (1969); *J. Chem. Phys.*, 51:263 (1969).

93. S. D. Worley, *J. Chem. Soc., Chem. Commun.*, 980 (1970).

94. J. A. Connor, L. M. R. Derrick, M. B. Hall, I. H. Hillier, M. F. Guest, B. R. Higginson, and D. R. Lloyd, *Mol. Phys.*, 28:242 (1974).

95. J. A. Connor, L. M. R. Derrick, I. H. Hillier, M. F. Guest, and D. R. Lloyd, *Mol. Phys.*, 31:232 (1976).

96. M. B. Hall, I. H. Hillier, J. A. Connor, M. F. Guest, and D. R. Lloyd, *Mol. Phys.*, 30:839 (1975).

97. J. C. Green, P. Powell, and J. van Tilborg, *J. Chem. Soc., Dalton Trans.*, 1974 (1976).

98. S. D. Worley, T. R. Webb, D. H. Gibson, and T.-S. Ong, *J. Electron Spectrosc. Relat. Phenom.*, 18:189 (1980).

99. M. C. Böhm and R. Gleiter, *Chem. Ber.*, 113:3647 (1980).

100. M. C. Böhm and R. Gleiter, *Z. Naturforsch.*, 35B:1028 (1980).

101. R. D. Lloyd and N. Lynaugh, in *Electron Spectroscopy* (D. E. Shirley, ed.), North-Holland, Amsterdam, 1972, p. 445; D. A. Brown and A. Owens, *Inorg. Chim. Acta*, 5:675 (1971).

102. C. D. Batich, *J. Am. Chem. Soc.*, 98:7385 (1976).

103. M. C. Böhm, R. Gleiter, and C. D. Batich, *Helv. Chim. Acta*, 63:990 (1980).

104. M. C. Böhm and R. Gleiter, *Theor. Chim. Acta (Berlin)*, 57:315 (1980), and the following references therein: A. Veillard, *J. Chem. Soc., Chem. Commun.*, 1022:1427 (1969); M. M. Rohmer and A. Veillard, *J. Chem. Soc., Chem. Commun.*, 250 (1973); M. M. Rohmer, J. Demuynck, and A. Veillard, *Theor. Chim. Acta (Berlin)*, 36:93 (1974).

105. J. C. Green and E. A. Seddon, *J. Organomet. Chem.*, 198:C61 (1980).

106a. J. C. Green, D. R. Lloyd, L. Galyer, K. Mertis, and G. Wilkinson, *J. Chem. Soc., Dalton Trans.*, 1403 (1978).

106b. M. H. Chisholm, A. H. Cowley, and M. Lattman, *J. Am. Chem. Soc.*, 102:46 (1980).

106c. M. Basso-Bert, P. Cassoux, F. Crasnier, D. Gervais, J. F. Labarre, and P. de Loth, *J. Organomet. Chem.*, 136:201 (1977).

107a. J. A. Ulman, E. L. Andersen, and T. P. Fehlner, *J. Am. Chem. Soc.*, 100:456 (1978).

107b. C. Cauletti and C. Furlani, *J. Chem. Soc., Dalton Trans.*, 1068 (1977).

107c. C. Cauletti, N. V. Duffy, and C. L. Furlani, *Inorg. Chim. Acta*, 23:181 (1977).

107d. D. M. P. Mingos, *J. Chem. Soc., Dalton Trans.*, 602:610 (1977).

108. F. A. Cotton, N. F. Curtis, C. B. Harris, B. F. G. Johnson, S. J. Lippard, J. T. Mague, W. R. Robinson, and J. S. Wood, *Science*, 145:1305 (1964).

109. F. A. Cotton, *Acc. Chem. Res.*, 2:240 (1969).

110. F. A. Cotton, B. G. de Boer, M. D. La Prade, J. R. Pipal and D. A. Ucko, *Acta Crystallogr.*, B27:1644 (1971).

111. F. A. Cotton and C. B. Harris, *Inorg. Chem.*, 4:330 (1965).

112. F. A. Cotton and C. B. Harris, *Inorg. Chem.*, 6:924 (1967).

113. F. A. Cotton, *Inorg. Chem.*, 4:334 (1965).

114. F. A. Cotton, G. G. Stanley, B. J. Kalbacher, J. C. Green, E. Seddon, and M. H. Chisholm, *Proc. Natl. Acad. Sci USA*, 74:3109 (1977).

115. F. A. Cotton and B. J. Kalbacher, *Inorg. Chem.*, 16:2386 (1977).

116. F. A. Cotton and G. G. Stanley, *Inorg. Chem.*, 16:2668 (1977).

117. A. P. Mortola, J. W. Moskowitz, N. Rösch, C. D. Cowman, and H. B. Gray, *Chem. Phys. Lett.*, 32:283 (1975).

118. J. G. Norman, Jr., and H. J. Kolari, *J. Chem. Soc. Chem.*, *Commun.*, 649 (1975).

119. J. G. Norman, Jr., H. J. Kolari, H. B. Gray, and W. C. Trogler, *Inorg. Chem.*, 16:987 (1977).

120. J. G. Norman, Jr., and H. J. Kolari, *J. Am. Chem. Soc.*, 97: 33 (1975).

121. C. D. Garner, I. H. Hillier, M. F. Guest, J. C. Green, and A. W. Coleman, *Chem. Phys. Lett.*, 41:91 (1976).

122. M. Benard and A. Veillard, *Nouv. J. Chim.*, 1:97 (1977).

123. M. Benard, *J. Am. Chem. Soc.*, 100:2354 (1978).

124. M. F. Guest, I. H. Hillier, and C. D. Garner, *Chem. Phys. Lett.*, 48:587 (1977).

125. H. van Dam, J. N. Louwen, A. Oskam, M. Doran, and I. H. Hillier, *J. Electron Spectrosc.*, 21:47 (1980).

126. H. van Dam, D. J. Stufkens, A. Oskam, M. Doran, and I. H. Hillier, *J. Electron Spectrosc.*, 21:57 (1980).

127. W. Heyser, Thesis, Free University, Amsterdam, 1979.

128. W. Heyser, E. J. Baerends, and P. Ros, *Faraday Symp.*, 14:13 (1980).

129. I. H. Hillier, C. D. Garner, G. R. Mitcheson, and M. F. Guest, *J. Chem. Soc.*, *Chem. Commun.*, 204 (1978).

130. A. W. Coleman, J. C. Green, A. J. Hayes, E. A. Seddon, D. R. Lloyd, and Y. Niwa, *J. Chem. Soc.*, *Dalton Trans.*, 1057 (1979).

131. M. F. Guest, C. D. Garner, I. H. Hillier, and I. B. Walton, *J. Chem. Soc.*, *Faraday Trans II*, 2092 (1978).

132. M. Benard, P. Coppens, M. L. De Lucia, and E. D. Stevens, *Inorg. Chem.*, 1924 (1980).

133. F. A. Cotton, S. Koch, and M. Millar, *J. Am. Chem. Soc.*, 99: 7372 (1977).

134. C. D. Garner, I. H. Hillier, A. A. McDowell, I. B. Walton, and M. F. Guest, *J. Chem. Soc.*, *Faraday Trans. II*, 485 (1979).

135. I. H. Hillier, *Pure Appl. Chem.*, 51:2183-2195 (1979).

136. B. E. Bursten, F. A. Cotton, A. H. Cowley, B. E. Hanson, M. Lattman, and G. G. Stanley, *J. Am. Chem. Soc.*, 101:6244 (1979).

137. M. Berry, C. D. Garner, I. H. Hillier, A. A. McDowell, and I. B. Walton, *Chem. Phys. Lett.*, 70:350 (1980).

138. F. A. Cotton and J. G. Norman, *J. Am. Chem. Soc.*, 93:80 (1971).

139. R. M. Richman, T. C. Kuechler, S. P. Tanner, and R. S. Drago,
     J. Am. Chem. Soc., 99:1055 (1977).

140. J. G. Norman and H. J. Kolari, J. Am. Chem. Soc., 100:791
     (1978).

141. M. Berry, C. D. Garner, I. H. Hillier, and A. A. McDowell,
     J. Chem. Soc., Chem. Commun., 494 (1980).

142. R. S. Dickson, F. Carnovale, and J. B. Peel, J. Organomet.
     Chem., 179:115 (1979).

143. J. F. Nixon, R. J. Suffolk, M. J. Taylor, J. G. Norman, D. E.
     Hoskins, and D. J. Gmur, Inorg. Chem., 19:810 (1980).

144. J. G. Norman and D. J. Gmur, J. Am. Chem. Soc., 99:1446
     (1977).

145. A. Serafini, R. Poilblanc, J. F. Labarre, and J. C. Barthelat,
     Theor. Chim. Acta (Berlin), 50:159 (1978).

146. D. E. Haycock, D. S. Urch, C. D. Garner, I. H. Hillier, and
     G. R. Mitcheson, J. Chem. Soc., Chem. Commun., 262 (1978).

147. D. E. Haycock, D. S. Urch, C. D. Garner, and I. H. Hillier,
     J. Electron Spectrosc., 17:339 (1979).

148. W. C. Trogler, D. E. Ellis, and J. Berkowitz, J. Am. Chem.
     Soc., 101:5896 (1979).

149. B. E. Bursten, F. A. Cotton, J. C. Green, E. A. Seddon, and
     G. C. Stanley, J. Am. Chem. Soc., 102:955 (1980).

150. E. L. Andersen and T. P. Fehlner, Inorg. Chem., 18:2325
     (1979).

151. H. van Dam, D. J. Stufkens, and A. Oskam, Inorg. Chim. Acta,
     31:L377 (1978).

152. A. B. Anderson, Inorg. Chem., 15:2598 (1976).

153. D. L. Thorn and R. Hoffmann, Inorg. Chem., 17:126 (1978).

154. B. K. Teo, M. B. Hall, R. F. Fenske, and L. F. Dahl, J.
     Organomet. Chem., 70:41 (1974).

155. B. K. Teo, M. B. Hall, R. F. Fenske, and L. F. Dahl, Inorg.
     Chem., 14:3103 (1975).

156. M. F. Guest and I. H. Hillier, Quantum chemistry--the state
     of the art, SRC Atlas Symp., 4:205 (1975).

157. M. Doran, I. H. Hillier, E. A. Seddon, K. R. Seddon, V. H.
     Thomas, and M. F. Guest, Chem. Phys. Lett., 63:612 (1979).

158. J. M. Foster and S. F. Boys, Rev. Mod. Phys., 32:300 (1960).

159. P. S. Bagus and H. F. Schaefer III, J. Chem. Phys., 56:224
     (1972).

160. A. Denis, J. Langlet, and J. P. Malrieut, *Theor. Chim. Acta (Berlin)*, 38:49 (1975).

161. C. P. Keyzers, P. S. Bagus, and J. P. Worth, *J. Chem. Phys.*, 69:4032 (1978).

162. J. Müller, E. Poulain, O. Goscinski, and L. Karlsson, *J. Chem. Phys.*, 72:2587 (1980).

163. R. Broer and W. C. Nieuwpoort, *Chem. Phys.*, 54:291 (1981).

164. G. A. Sawatzky and A. Lenselink, *J. Chem. Phys.*, 72:3748 (1980).

165. E. L. Anderson, T. P. Fehlner, A. E. Foti, and D. R. Salahub, *J. Am. Chem. Soc.*, 102:7422 (1980).

166. D. Ajò, G. Granozzi, E. Tondello, and I. Fragala, *Inorg. Chim. Acta*, 37:191 (1979).

167. J. C. Green, E. A. Seddon, and D. M. P. Mingos, *J. Chem. Soc., Chem. Commun.*, 94 (1979).

168. B. R. Higginson, D. R. Lloyd, S. Evans, and A. F. Orchard, *J. Chem. Soc., Faraday Trans. II*, 71:1913 (1975).

169. M. Elian, M. M. L. Chen, D. M. P. Mingos, and R. Hoffmann, *Inorg. Chem.*, 15:1148 (1976).

170. J. C. Green, D. M. P. Mingos, and E. A. Seddon, *J. Organomet. Chem.*, 185:C20 (1980).

170a. W. N. Lipscomb, *Boron Hydrides*, W. A. Benjamin, New York, 1963.

170b. G. Granozzi, S. Agnolin, M. Casarin, and D. Osella, *J. Organomet. Chem.*, 208:C6 (1981).

170c. G. Granozzi, M. Casarin, E. Tondello, and D. Ajò, *Inorg. Chim. Acta*, 48:1981.

171. S. C. Khandelwal and J. L. Roebber, *Chem. Phys. Lett.*, 34:355 (1975).

172. S. Kitagawa, I. Morishima, T. Yonezawa, and N. Sato, *Inorg. Chem.*, 18:1345 (1979).

173. D. Sangler, G. M. Maggiore, L. L. Shipman, and R. E. Christophersen, *J. Am. Chem. Soc.*, 99:7487 (1977).

174. H. Kashiwagi, T. Takada, S. Obara, E. Miyoshi, and K. Ohno, *Int. J. Quantum Chem.*, 14:13 (1978).

175. D. A. Case and M. Karplus, *J. Am. Chem. Soc.*, 99:6182 (1977).

176. S. Muralidharan and R. G. Hayes, *Chem. Phys. Lett.*, 57:630 (1978).

177. J. Berkowitz, *J. Chem. Phys.*, 70:2819 (1979).

178. J. C. Green, M. R. Kelly, M. P. Payne, and E. A. Seddon,
     D. Astruc, J.-R. Hamon, and P. Michaud, *Organometallics*, 2:
     211 (1983).

179. D. E. Cabelli, A. H. Cowley, and J. J. Lagowski, *Inorg. Chim.
     Acta*, 57:195 (1982).

180. B. J. Morris-Sherwood, B. W. S. Kolthammer, and M. B. Hall,
     Inorg. Chem., 20:2771 (1981).

181. D. C. Calabro, J. L. Hubbard, C. H. Blevins II, A. C. Camp-
     bell, and D. L. Lichtenberger, *J. Am. Chem. Soc.*, 103:6839
     (1981).

182. C. Guimon, G. Pfister-Guillouzo, and E. Rose, *J. Organomet.
     Chem.*, 224:125 (1982).

183. M. C. Böhm, *Inorg. Chim. Acta*, 62:171 (1982).

184. J. C. Green, M. P. Payne, and J. H. Teuben, *Organometallics*,
     2:203 (1983).

185. C. Cauletti and J. Sima, *J. Electron Spectrosc. Relat. Phenom.*,
     19:1 (1980).

186. S. Kitagawa, I. Morishima, and K. Yoshikawa, *Polyhedron*, 2:43
     (1983).

187. M. C. Böhm, *J. Mol. Struct. (Theochem. Vol. 5)*, 89:165 (1982).

188. N. M. Kostic and R. F. Fenske, *Chem. Phys. Lett.*, 90:307
     (1982).

189. J. C. Green, M. R. Kelly, P. D. Grebenik, C. E. Briant, N. A.
     McEvoy, and D. M. P. Mingos, *J. Organomet. Chem.*, 228:239
     (1982).

190. S. D. Worley and T. R. Webb, *J. Organomet. Chem.*, 192:139
     (1980).

191. G. Granozzi, D. Ajò, T. Boschi, and R. Roulet, *J. Organomet.
     Chem.*, 224:147 (1982).

192. M. C. Böhm, M. Eckert-Maksic, R. D. Ernst, D. R. Wilson, and
     R. Gleiter, *J. Am. Chem. Soc.*, 104:2699 (1982).

193. M. C. Böhm, *Ber. Bunsenges. Phys. Chem.*, 86:63 (1982).

194. S. D. Worley, D. H. Gibson, and W.-L. Hsu, *Inorg. Chem.*, 20:
     1327 (1981).

195. J. N. Louwen, J. Hart, D. J. Stufkens, and A. Oskam, *Z.
     Naturforsch.*, 37B:179 (1982).

196. M. C. Böhm, *Inorg. Chim. Acta*, 61:19 (1982).

197. M. C. Böhm and R. Gleiter, *Angew. Chem.*, 95:334 (1983).

198. G. M. Bancroft, T. Chan, R. J. Puddephatt, and J. S. Tse,
     Inorg. Chem., 21:2946 (1982).

199. G. M. Bancroft, T. C. S. Chan, and R. J. Puddephatt, *Inorg. Chem.*, 22:2133 (1983).

200. C. Furlani, M. N. Piancastelli, C. Cauletti, F. Faticanti, and G. Ortaggi, *J. Electron Spectrosc Relat. Phenom.*, 22:309 (1981).

201. C. Cauletti and R. Zanoni, *Z. Anorg. Allg. Chem.*, 496:143 (1981).

202. J. C. Green, M. Payne, E. A. Seddon, and R. A. Andersen, *J. Chem. Soc., Dalton Trans.*, 887 (1982).

203. M. C. Böhm, M. Eckert-Maksic, R. Gleiter, G. E. Herberich, and B. Hessner, *Chem. Ber.*, 115:754 (1982).

204. R. L. DeKock, P. Deshmukh, T. P. Fehlner, C. E. Housecroft, J. S. Plotkin, and S. G. Shore, *J. Am. Chem. Soc.*, 105:815 (1983).

205. E. Ciliberto, L. L. Costanza, I. Fragal, and G. Granozzi, *Inorg. Chim. Acta*, 44:L25 (1980).

206. J. N. Louwen, D. J. Stufkens, and A. Oskam, *J. Chem. Soc., Dalton Trans.*, in press (1984).

207. J. N. Louwen, D. M. Grove, H. J. C. Ubbels, D. J. Stufkens, and A. Oskam, *Z. Naturforsch.*, 38B:1657 (1983).

208. J. N. Louwen, R. Hengelmolen, D. M. Grove, A. Oskam, and R. L. DeKock, *Organometallics*, in press (1984).

209. J. F. Nixon, R. J. Suffolk, M. J. Taylor, J. C. Green, and E. A. Seddon, *Inorg. Chim. Acta*, 47:147 (1981).

210. G. Granozzi, E. Tondello, D. Ajò, and F. Faraone, *J. Organomet. Chem.*, 240:191 (1982).

211. G. Granozzi, M. Casarin, D. Ajò, and D. Osella, *J. Chem. Soc., Dalton Trans.*, 2047 (1982).

212. J. Vites and T. P. Fehlner, *J. Electron Spectrosc Relat. Phenom.*, 24:215 (1981).

213. G. Granozzi, M. Casarin, S. Aime, and D. Osella, *Inorg. Chem.*, 21:4073 (1982).

214. N. C. V. Costa, D. R. Lloyd, P. Brint, W. K. Pelin, and T. R. Spalding, *J. Chem. Soc., Dalton Trans.*, 201 (1982).

215. D. E. Sherwood and M. B. Hall, *Organometallics*, 1:1519 (1982).

216. R. L. DeKock, T. V. Lubben, J. Hwang, and T. P. Fehlner, *Inorg. Chem.*, 20:1627 (1981).

217. M. Casarin, D. Ajò, G. Granozzi, E. Tondello, and S. Aime, *J. Chem. Soc., Dalton Trans.*, 869 (1983).

218. P. Deshmukh, T. K. Dulla, J. L.-S. Hwang, C. E. Housecroft, and T. P. Fehlner, J. Am. Chem. Soc., 104:1740 (1982).

219. R. L. DeKock, Kwai Sam Wong, and T. P. Fehlner, Inorg. Chem., 21:3203 (1982).

220. N. C. V. Costa, D. R. Lloyd, P. Brint, T. R. Spalding, and W. K. Pelin, Sur. Sci., 107:L379 (1981).

221. G. Granozzi, E. Tondello, M. Casarin, S. Aime, and D. Osella, Organometallics, 2:430 (1983).

222. G. Granozzi, E. Tondello, R. Bertoncello, S. Aime, and D. Osella, Inorg. Chem., 22:744 (1983).

223. G. Granozzi, R. Bertoncello, S. Aime, and D. Osella, J. Organomet. Chem., 229:C27 (1982).

224. G. Granozzi, R. Bertoncello, M. Acampora, D. Ajò, D. Osella, and S. Aime, J. Organomet. Chem., 244:383 (1983).

225. J. N. Louwen, R. R. Andréa, D. J. Stufkens, and A. Oskam, Z. Naturforsch., 37B:771 (1982).

226. J. N. Louwen, R. R. Andréa, D. J. Stufkens, and A. Oskam, Z. Naturforsch., 38B:194 (1983).

227. J. N. Louwen, D. J. Stufkens, and A. Oskam, Z. Naturforsch., in press (1984).

228. J. C. Green, Struct. Bond. (Berlin), 43:37 (1981).

229. D. C. Calabro and D. L. Lichtenberger, J. Am. Chem. Soc., 103:6848 (1981).

230. D. B. Beach and W. L. Jolly, Inorg. Chem., 22:2137 (1983).

231. G. Granozzi, E. Tondello, M. Casarin, and D. Ajò, Inorg. Chim. Acta, 48:73 (1981).

232. P. T. Chesky and M. B. Hall, Inorg. Chem., 22:2103 (1983).

233. M. Bénard, J. Am. Chem. Soc., 100:7740 (1978).

Index